NOT SOMEV ___

BUT HERE

A CONTEMPORARY ANTHOLOGY
OF WOMEN AND PLACE

Sundress Publications • Knoxville, TN

Copyright © 2014
ISBN: 978-1-939675-11-8
Published by Sundress Publications
http://www.sundresspublications.com

Editor: Erin Elizabeth Smith
Nonfiction Editor: T.A. Noonan
Poetry Editor: Rhonda Lott
Fiction Editor: Beth Couture

Readers: Margaret Bashaar, Sarah Black, Bob Boyd, Luci Brown, Danielle Favorite, Stacia M. Fleegal, Susan Graybeal, Adam Houle, Kate Johnsen, Melanie Jordan, Sophia Kartsonis, Jan LaPerle, Sara Lovelace, Samantha Milowsky, Shannon O'Brien, Nicole Oquendo, Jacqueline May Parkison, Chris Petruccelli, Jake Ricafrente, Sarah Jordan Stout, Donna Vorreyer, Gary Wilkens, Taryn Wolf

Special Thanks to Lyric Dunagan, Sarah Bohlman, Taryn Wolf, Daniel Daws, and Stephanie Phillips.

Colophon: This book is set in Adobe Caslon Pro.

Cover Image & Design: Rhonda Lott

Book Design: Erin Elizabeth Smith

NOT SOMEWHERE ELSE BUT HERE

A CONTEMPORARY ANTHOLOGY OF WOMEN AND PLACE

EDITED BY ERIN ELIZABETH SMITH,
T.A. NOONAN, RHONDA LOTT,
& BETH COUTURE

CONTENTS

NONFICTION

POETRY

FICTION

NONFICTION

Judith Arcana

Walking the Lake's Edge in Winter

Everyone who knows Chicago knows winter there is cold, really cold, and pretty often filled with snow. The snow lands thick, in great dunes that blanket the city's dirt. Or it lies hard and gritty in the street, like the salt crystals scattered to break it down to slush. Or maybe the snow never lands; it just cuts, sharp and hard, slashed by the knife of the wind.

Not everyone knows what Chicago winters do with the big lake; few walk the ice edge in early February. Lake Michigan is so big it freezes only rarely, and the wind in winter moves the water much as it does in the hot months, lifting it into waves as clear in their hearts of gray light as summer's waves of green. The lake's body rises and falls all winter long.

By February of a freezing winter the shore is no longer flat, and the lake no longer throws its fans across the sand. By February there are ice caves, built up and hollowed out by the waves, some four and five feet high above the beach. Most days the sky is low, colored milk, and sand suspended in the wave-carved ice is coarse enough to smooth fresh cut wood. But when the low sky opens, and the brittle winter light pours through, its pale gold illuminates the waiting shadow of the ice caves. Suspended sand glitters like gemstones; hollows become diamond mirrors.

Between Fullerton Parkway and North Avenue, a stretch with a breakwater of long narrow concrete piers, the ice caves gleam green and silver. Even the white of that frozen architecture glistens. New waves make no splash, but crack where they land. They shatter as they freeze.

I walked that shore in February. I want to go to the beach, I said inside my head, and pulled on high boots lined with fleece. My mind was changing like the landscape; I needed to be there. I needed the comfort that comes when inside and outside are one thing, no separation.

I understood this, why I was going to the lake, when I crossed under Lake Shore Drive and the cars roared over my head, trembling the walls of the concrete tunnel, rumbling its dark cracked ceiling. On the other side, the hotdog-popcorn-ice cream wagon was boarded up, and the drinking fountains covered. There were no gulls, and after the roar of the Drive, the beach seemed silent.

Then, in that sudden quiet after the tunnel, I heard the creaking ice, moved to sound by the insistent lake, heard my bootsteps crunching the dense snow. I saw that the long piers were gone – no, they were invisible, a skeleton for the carved ice and frozen sandsnow.

No fish smell, but the smell of my own body rose on the heat coming out of my collar, warming my throat, wrapped in its layers of flannel and wool. I stumped over to what had been the summer edge of the beach, and stopped. There I saw that light was trapped in the ice, shining. The sand itself shone, silica and mica glistening like tiny stars in icelocked space. The ice looked green as I approached it, silvergrey when I finally stood there, watching water from Gary and Milwaukee come to freeze at the tips of my boots.

Here was the science lesson made palpable: all about freezing, all about how one thing, water, could be many things, and yet be itself. Solid—the ice, and liquid—the lake, even gas—my wet breath like hot steam; and in all of these, itself. Was this true of me? My mind expanded like the lake at freezing, and took new shapes, like the ice caves.

Here was the philosophy lesson, biology of the spirit, teaching the physical nature of mind in Chicago, as fresh water mingles with salt when the St. Lawrence finds the sea, that briny offshore current freshening then, there, just there and then in a moment – and all of it changing: going, coming, moving, changing, coming on through these great lakes to me, here on this winter beach. Like the water that makes me, the water inside me, moving from lips to heart, cells to systems and back again in tides of myself, so this water, rising from the heart of the continent, surges from Mackinaw City to Toronto, from Portneuf to Riviere au Renard. Here was the lesson that teaches how everything changes, how transition is never complete, how whatever we are is whatever we've been, whatever we ever will be.

JENNIFER ARIN

¡SEVILLA, NO HAY MÁS QUE UNA!

Loosen your hips, the teacher commands us in every flamenco class: *move them!* Not only are we as stiff as the hard floor we dance on, but someone *else* has to teach us how to be sensual. Pretty embarrassing. If this prudishness stems from our Puritan culture (what else?), why do Spanish women, with their country's fiercely Catholic past, have no problem shaking it up? I remember watching a shapely woman in her fifties take the dance floor at a club in Sevilla and launch into a low rumba. Bent forward at the waist, rump out, she pulled her skirt tight, clutching any loose fabric so that each swish of her hips had full impact. The men went crazy. The women laughed and clapped.

I'd never planned to study this kind of dance—nor any kind. But who among us can predict where our lives will lead? And who can tell what will become home? I'd never planned to move to Paris, either—the place where, in a twist of fate, I first heard the music of Sevilla. But from the first day of a three-week summer vacation in Paris, the city had been irresistible: its grand esplanades; its river which reflected the light differently each day; its language which I'd studied and loved becoming fluent in, even though my mouth ached, at first, from days on end of those puckered vowels. I interviewed for one job after another until, at last, an international agency hired me to enter computer data. Dull work, but the perks were grand: long lunches, eight weeks of vacation per year, a health plan that justified the *pharmacie* on each block, and a salary increase for every language employees proved competent in. I passed the company's French test, and liked anyway the idea of learning another tongue, so I began lessons with Nora, a teacher who held classes on the premises, and who introduced nine colleagues and me to Spanish language and culture. One day, she played for us a *sevillanas* tape:

Fiesta, Feria, Juerga y Vino,
Duende y Ole, Ole y Ole
Las sevillanas, y Ole y Ola
¡Ole!

So many vigorous *¡oles!* It was a welcome contrast from the hushed manner of the French; I was always the one laughing and talking loudest, until Spaniards, Italians, or drunken tourists from *any* country turned up. But what made the Spanish singer so passionate? Was it the *vino*? Or the *duende*, that deep expression of the soul? Either way, the song made it seem that each *fiesta*, each *juerga* or gathering, and even each city fair was a non-stop dance party.

This was well worth seeing! From Paris, the flight to Sevilla was quick and easy. Guidebook in hand, I checked into a *pensión* in the center of the city, then headed off to a *tablao*—a club where people dance *sevillanas*—following Nora's suggestion and a map: cross the River *Guadalquivir*, veer left, head a couple of blocks east, and *voilà!* *La Candela* appeared.

The moment I walked into the club, the music I recognized as *sevillanas*—melodious, fast, upbeat—enveloped me. Once my eyes adjusted to the soft light, I could discern the band: four middle-aged men with dark, slicked-back hair, and stomachs that hung over their belts. People of all ages and shapes were dancing, too. The place was packed not only with couples, but with whole families, many of whom were seated at large tables spread around the dance area. Mothers, daughters and sons; aunts, nephews, nieces: a strikingly cross-generational crowd.

Couples moved vigorously to the beat, and in perfect sync with one another, steps matched, arms rising in unison. The partners never touched, but they circled each other closely, hands *nearly* on each other's waist. Sometimes women danced together, their comfort reflecting the deep bond of friendship, or kinship. When men and women danced together, their bodies radiated the heat of desire barely withheld. At one point in the dance, a flash of footwork by all the couples made the floor resound like a drum.

The music thumped on, beckoning. I squeezed past a crowd of people to make my way to the dance floor's edge, where a handful of *sevillanos* were clapping to the beat and waiting to take the floor next. I would have loved to dance, too—the music and scene were compelling—but the fast footwork baffled me. Surely, there was a pattern. I could see some steps repeated, but what exactly those steps were eluded me. The rhythm was just as confusing. Each *sevillana's* beginning varied in length, the lead singer stretching out his vowels according to emotion and lung power. Equally puzzling, every song had a last note that seemed one too many. How on earth could anyone born elsewhere know when to take that first step, or the last? The couples started and stopped on a dime, hitting that final note with their arms up high, an expression of triumph and joy. I'd feel the same if I could figure out the beginning and end—or middle, for that matter.

¡Ole! everyone called out together, during a pause in the music, to praise the band. It was little wonder they all were so enthusiastic; I was catching *sevillanas* fever myself. Each night for a week I went back to the *tablao,* even dancing when men would ask, as they inevitably did since I was always by the dance floor, standing alone—no mothers and aunts whose approval was needed!—intently watching the couples. Each time I joined in, the amused smile of every last observer made it clear I wasn't fooling anyone. No surprise there! It took all my effort just to avoid bumping into my partner or the other dancers, with all those place-swapping turns. Still, I figured it was the only way to learn, and it was fun—exhilarating!—to move to those songs, even if I barely caught the words being sung, or what my partners said.

¿Como te llamas? each man would begin, his mouth pressed against my ear, a sensual and, amidst the music, necessary gesture. Then each would give up trying to converse when I couldn't say much more than my name and where I was from, answering most questions with *¿Qué?* and *No entiendo.* How awful to be fluent in

neither the language nor the dance! The steps felt as unnatural as the rolling Spanish "r" that always stuck on my tongue. No matter how often I practiced aloud words like *carro*, *perro*, and *ferrocarril*, my "r" in those words—for *car*, *dog*, *railroad* sounded like an engine that couldn't turn over.

To grasp the dance and its vocabulary, I wandered into a music store a few doors down from the club and asked, in a wonderfully "r"-less phrase, *¿Dónde hay discos de sevillanas?* I bought a couple of CDs, grateful to find printed lyrics stuffed into each clear case. Remarkably, whatever the song's topic—most often, love—the lyrics also praised some prized aspect of Sevilla: its flowered balconies, whitewashed houses, lively festivals, gorgeous women, and even the joy of *sevillanas* themselves. Sevilla, each song concluded, is beyond compare. One chorus proclaimed enthusiastically, *¡Sevilla, no hay más que una!* Never mind that there's no more than one of *any* city: *there's only one Sevilla*, the refrain goes, and every *sevillano* seems to agree. No wonder the singer I'd first heard *ole*-ing back in Paris had been so enthusiastic! *Sevillanas* may be the happiest music on earth; it's certainly the proudest.

Each day I listened, in my hotel room, to those CDs. The cheery, fast-paced music was irresistible, especially once I began to crack its rhythmic code by singing along with the lyrics. Even singing, though, I was always behind the beat. Over and over, I chanted along to get the words and rhythm down, and did sweeps across the floor as grandly as I could, short of knocking into the table or bed. Between the alluring half notes the singers intoned, and the unabashed enthusiasm of it all—*¡ole! ¡vamos! ¡eso!* the musicians cried out—I couldn't get enough.

But I would be leaving soon to go back to Paris. The dance would be gone, and the music a handful of recordings, nothing more. France was still home, but now, like most any home, it would feel incomplete. I loved the language and beauty of Paris, the bookstands along the Seine, the late-night outings with friends, and the rich history found everywhere—not only in grand places like the *Conciergerie*, where Marie Antoinette was imprisoned, or Henry IV's majestic brick pavilions at the *Place des Vosges*, but even underfoot.

Most evenings, as the setting sun colored the sky and Seine, I lingered on the *Pont au Change*. Sculpted into that bridge's side are laurel wreaths encircling a big letter "N": the imperial insignia of Louis Napoleon. In Paris, the past is everywhere.

Absent from its midst, though, is that open display of joy Andalusians so willingly engage in. Most Parisians are introverted, even indifferent, except when they're annoyed. Back in Paris, I took my beloved *sevillanas* to the office one day and, when everyone went to lunch, put on a song and began to dance. Apparently, not everyone had left. A colleague from the adjoining office burst through the door and shouted, "*Arrête cette musique de merde!*" How anyone could hear that music and cry "Turn that shit off!" was beyond me—but clearly, not everyone was enamored with *sevillanas*. Still, maybe I could find others in Paris who were.

Heading home that evening, I stopped by a dance studio near my neighborhood. I'd never paid much attention to it before, but now I followed a long, cobbled alley to an office where brochures lined the counter. *Allez-y*, a bearded fellow behind the counter said without looking up, *take one*. The brochure touted how the *Centre de Danse du Marais* had classes in *toutes les disciplines*: *afro-cubain, danse classique, danse orientale*. The list went on … *salsa, samba—sevillanas!*

Astonishingly, the *débutant* level was offered several times a week. The instructor, Patricio Martín, was surely a Spaniard, and probably, I figured, from *Andalucía*. Who else would be teaching *sevillanas*?

But the teacher turned out to be a flamboyant Frenchman named Patrick Martin, as in PaTREEK MarTAN—no rolling "r" to be found. This, rather than the dance, was my first lesson: all non-Spanish *flamencos* give themselves Spanish names. Another teacher, Monique, was listed as Monica; a dancer named Phoebe rose again as La Fibi; and since my Anglo name wasn't easily converted, I was simply dubbed La Flama, the Flame, after pounding out some steps so passionately I broke a floor tile. Sadly for French floor tiles but happily for me, the culture of Spain was becoming integral to my life. The body, too, is a kind of home, and mine was delighted to be dancing *sevillanas.*

And yet, after four years in Paris, I began to consider a return to the States. Over time, my job felt more and more dull and dead-end. And my family was halfway across the globe, in California.

Une autre américaine déracinée, a friend remarked, enthralled with her observation that I was a typically "rootless" American in Paris. As if I had anything in common with the parade of Americans and assorted Anglos who arrived each tourist-crammed summer, and spent their days and nights eating baguettes and downing bottles of cheap wine by the Seine. For me the city, no matter what the season or scene, was home. Still, the time finally came when I packed boxes and peeled posters off the walls of my apartment, wretchedly unsure if I was making the right choice. The last item to join the other boxed ones was the painting a Parisian friend made for me. In his condensed version of the city, the two of us dance beneath a twilight sky, near an illuminated Eiffel Tower and fiery Moulin Rouge.

Was I leaving home, or returning to it? On the long flight to California, I looked out the window as the plane slowly crossed the Atlantic, casting a steady shadow on the surface. And then, back on the West Coast, I felt as foreign as I had during my first months in France. Whenever I opened my mouth—at the grocery store, post office or bank—everyone asked where I was from. Without realizing it, I'd acquired French gestures and habits of speech, from the high shrugs to an accent born of miming French sounds for so long. Also, having long ago traded my American clothes for French ones, everywhere I went I was now uncomfortably overdressed. How I missed Paris! Not just the *soignée* way the French dress, and not just the language (though I did grieve the language), but the grand architecture, the convenient *métro*, the restaurants and clubs open until morning, and of course, I missed my friends—even the one who'd called me an *américaine déracinée*. What would she say now?

To lessen the ache, I found a dance studio that offered classes in *sevillanas.* Such a find seemed a miracle—almost. Unlike the Paris studio, in the midst of a cobblestone courtyard and chic *quartier*, the

California studio was in a poverty-stricken area downtown, and required walking past panhandlers and addicts. I took my chances and went to the studio once, then twice a week. The instructor, Miguel, was a sweet-tempered man of Mexican descent, lean and dark with a thin mustache. After a couple of weeks, some of his students invited me to join them after class, to rehearse new steps. Over dinner, they talked about Spain, where most of them had taken flamenco classes.

Much as I loved *sevillanas*, aspirations to flamenco were foreign to me. Where *sevillanas* are more of a folk dance, joyful and social, flamenco is gritty, and usually danced solo. A couple of light-hearted flamenco dances do exist—*alegrías*, whose name means happiness; *peteneras*, where the dancer often uses a fan or shawl—but most flamenco dances require a deeply furrowed brow and "don't fuck with me" attitude. When I asked Miguel about the difference between two flamenco dances, *soleás* and *seguiriyas*, he explained, "*Soleás* are when someone's hurt you badly and you hate them. In *seguiriyas*, you want to kill them."

Arriving early to class once, I found Miguel sitting on a bench outside the studio, waiting for an earlier class to end. We chatted about dancing, and even about the flower shop he owned: a fallback, I assumed, for the years when he could no longer teach or perform. Though he looked at least twenty years younger, rumor had it he was in his 70s.

Miguel confided that he'd been considering whether to retire:

> *It's finally time.*
> *Yes*, I said sadly, *I understand.*
> *It was a hard decision, but I figure it's time to sell the flower shop so I can dance full-time.*

Apparently, Miguel himself was still in full bloom! He asked about my own plans, then encouraged me to pursue flamenco, offering me a small role in an upcoming performance with his troupe. I was too surprised and flattered to say no. The rehearsals, though, proved daunting. Instead of the casual fun of *sevillanas* classes, these sessions were filled with intensely ambitious, competitive dancers, many of whom had long trained in ballet before falling in love with flamenco. Some were even teaching their own flamenco classes. No wonder they felt comfortable dancing in the front of the room, up close to the mirror and entranced as they gazed at themselves. How well they moved, doing with ease the *vueltas*, those turns that made my head spin even more than the new choreography. I decided to do what other students did: study in Spain. Summer would be the perfect opportunity, since a teaching job I'd found at a local university offered that time off. A trip back to Sevilla, then north to Paris, which I still missed dearly, would be the ideal homecoming.

Juana Amaya was one of the teachers in Spain everyone spoke of: a renowned gypsy dancer. In June, I flew to *Sevilla*, checking into the same *pensión* as before. It felt almost like home this time. The next day, I set off to the studio where Juana taught. The place was easy to find, with the class's intense footwork audible half a block away—the unmistakable sound of each nail-soled shoe forcefully hitting the floor. The first sight I caught was not of Juana, but of the women who filled the packed room, all wearing full, colorful skirts: fuchsia with three ruffles, black-and-red with two, polka-dotted with a shawl around the waist. I looked with regret at my own skirt, an ordinary, barely flared black one to whose bottom hem a friend had sewn a neon-blue band of fabric, to give the illusion of a ruffle. A real flamenco skirt costs hundreds of dollars, too much on a teacher's salary—and who knew if I would even keep up the dance?

Juana made you want to, though. I could see her now, talking to the guitarist in the front of the room. Tall, elegant, with thick hair that cascaded past her shoulders, she kept her eyes downcast when she danced, as if our presence was irrelevant. When she "marked" some steps for us, her movements exuded both the intense heat of sharp turns and strikes, and the cool of supreme control. Between each series of steps, Juana switched the rows of students, so we all could watch her easily at some point. But the more aggressive students kept pushing their way into the first and second rows again; I spent most of the class looking at their backs. Afterwards, I approached Juana and, braced for rejection, asked if she would give me a few private lessons, which I figured would cost little more than all the group classes I'd planned to take. The request was, I knew, far-fetched. Why would Juana spend time on a beginner when so many advanced students swarmed around her, surely also wanting private sessions? And with her performance schedule, how much free time could she have?

But she agreed, which only made me more nervous. What on earth was I doing? And what would it be like to dance directly under the gaze of someone so intense? I found out a couple of days later, when I went to her home—a lovely *casa* whose balcony was dotted with white, red and pink *claveles* and *geranios*: just the kind of carnations and geraniums sung about in *sevillanas*. Juana answered the door herself, but it was clear we weren't alone. Male and female voices and the happy squeals of children echoed around an upper floor. Juana led me to a blank-walled, windowless room, where I made two unfortunate discoveries: in June, the heat of Sevilla becomes overwhelming, especially in rooms with no windows; and in private lessons, you do a lot more dancing.

Juana demonstrated, two or three times, a pattern of steps, then clapped out the music's accents while I duplicated her movements again, again, again. It didn't take long for sweat to start running down the inside of my leotard. When I stopped to take a swig of water, Juana looked impatient.

"*Otra vez!*" *Again!* she demanded. When I left, a sweat-soaked hour later, it took two large bottles of water to quench my thirst. Evening was the only respite, when even the sun couldn't hold itself up any longer. Only then could I recover from the nearly Saharan heat. The next afternoon, I went to another lesson with Juana, to suffer in the name of flamenco. She was even tougher this time, insisting I do the steps over and over until each was executed to perfection. Her rigor would have been welcome if I hadn't been on the verge of heat stroke. At least I was getting the requisite furrowed brow.

By the time I returned to my *pensión*, drained and dehydrated, I couldn't help longing, just a little, for the happy *sevillanas* of days past. When the sun dipped toward the horizon, I headed to a *tapas* bar where a *tuna* was playing. This is not some highly talented fish, but a Renaissance-style band of college students, who dress like troubadours in colorful tights and cloaks and feathered hats, and who play lutes as well as guitars. I asked the band if they knew any *sevillanas* tunes.

It didn't take much prompting. They struck up a song, and the fatigue of the flamenco lesson fell away. Here was a dance I was at home with now, and its quick rhythms and cheery tune stirred me to my feet. The musicians played on while I danced, facing them. I spun around for the final turn—*¡ole!* the singer shouted—and my legs almost buckled out from under me.

Deeply immersed in the music, I hadn't noticed the swarm of tourists filming me—for how long now? They must have stumbled upon the scene—a band, a bar, a show—and were eagerly capturing what they thought was a typical *sevillana* doing her dance. All the windows of the bar had bulky video cameras thrust through them. A horizontal row of the blocky cameras was perched heavily on each ledge, with other video cameras leaning upon *those*, in vertical stacks that obscured almost all the outside light.

If a friendly group had approached the tucked-away bar, smiling and maybe asking for a picture, how flattering that would have been! But the faces of this group were hidden by the cameras they peered through, making it seem I was under cold scrutiny. And the fast, aggressive surrounding of the place felt like a surprise attack. They had me trapped.

I stopped dancing, but they kept filming. I moved into a corner, trying to hide from those relentless lenses that, incredibly, still swerved toward me. Finally convinced the dancing was over, the tourists put down their cameras and grumbled to each other in a language I didn't speak, but whose irritated tone was as clear as the annoyed looks on their faces, visible now. I'd spoiled their movies, ruined their fun. They abandoned the scene, one by one, slowly boarding the buses that had brought them. The bars' windows let in the dusky light again. When the tourist buses departed, motors roaring, I left also.

The night deepened. In the surface of the *Guadalquivir* River, the lights of the city appeared as pretty neon streaks. Even the reflected *Tio Pepe* billboard looked beautiful, the river's currents softening the oversized image of a man holding a huge bottle of liquor. At the bar that night, maybe a little *Tio Pepe* would have helped.

The air was comfortable now, even slightly cool by the river's edge. Though no stars were visible in the city-hazed sky, the moon was bright and bold. So many *sevillanas* mention that moon. *Nuestro amor bajo la luna*, one refrain goes, singing of love beneath that moonlight, and then, sexily, of a woman dancing: *el lucero tiene celos cuando mueves tu cintura*—starlight is jealous when you move your hips. I couldn't help softly singing that refrain, a quiet offering to the river. The lyrics reminded me of the woman I'd seen on the dance floor once, swinging her hips and clutching her skirt tight. She was breathtaking in her boldness, her movements so free.

Maybe it wasn't terrible, in the end, that I'd attracted those tourists. There are fates far worse than growing from a young woman lost at a *tablao*, to one discovered in a *tapas* bar and taken for a Spanish dancer.

Tara Isabella Burton

Fatherlands

I came to Palermo because it was home, and because nowhere else yet had been. I had too many stamps in my passport and too many languages I only half-spoke, and a room in a shared house in England piled high with talismans of my wanderings: Orthodox icons, Croatian carvings, Armenian carpets festering with mold and fenugreek. Every six months or so I panicked and impulse-bought Ryanair tickets to Marrakech, or Istanbul, or Madrid, because a book or an article or snippet of overheard conversation convinced me that there, *there*, I could belong. I compulsively checked house-prices in cities I'd never been to, *just in case.* I spent my second year of university ostentatiously forgoing bacon in a misguided attempt to revive my Jewish roots.

I'd grown up in a breathless sequence of countries, my mother eternally convinced that the next one would welcome us. I'd met my father for the first time the previous summer, when I was nineteen. I'd tracked him down on Facebook, and after awkward pleasantries we'd driven through Umbria and played at small talk until his English and my Italian, gave out (we got stuck on the word "rewind" halfway through his attempt to explain our relationship; he gave up and bought me an ice-cream cone instead). We hugged goodbye; we traded text messages; I was no closer to homecoming than before.

I hadn't felt what I'd expected to feel—a tug of belonging, my blood boiling when it came close to his. My father was affable; he was genial. But no cataclysmic force had risen up from the hills to claim me; I had not fallen to my feet, renting garments with the Italian extravagance that was now my birthright. I'd only smiled and nodded, and not belonged.

But I had taken one tangible fact from that first meeting. My father told me that that he'd grown up in Palermo, near a town that still bore his last name.

I'd always been better with places than with people.

I pictured how it would be. Third-cousins in subterranean cafes would recognize me by the color of my eyes and the shape of my brow; they would gather me to their breasts and stroke my hair and force-feed me pasta with fennel and sardines. I would traipse over ruins like a mountain goat; I would eat tomatoes whole and let the juice pool in my palms. I would throw myself like a mermaid into the crashing of the sea, and the atavistic power of my homeland would wash over me with the waves. I built for myself a Palermo of frescoes and mosaics, alleys and marketplaces, Moorish domes and candied fruit, a scrapbook of images that I thought—for a moment —could signify home.

When I stumbled out of the train-station the following March, tripping on slick cobblestones, pulling at my ill-fitting dress, I realized just how much of a stranger I was. I dragged my suitcase past packs of Sicilian teenagers (smoking furiously, lithe like cats), and they did not recognize me or press me in their arms but only mocked, in slang they thought I did not understand, my *mozzarella* complexion, my frizzy hair, my dress. In broad, slick English one of the boys asked me if I'd like *to fuck*.

No ancestral spirits sprang up from the earth of Etna to defend my honor. No long-lost cousins emerged from the town, five miles off, that bore my father's last name, which I had claimed—mentally at least—for my own.

But the boys on the Via Maqueda did not know me. They didn't know that I was one of them, that my romanticized devotion to blood-kinship meant that they should have leaped to defend me against that profoundly foreign charge of being *fuckable*. All they knew was that I was blonde and pale and poorly dressed, and that I did not belong.

That night I barricaded myself in the mildew-dank *Hotel Casanova* and stared out at the sea, towards the horizon of a Sicily that did not exist. It rained for the next three days.

There is a certain discourse we get used to when we travel, a certain double-voiced loneliness that happens when we go someplace that is at once strange and known, because we have already imagined it. We tell ourselves stories about somewhere, stories that are really about *us*. We press our dreams and our memories into the clay of new streets and new cities, and because they are a part of us we are never alone.

But Sicily silenced me. Palermo overwhelmed me. It smashed the ramparts of the invisible city I'd built for myself. It smeared its chaos into my face. It laid waste to my fantasies and left me to wade through the visceral, greasy reality of Palermo-that-was.

I had no time to think; I had no space to dream, to impose my visions of Palermo upon this dank and labyrinthine city, where blistering suns snapped at the heels of storm-clouds. Geriatric flower-sellers massaged my bare legs near the Cathedral, crowing that I must be cold. Chickens squawked and stank as men loaded them into the backs of jeeps near the old Zisa. In the Vuccira, a warren of marketplaces snaking through the crumbling-plaster streets of the old town, a fishmonger thrust a handful of squelched squid into my face, and its tentacles flicked brine into my eyes.

I could no longer tell myself stories. I was as permeable as rice-paper, as malleable as clay. The city shook me through; it left me breathless. At times, wild with the savage force of this loneliness, I broke down in tears—at bus-stops, on trains. I wanted, desperately, for something to come between me and the truth of it, a barrier to defend me from this city that was not mine.

My last day in Palermo, I broke down in tears in the heart of the Vuriccia, stinking of squid, and pleaded with the silent household gods to make Palermo the end to my wanderings, to make it home.

Home, after all, is where everything is safe, where everything is known. It is where we curl into our delusions, sidle up like cats against our imaginations. As long as we are safe; as long as we can lie to ourselves, then we are home. Istanbul, Marrakech, Madrid had never been foreign to me. They had all, in a sense, been home— places where I could cultivate my carefully-held illusions about myself (I was an Edwardian lady explorer; I belonged everywhere; I could curse in five languages; I was the bastard daughter of the tenth son of an unknown Italian count). But Palermo, where my father was born, could never be home. It sent me ricocheting through the chambers of my loneliness, careening away from my familiar, lazy fictions, the lies I told myself about myself. Here in Palermo, for the first time, I was nobody at all.

So I remember Palermo, as I do not remember Marrakech or Istanbul. It is the city that I cannot tame, the city I cannot control, the city that will not be circumscribed or comprehended, that will not let me wrap my arms around it, and that will never wrap its arms around me. It is the only city that does not belong to me, and it will not let me go.

WENDY CALL

TILLED PATHS THROUGH WILDS OF THOUGHT

1: Containing Wilderness

Between a pair of gift-shop thermometers, above a trio of 1970s ceramics (an eggplant gravy boat and two rainbow-headed cockatoos), hangs Albert Bierstadt's *Cathedral Rock*. The granite mountain glows in the summer-pink light of a day just beginning, or just ended; deer stand like set pieces under a green-leaved tree; dead branches resist Merced River's merciless pull. This painting—one of four versions of *Cathedral Rock*—hangs in the living room of a mansion that belonged, most recently, to the Rockefeller family.

In the 1860s, the price for this Vermont home on two hundred fifty acres of land, or for a single oil painting by a German immigrant from the City of Blades, was the same: twenty-five thousand dollars. Land under your feet or a landscape you might never see—or that might never have fully existed—held the same cash value. Bierstadt's lifetime of Western paintings came from just three trips he made to the West. His work was the product of more time in France and Italy than in the American West.

Natural and cultural reserves were once called "reservoirs," containers for wildlife and forests and other wild landscapes. We place into reservoirs water or money or objects reserved for later use. They are saved, not protected. It is a system for commodities, not treasures.

George Perkins Marsh, a Vermonter who lived in that Rockefeller home before it grew into a mansion, tried to warn us all. In 1864 he wrote: "Man has too long forgotten that the earth was given to him for usufruct alone, not for consumption, still less for profligate waste."

Bungalow, a word brought to us from India: *bangla*, meaning something from Bengal. The word came to mean a one-story home with a thatched roof. And then, any one-storied home with a wide veranda offering plenty of shade. Now, it means a home like the one where I worked while at Woodstock, Vermont's national park, Marsh-Billings-Rockefeller, or like the one where I've lived in Seattle for the past seven years.

The Elizabeth Billings's Woodstock bungalow is best in the rain, when it falls like a mist or in fat, furious drops, the water drumming a deep rivulet that draws a perfect square into the soil around the house. This house is not yet a century old, does not know so much of what this land knows.

It did not see the Western Abenaki, the People of the Dawn, clear the undergrowth from Vermont's original forests. Or witness Thomas Knox, fugitive from Harvard University, mending a broken heart by hunting and trapping animals that are no longer found in Vermont. Or know the homestead built by the Cady family on the hill northwest of a sharp bend in the Ottauquechee River. Or smell the once-boggy Pogue dredged for fertilizer.

This bungalow has stood for fewer than one hundred years. It barely noticed the 2011 torrents of Tropical Storm Irene, stood impassive as the houses below swirled with mud and river rage. In the aftermath, the bungalow's well provided water for the entire park, slim red hoses snaking down the fern-furred hill.

After the rain stops, sun beams phosphorescent; the velvet-bright sky fades to grey. Mist lifts from silver-dipped leaves as this house shelters all.

The land underneath the bungalow has always existed—so say Vermont's longest-time residents, the Abenaki. The Great Tabaldak created the earthly beings that inhabited this place, but the place itself was already here. Odzihózo, Tabaldak's helper, built himself a body limb by limb, from dust graced by the creator's touch. Odzihózo, the Transformer, moved the earth, pushed up mountains, carved rivers and lakes, and persuaded wild animals to fall under hunters' arrows and spears. He made Vermont into a suitable home place: created fresh-water rivers of shad and salmon and hills filled with moose and bear and deer, then finally came to rest in his most cherished creation: Lake Champlain. He lies there still.

For the Abenaki, the lands we now call Vermont had a *genius loci*, a guardian divinity. A century before George Perkins Marsh published *Man and Nature, Or, Physical Geography as Modified by Human Action* in 1864, the term *genius loci* came to mean the genius of a place, but for much longer it has meant the genius *in* a place, a guiding spirit.

3: Circle of Elders

Every morning we climb up the hill away from the town of Woodstock and into the park, past the Victorian-gingerbread garden house, past the waterfall garden, past the pile of acorns that my four-year-old goddaughter began gathering her first day in the park. Lesley has come to visit me from Seattle, to experience a national park that could not be more different from the one she knows: the North Cascades.

Each morning Lesley and I pass the white-feathered star in the middle of the path and she bends over it, waving her short arms, fingers splayed. *Don't step here, don't step here!* She tells me, her voice firm. She knows, though I have said nothing, that this was once a bird, a life soaring overhead, not a splay of feathers on dun soil.

We must keep a wide berth, give death the space it deserves. I don't know why she insists on this, or how she knows that this is some glimmer of quotidian sacred. The Abenaki have always known that the bones of hunted animals must be treated with respect. Bear and beaver and muskrat and mink granted the gift of a successful hunt; it was a privilege they could withdraw. In this way, the Abenaki had long since known what George Perkins Marsh tried to tell us so long ago.

Lesley finds lost life all over the park: a mouse curled in a death clutch outside the bungalow's back door, a black-and-orange butterfly brittled at the edge of a road. *Who killed them?* She wants to know. I try to explain the natural cycle of life. That not all death is murder. That their mothers are not, as she worries aloud, over and over, missing them.

Crouching once again over the feathered star, Lesley stares past my failed words. She looks expectantly toward the circle of old-growth white pines—*weit* pines, Weymouth pines, wide pines, the trees the Iroquois called Trees of Peace—that tower over both our heads.

4: Undimmed by Tears

The year that I turned eight and the United States of America turned two hundred, my family took the National Parks tour. So many landscapes and vistas and miles crammed thirty days: Yosemite and Sequoia (but not Hospital Rock), then Mount Rushmore (but not Wounded Knee), then Bryce and Zion (but not the Anasazi Village), and then the Grand Canyon (where my mother bought me a blue-beaded necklace from a Hopi jewelry-maker). The final national park on our tour stayed most deeply with me. I carried home the memory of the Petrified Forest, close to our home in the desert of Southern California's Imperial Valley. I carried the memory in the slickness of wood turned to stone under my calloused fingers, in the glint of petrified sap under desert sky.

And I carried it in a vial of tumbled wood—an irony that was, even at age seven, not lost on me. I could not pick up ancient once-wood pebbles that littered the ground, but my father could buy a small container of them at the park gift shop.

When we love things, we want to take them home, rather than stretch our idea of home so that it might include them.

5: Fallen Stones, Fallen Walls

The creator Tabaldak first built the Abenaki people out of stone, but this left their hearts too cold; he broke up these original, failed humans and scattered their stones across the land. He tried again with wood; this time, he succeeded.

Vermont's forests blanket a history of fences, fields, feedlots; they lie like a featherbed over a landscape scarred and scarified. Pull back the sylvan quilt, the pine-needle bed, the leaf litter; find micaceous greenschist and quartzite, uncover the terrain that so vexed nineteenth-century farmers. The Wisconsin ice sheet laid waste to this terrain long before we did.

Yet we did. Vermont farmers built walls from stones, heaved up from the deep each cold winter, because there were no trees left to fell. A park ranger stands in the circle of old-growth white pines and says, "It's been a long time since we've seen that sylvan tunnel." So many American trees—elm, chestnut, beech—lost from this landscape.

The Abenaki and their forebears, sustained by their home in Vermont for one hundred centuries before Europeans arrived, usually hunted from one-quarter of their forest each season. Even if rivers flooded, or first frost descended devastatingly early, or winter turned bitterly cold, they would not starve.

6: A Destiny Not Manifest

On a train trip from Seattle to Chicago, I am surprised to learn at the Empire Builder railway passes right through Glacier National Park. I think of this, ignorantly, as a happy coincidence, a way that I might take a backpacking trip in a national park without a car. I look back on my naïve enthusiasm and laugh. When will I learn that there are no simple coincidences, happy or otherwise?

Frederick Billings's Northern Pacific Railroad carried visitors west, to the places we call Yellowstone, Glacier, and North Cascades National Parks, to the places that the Blackfeet, Chelan, Cheyenne, and Sheepeater Shoshone had called home.

Billings—who lived in the park mansion after the Marshes and before the Rockefellers—headed west from his hometown of

Woodstock, Vermont in 1849. He went to seek his part of a fortune that had, until the previous year, belonged to Mexico. At the time of his departure, Vermont's first railroad tracks had just been laid downriver from his home, in White River Junction. By the time Billings returned home to Vermont in 1864 with his gold-rush-land-claims fortune—the same year George Perkins Marsh published *Man and Nature*—railroads covered his home state and trees no longer covered its once-green hills. The Vermont railroads created their own destruction: the end of lumbering meant the end of the Woodstock railroad, among many others.

"With the disappearance of the forest, all is changed," George Perkins Marsh observed.

7: Amber Waves of Sound

A rock-laden truck climbs Elm Street in low gear; gravel crunches under sightseers' feet; ladders squeak open; mowers grind green turf. Over it all, two birds force their song. One mower grinds closer, insistent and grating. Closer, suffocating bird song. Breeze rattles leaves; birds insist on their notes; a mother, father and son speak of mansions and flower gardens; two cameras click. Thunder rumbles in the long distance and the moment breaks.

Landscape, seascape, heartscape, soundscape. Perhaps the last is hardest to protect, with so many predators encroaching on our national parks: Jet Skis, chainsaws, snowmobiles, campground boom boxes, airboats, generators, snowplows, riding mowers, backhoes, and cars, cars, cars.

In the Everglades, manatees skim the surface of a bay called Snake Bight, their wide skulls tracked with scars sliced by Jet-Ski propellers. In Miami, billboards at boat launches politely request that Jet-Ski riders stay away from the manatees; they are so tame, so torpid, so trusting. Thick black graffiti blot out the billboards' pleas.

In Northern California lumber trucks rumble roots, driving the world's tallest trees to an early death. A judge finally rules: "The public interest is best served by letting the ancients thrive a little longer." Government road-builders wanted to widen the highway through a redwood grove, but the judge insisted, "the scale tips sharply to the safety of our 3,000-year-old redwood trees."

Park rangers manage trails, gardens, endless questions, carriage roads, historic buildings, first-aid emergencies, stands of pine and spruce and maple. And now, they have a mandate to manage soundwaves. Preserve sound; eliminate noise. Or at least hide it. Every week, mowers big as tractors manicure the park mansion lawn, but only after visitors have gone home for the night.

On the bungalow porch, Lesley tries to read a book as I try to begin writing one. (We are both at a loss.) A mechanical whine rips into our shared silence. I can't place the noise: too low-pitched for a weed whacker, too high for a chainsaw. Lesley abandons her book, eyes wild. "Not here!" she says. "Mucho ruido!" *So much noise!* I nod, catch sight someone working his way through the hillside underbrush, waving an enormous weed whacker like a dousing rod. Lesley presses her hands to her ears; her cheeks redden with alarm. Her eyes insist that I make it stop. The whine continues, oblivious. She jumps up, runs down the hillside to the line where grass meets forest. "No, no, no!" She yells to the weed-douser.

He can't hear her; doesn't notice the child trying to defend the soundscape, her long braids whipping.

8: Awaiting Halcyon Skies

On a Sunday afternoon in August, Lesley and I sit down to lunch at a Woodstock community table set for seventy-five. The meal is a collective effort. A master furniture-maker taught many hands to sand and polish wood from local trees, building the tables. Those tables hold food that many other local hands sowed and harvested and fed and milked and slaughtered and stirred and seasoned.

The man who directed the Marsh-Billings-Rockefeller park for its first dozen years welcomes the group. He reminds us of Wendell Berry's words: *We are living on the far side of a broken connection.* Rolf Diamant says, "I think by 'broken connection,' he was really talking about the difficulty of living more sustainably, and living as a community. I believe we are beginning to reestablish that connection. We are bridging the divide between what our values and aspirations are, and what our relationships and accomplishments are. So perhaps it is particularly fitting that we're all having lunch on a bridge."

And we are. This table set for seventy-five spans Middle Bridge, one of the covered bridges over the Ottauquechee River, connecting park to town. We savor arugula and leek puree; pull bits from grilled quail. Just as we spoon peach and blueberry cobbler, the sky drops a fury of rain. Many leap up from our long table, the moment of fellowship broken, rain pushing them home. I imagine a short summer squall and stay on the bridge with the diminishing group, safely enclosed, as the Ottauquechee River churns and froths below us. Lesley and I walk home under nearly dry sky.

A week passes. Lesley and I spend a full day inside, watching the rain. We've been warned that high winds from Hurricane Irene might reach us; everyone in town has tied down everything that might fly. It has been raining all day, but there has been little wind. Lesley raises a fat hand and gestures politely, palm open and fingers together, not pointing. "Look, Wendy, a waterfall," she says, happiness in her voice, her eyes on the road in front of my rented duplex. I follow her enthusiastic gaze.

What was solid asphalt has fallen clean away; rain tumbles down the hill and into a cataract fifteen feet across and just as deep. "You're right, Lesley, a waterfall!" I reply, as fear bolts through me. *Should we leave?* I ask myself. We don't have a car. The park is closed. This mid-1800s house has clung to the side of this hill through seven generations. I decide it will remain solid, even as the rain pours, even as Kedron Brook, usually five feet wide, spreads across three hundred feet of valley below us.

Lesley and I watch Kedron Brook drag enormous tree branches, the deck from someone's house, and a gas tank toward Ottauquechee River. We can't see that distant river tearing down most of Middle Bridge and tearing through the rooms of many homes—including

Rolf Diamant's.

More weeks pass. Bridge repairs begin. Hundreds of volunteers shovel mud from hundreds of houses. Communal meals pulled from defrosting freezers in dark houses are shared on plastic folding tables and chairs on Woodstock's Village Green.

As soon as a floor is laid and a heating system installed, Rolf and his wife Nora can move back home. When I express my sorrow for all that they have lost, Rolf shakes his head, calm. "I really liked those things, but I didn't cherish them. I didn't cherish any of those things."

9: The Names of Things

A half-century-old photograph of Mount Rainier, the mountain that guards my home in Seattle, hangs on a wooden wall of the park bungalow. The National Park Service has filled Mount Rainier with places named after Native tribes: Yakima Peak, Cayuse Pass, Puyallup Glacier and Point and River, and Nisqually Cirque and Cleaver and Icefall. Nevertheless, our maps don't label the mountain by its original name, Tahoma, just as some still call the Alaska Koyukon's Denali "Mount McKinley."

Few Native place names survive on the simple brown signs that fringe Vermont's roads and highways. Ottauquechee, one of the few, is probably not an Abenaki word, but a Natick one. The word might mean "swift mountain stream," or perhaps "place with many rushes and cattails." This erasure is an old loss. Two centuries ago, Vermont historian Samuel Williams insisted, futilely, "On account of their originality, antiquity, signification, singularity, and sound, these [Native] names ought to be carefully preserved. In every respect they are far preferable to the unmeaning application, and constant repetition of an improper English name."

When I was in kindergarten, living on a military base in the California border town of Seeley—named for a white developer, and previously called Silsbee, for a white rancher—we lived on Gila Bend Drive. We were lucky to live on a street named for a native creature, the country's only venomous lizard. Streets labeled only by single letters or numbers filled our military neighborhood. Four years later we left Gila Bend for Sparrow Drive, named for a Navy missile (only indirectly for the bird). And four years after that, we moved to Constellation Street, in a neighborhood "off-base," as we called it, with streets named for Navy ships and aircraft carriers.

My childhood street addresses tell a story about the places I lived. They tell another story, too: my father's changing work moved him through many places, but into none. As a twelve-year-old my father built vegetable crates for Michigan muck farmers; as a thirty-year-old he designed parachutes for Navy pilots.

While in my twenties, I lived on a Boston street called Glade, next to a city park larger than Vermont's national park. Boulders marked the boundary between private backyard and public park. Conglomerations of grayish-brown rocks, with bits of a dozen different colors embedded in them, they spread thirty feet in diameter. These rocks, half a million years old, did not originate here, but likely belonged originally to the land that is now Africa. My Boston-backyard boulders, called "Roxbury Puddingstone," have this history in common with eastern Vermont.

Four hundred million years ago, what is now Vermont sat on the equator. The tectonic plate that contained what is now the African continent crashed into the one that is now North America, leaving behind a margin of earth, the violence of the collision creating the Green Mountains. The land of this national park, of all eastern Vermont and Massachusetts, lies on what seems to have been destined to be African soil.

10: New Lands, New Roots

A ribbon of sadness threads through the story of our national parks, floating back more than a century and fluttering into the future. Yes, our national parks belong to us all. Still, before these lands became national parks, they belonged to some of us. Or, to say it more correctly, some of us belonged to those lands, then were forced to leave.

In our nation of peoples immigrant and invaded, nothing is more American than pulling up stakes and moving on to pound new ones, and nothing is more American than yearning for home. I think constantly about the search for a home place because I grew up without one. Perhaps so many of us speak of "creating a sense of place" because most of us lost that sense generations ago, and we know it will take many generations to regain. Or perhaps it's a sense we hold as children, but our grasp weakens as we age.

When I was thirteen and my brother was eleven, our family left California to move east. My brother and I were in mourning. Our last five days on the Pacific coast, after we'd moved out of our cement-block, military-issue house, we rented a small cabin on the beach, walking distance to my father's cement-block, military-issue office. My brother and I sat on the big shoreline rocks for hours during that final week, tingled by Pacific spray, wondering what the other coast would be like. We had spent so many hours on that beach, visiting weekly from April through November, and daily during summer's long shimmer. We had explored every tide pool and rock crevice, stepped on sand sharks, collected gallons of shells and rocks, and walked far across the stinking, skin-prickling tidal lagoon at low ebb. One time, we fed seals by hand. Most times, we huddled by the campfire long after dark, begging for more time on the sand, under the stars.

My brother and I knew that beach as only children can know a place, not just with eyes and minds, but with full-body knowledge. My father never much liked the beach and my mother couldn't even swim—both had been born in flatland Michigan, as had all my grandparents and great-grandparents.

After spending two weeks in Vermont with me, Lesley returns home to Seattle. Her parents have been planning to move home to Mexico. Last minute, they change their minds; Lesley enrolls for a second year in a South Seattle preschool. Surprised and happy to see her, her teacher asks, *Weren't you moving back to Mexico?* Lesley has never been to Mexico. She answers, with a preschooler's bedrock confidence: "No! I'm here, teacher. I live *here*. Here, Seattle!"

Home is the place that exists nowhere else in the world, even as it might exist anywhere in the world. Like silver maples, we can sprout new roots wherever a branch touches ground.

11: Shedding Grace

A park ranger explains the Hudson River School to park visitors staring at a painting in the Rockefeller mansion's front hallway. (Earlier, one of the visitors asked another, "How do you feel about art?" The other said, "So-so.") "Nature wasn't something that you sought out; it was something that you feared. It was something to be conquered," the ranger says.

In my grandmother's only photo album, there is a snapshot from her childhood, taken around 1915: little Ida with her even littler sister, sitting on a log two feet across. Behind them is another log. Behind that, piles of tangled branches, then small trees waiting. My grandmother and her younger sister have matching wool coats, black-ribboned hats, lap-clasped hands, double-buckled shoes. Grandma Schust has written underneath the photograph's scalloped border, "Bursley's Mill."

At the time my grandmother visited that southeastern Michigan mill, long after Vermonters cut down their own forests, loggers began to take crosscut saws to the old-growth Douglas firs of my Seattle neighborhood. In a 1905 image captured just down the road from my Seattle home, a man sits on the lip of a charred stump yawning eight feet wide. Behind him lies sawed lumber, brush, and fallen logs. In the distance, fir-black forest. The man was a "powder monkey," the photo's caption tells us, who "knew how to carry and ignite explosives for the clearing of land."

Niagara (proper noun): the French interpretation of a Mohawk word meaning neck of land between the lakes.

Niagara (noun): a deluge.

Niagara (verb): to fall or cascade.

Niagarized (modifier): describes a place whose natural beauty has been destroyed.

12: Endangered, Extinct, Engendered

The resinous smell of an old growth hemlock forest has given way to flaming hills of silver and sugar maples. We little remember what we've lost.

More than nine thousand years ago, the very first Vermonters harvested beluga and bowhead whales, harp and hooded seals, from the salty Champlain Sea. An eon later, the inland sea closed. Rivers flushed out the brine within a decade and nearly all the ocean-going species died out of the sea-turned-lake. One of the only salt-loving creatures to survive this epic sea change was the salmon.

Not long after Hurricane-Tropical-Storm-Cyclone Irene, a fisherman catches an Atlantic salmon that has fought its way back to the White River. Proud of his catch, he publishes a photograph of the (so he thinks) stunningly large brown trout (thirty one inches!) in the local newspaper. This endangered fish had returned home to White River by swimming from Greenland through the North Atlantic, to the Long Island Sound and up the Connecticut River, fighting the insistent current. Fisheries biologists realize the radio transmitter in their beloved salmon is sending its SOS from a freezer in the town of Bethel.

George Perkins Marsh tried to warn us.

Bethany E. Chaney

The Tiny House

I am a small person. I'm not abnormally short or underweight, I just don't take up that much space. My face is long and thin, my fingers are bony, and my wrists are as tiny as a young girl's. My shoulders, while nicely proportioned, slump inward on most days. My legs plow a narrow path as I walk, and when I sit I am as compact as a frog. I might have bulges on my knees and thighs, but still, on that horrendously long flight from Atlanta to Johannesburg, I'm the woman you want in the middle seat. When all the lanes in the lap pool are filled, I'm the one to swim beside. And depending on your point of view, I'm either a perfect date or a useless one—overlooked by other men at crowded bars, but also overlooked by the bartender.

It's not that I am just small in stature. I also have small breasts. Tiny ones. Bear with me here, but I'm 44 years old and my breasts are the same size they were when I was fifteen, about the time I first felt the tell-tale pubescent bruising in my chest. My mother was thrilled to learn about it. She rummaged through my sister's dresser and pulled out an old, tattered training bra. It featured broad, flat cups made of polyester fill, just like a mattress pad. "It will make you look bigger," she said with a knowing look.

But wearing a mattress pad didn't make me look bigger. It only made me itch. That year my nipples grew like broad, inverted mushrooms, but when the bruising went away, nothing else was different under my shirt. My mother chewed her nails. She brought home clothes with ruffled bibs and wide lapels, taught me how to stuff a bra, and suggested I get a perm to 'draw the eye' to my face. None of this solved the problem: that in the excess of the eighties, I was noticeably lacking.

Unlike some men with modest endowments, overcompensation

has never been my thing.

I learned early to dress in baggy shirts and cardigans pilfered from my father's closet. I slouched like a schoolboy at my desk and hid behind notebooks and other people in the halls.

Over the years I refined these and myriad habits of hiding not just my body but my better self, of finding comfort in the background while avoiding center stage. My academic credentials were average, sans honors courses and dean's lists and degrees from the best schools. I sabotaged better relationships and married, then divorced, not-so-well. My career ladder has not been high, nor have been my earnings.

Until recently I've had chronically bad haircuts. While I long ago learned to love my small breasts, in my middle age I am a classic underachiever by just about any other measure.

Except, perhaps, for my house.

Here's the thing, and this may come as a surprise: the house is small, too. Really small, with a footprint of just 440 square feet. This may not be out of the ordinary in a place like New York City, but the size is unusual in a Southern place like North Carolina, where there is both ample land and a sense of entitlement to it. At first I thought I was building the house because it was what I could afford after leaving a relationship and, with it, the opportunity to build something larger.

Later, after the digging and building and grading was compete, I realized I had done it for a different reason. It was how I would turn my fade-away habit finally on its head.

The contractor who built the house was a family friend. He raised his eyebrows when I showed him the plans. "You want to build this?" he said. "You're sure?" His tone was at once mocking and curious, skeptical and excited. He sketched out a budget, fudged the plans to pull a permit, and got to work. To keep expenses reasonable he kept a slim crew, including two industrious immigrants, an unemployed commercial contractor and, occasionally, his kids. The work was hard.

The lot was wet and muddy, and under the mud hid masses of

fetid blue clay, useless to most living things except the most dedicated of potters. The houseplans I purchased were designed in California and required modification to meet the more commonplace codes of the Southeast. There were engineering challenges and issues with utilities, all the usual stuff of the trade, but each new frustration was overcome by the crew. They enjoyed the job, even if they thought I was a little nuts.

There were plenty of moments when I thought myself nuts, too. When the footings had been dug and the crew had left for the day, I climbed into the hole that would be my crawl space and took a look around. It was no bigger than a college dorm room and I was instantly depressed. Had I gone too far in my approach to downsizing? Had I set my bar too high, or too low? Was I destined to be an ascetic with an ironically huge mortgage? Where would I put the litterbox? But as the framing came up and the walls were dried-in, the house lifted gracefully out of the clay, expanded like the pages of a pop-up book, a fascinating but simple creation in which I imagined my story unfolding.

It was fascinating to other people, too. Every day brought new visitors, most of whom I never met. My contractor would tell me about them: curious pedestrians, other contractors, realtors, neighborhood kids, even his own mother. Once, after I moved in, a new neighbor graciously declined my invitation to visit the house because she already had. When the crew left in the evening, she told me, she and the other neighbors would quietly file to the job site, braving the mud and construction debris to tour the latest progress.

I secretly enjoyed the attention during construction because it was focused on the house, not on me. People like the idea of a small house. There are so many big ones, after all. People in the Research Triangle, a fast-growing area of central North Carolina, are as much weary of the cookie-cutter sprawl as they are of the fancier kind, where 5,200 square foot houses seem unique by virtue of landscaping rather than actual design. There is an overabundance of conspicuous space here, good for flaunting or hiding, depending on your needs. Teenagers in large families never have to share their rooms, much less leave them. Parents can escape to ample master suites while live-in nannies look after the kids. Divorcees can celebrate their freedom, filling empty rooms with oversized beds and lots of well-bred dogs. Until recently, capital was not necessarily a requirement to get this kind of space. It only took a jumbo mortgage with innovative features, and for those with less rugged ambition, a good cleaning service.

I don't know anyone who has a jumbo mortgage, or if I do they choose not to discuss it. Most of my friends live in average four-bedroom, two and one-half bath homes with an extra den and good resale value, at least when market conditions are good. Theirs were practical decisions made in anticipation of growing families, relatively flat income, or at the very least, a modest return on investment.

Their choices weren't arrogant, unhealthy, or environmentally unsound, although, if pressed, they might admit they live the way they thought they never would: like their parents. There are those among my friends who, while calculating the difference between their spaces and mine, controlling for height, girth, family size, and seasonal conditions, sigh wistfully.

They let their eyes roam from floor to ceiling, along the lines of the loft, and through the galley kitchen to the small bedroom in the rear, taking in the whole house without ever moving their feet. "It would be really nice to downsize," they say. "Easy to clean." Then I tell them about my electric bills, which are less than thirty dollars a month. Their shoulders shake with laughter and their chins move from side to side.

So while it may have been a timely subject, when a columnist for the newspaper asked to write a story about my house, I demurred. Strangers would learn my address and seek out the house, disturbing the neighbors with whom I share a drive. They'd upset a delicate balance between my modesty and pride. And I certainly was not interested in being a poster child for small living, or for single women with cats and chronically low self-esteem.

There are plenty of people who live in small spaces, and plenty of small spaces to live in. There are studio apartments in Manhattan and two-room millhouses in towns like mine. People live in barns and sheds, yurts and teepees, and plenty of souped-up campervans. Some people choose these spaces gratefully, others, experimentally. Then there are the highly-principled who seek only to live sustainably, to reduce their footprint on the earth, net zero waste, that sort of thing. Others have little choice in the matter, like those who live in tin-covered shanties, truckbeds and Katrina trailers, or prison cells. People live in cheap hotel rooms, flophouses and cars. Whole families in converted schoolbusses. Once, on my regular jogging path, I saw a returned soldier living camp-style beneath the trusses of a bridge. None of this is experimental living, really. It is rarely chosen on principle. If a newspaper published a story about these small homes, the message would have been quite different than the one they would publish about mine.

I am more grateful than principled, but I am selfish all the same. Sometimes I pour a shot of bourbon and dance in my living room to whatever I might be playing: bluegrass or jazz, folk tunes, old techno hits or southern rock. I clog, belly dance, waltz, or writhe like a hippie white man as if being swarmed by bees. I'm not a good dancer. I lose my balance a lot. But I like to move to a good beat, especially in the soft light of afternoon, barefoot on my smooth pine floors, rapt with my own music. Sometimes I pretend there is someone watching me and I feel sexy and foolish all at once. I laugh at myself and my imagined someone, and then I am lost again in the rhythm, one I've chosen all the same.

Children love the house, too. It's like a playhouse to them. They scramble up and down the ladder to the loft, finger the books on their low, crammed shelves, and chase the cats until they squirm beneath the bed. They are charmed by the dimensions of each room and give me pointers on hiding my toys, where to put the television, and whether I should sleep upstairs or down. The girls like my purple bathroom, and the boys, the swank washer-dryer combo tucked underneath the counter in my slim, orange kitchen.

Men, especially contractors, admire my house the most. They

enjoy the quality construction, hand-built cabinetry and custom trim. They ask questions about insulation, airflow and egress, and whether the loft technically can be considered finished space (it can't). They tap their knuckles against the inverter unit and shake the ladder that leads to the loft, salvaged from a bankrupt bookstore. "Why don't we build more of these," they say, "and learn to live simpler lives?" Their eyes grow soft and distant, and I know what they're thinking. The construction business stinks, but their families depend on their hustling, on the larger, more expensive projects that pay the mortgage, college tuition, and medical bills. They are tired and weary and fantasize about being alone, about a self-sufficiency without all the demands of the homes and the families they've been asked to build. Every man needs his cave, so goes the old joke, but they don't come out and say it that way.

Recently I swayed from my policy against press and entertained a film crew, three teenagers making a video about green living for a class project. They found out about my house on a blog entry posted by the company from which I'd bought my plans. The company had included my first name but omitted other personal details at my request. This was no deterrent for the kids. Within minutes they had found my e-mail and home address and arrived on a Friday afternoon, spilling out of a bright blue, fashionably boxy car, the kind spirited teenagers love. It was a gaggle of oohs and ahhhs. "We want to live like this!" they said. "Except next to each other, of course." I smiled and hoped they would never change their minds.

The first shot was scripted, outside in the drive. "Just walk out the door," they said, "like you're going to work." I told them that I work at home. They staged the shot anyway and then came inside, crowding the living room with youthful bodies and loads of expensive equipment. The cameraman gave his orders: where to move, where to plug in the cords, whether to turn the lights on or off. The two girls conducted the interview, reading their questions from colorful index cards. They were important questions for which I felt ill-prepared: What is different about living in a small house? Is it hard for people to build houses like this? Did you have to leave anything behind?

I answered best I could, wondering whether I sounded pompous or sincere, or whether I was making anything up, which happens sometimes. I watched their faces as I struggled to respond, looking for signals that I was on the right track. I was dancing in my living room to a live audience, wracking my nerves, like baring my chest once did.

"Why *should* people live in small houses?" they asked.

I looked around the room, found my grandmother's watercolors and my nephew's baby picture, the antique hutch I purchased twenty years ago that serves as my linen closet and my liquor cabinet, both. I dug my toes into the expensive floral rug and thought about why I'd built the house, why I lived here hunkered down amongst a few important things. There were the merits of living small in an increasingly wasteful society, learning new boundaries and new restraint. There also was the achievement of it - the energy efficiency, the affirmations, the sheer delight of one's own, right-sized home. Therein lay the irony of my story: that in my tedious attention to becoming small, I inadvertently had built myself a more expansive space. I had built myself the opportunity to grow.

"That's a complicated question," I said. "I'm not sure I can tell you that anyone should."

I told them that people live in small spaces for many reasons, that sometimes it is all they can afford or it is culturally preferred. Sometimes the way we live in one part of the world leaves fewer resources available to others to live as they please. Maybe we are asking the wrong questions, I said. Maybe it isn't about how big we live but how mindfully we do that makes a difference.

The kids were gracious, perhaps even relieved. They shut down the camera and unplugged the lights, packed up their things and stroked the cats goodbye. I watched their shiny blue car turn the corner before closing the door behind me. Then I stood alone again in the quiet, in the soft light of late afternoon. I lifted my dress over my head, along with my bra.

Yvonne Battle-Felton

The Other Side of the Pond

I have reached an understanding with death.

I do not seek it out. It does not seek me.

I like to think I've maintained a respectable distance since reaching this bargain though I can't recall with certainty when it was reached. It may have been the day my Volkswagen Jetta twirled along the New Jersey Expressway, skidding in furious circles—first in one and then the opposite direction. Eventually gaining momentum on slick patches of grass in the median, my car and I flipped side over side over side. We spiraled over the grassy divide and landed in the middle lane on the opposite side of the highway. It was an inspiring distance. Most areas of the expressway are divided by trees and concrete. The grass was one of many miracles. The witnesses thought I had died.

And perhaps, a part of me had.

There was a time I maneuvered the occasional Ouija Board, a time I wandered through cemeteries. Years ago, I entertained thoughts of hot boys pressing my naked back into cool headstones. But, I've denied myself the delectable energy that rises like mist between marble graves at dawn. I romanticized death. I have been mystified by the aura of it, a fascination only those less intimate with death can afford. Mine has always been a periphery attraction, one not borne of the actual realization of the permanence of death.

At least once a month I take my children to Woodlawn's duck pond to feed the growing population of Canada geese, swans, seagulls and the occasional duck. The air smells like earth here. It doesn't smell like the masses of bird droppings my children try desperately to avoid. It doesn't smell like hungry, possibly diseased, bird bodies flinging feathers, dripping water and impatiently hissing. The air smells like earth.

During these trips, my primary interest is to keep tiny feet from wandering too close to the water's edge. The water is not deep. If not for the haphazardly sprinkled, jagged boulders, a child tumbling into the pond would likely be more of an inconvenience than a danger. The growing flocks of seagulls delight in the frenzy. They nip and fight, young and old, seagull and goose—they don't discriminate—but to their credit, they stay near the rippling edges of the pond. It is the geese that challenge my reality.

My daughter and oldest son stand guard as my little one rationalizes rations: he gives more food to the geese who twitter along the edges than to the bolder, hissing flock near his feet. The occasional duck receives smiles and indigestible, sweaty bread balls. To the seagulls, he gives nothing. Once they've grown exhausted from fighting for crusts of bread, pretzels and whatever else my two-year-old decides they can have, the large brown and white geese wander through sparse grass, across the worn path of road that lies along the pond, and file one after another from view. Perhaps, at those times, I am tempted to gaze across the pond.

Beyond the pond's edge, above the tiny crowned heads of geese, lie the dead. That the duck pond is also Woodlawn Cemetery is not often relevant.

Lately, it is.

My grandmother died of cancer in March 2006, just before my daughter's eleventh birthday. My fingers were laced through her long, chestnut-brown fingers when she died. I lay with her as she grew cold.

Still, I can go entire days without remembering. I can reach for the phone, one hand slippery with turkey innards, the other poised to dial, lips parted to ask my grandmother how to cook a turkey. But then I remember. The permanence of her death manages to shock me each time.

Only once have I stood at my grandmother's grave. The coffin closed. The casket sealed. The plot covered. There was no room for mysticism at my grandmother's funeral; no time to linger amongst graves, no desire to do so.

My distance from death has diminished.

I am helping a friend deal with her husband's death. Often I sit with her in silence. It's better this way. I don't know how to say: "There will be days you will forget he is dead. There will be times you will reach for him and the space where he is not will appall you. There will be days you will remember he is dead and you will smile because you loved him, and days you will feel guilty for smiling.

Weeks later, I am again at the duck pond. Today, I watch a family cascade out of an SUV. A mother, her daughters and a granddaughter: three generations of women. One of the daughter strokes her brown hair as the wind gently brushes it. "I come here once a week," she tells me. "I have family here."

I follow her gaze across the pond.

I am suddenly surrounded by graves.

JUDITH GILLE

THE DEVIL AND THE VIRGIN

Not long after I purchased my home in San Miguel de Allende in 2002, friends and family began barraging me with magazine and newspaper articles about the city. Its abundant colonial charm and affordable real estate had not escaped the attention of the media, who were as smitten as I was with the colorful Mexican hill town. At least once a month, I'd find some new review on my desk at work or in my email inbox. *Condé Naste, The New York Times, The Washington Post, The Wall Street Journal, U.S. News and World Report, Travel and Leisure, Town and Country, Architectural Digest* and *Elle*— all published articles extolling some aspect of San Miguel's *buena vida*. When my mother sent one she'd clipped from *Money Magazine* decreeing it as one of the "Top Ten Places to Retire," I knew my investment acumen had shot up in her esteem. But I was also aware of the consequences of such an article: more Americans would be arriving in San Miguel.

Of the Americans pouring into town, a disproportionate number of them were women over fifty. The allure of this irresistible Mexican town seems to fan the flames of postmenopausal passion, making middle-aged women fall hard in love.

When the sirens of San Miguel call, some of these women tumble into a state of love-induced insanity that lasts long enough for them to imagine a whole new life here. Many even purchase a whole new house to go with their whole new life— just like I had.

But the expat women I know are drawn to more than just the brightly-colored walls, picturesque churches, cheaper housing prices and bargains in the markets. They're drawn to San Miguel because they want to be part of the lively Mexican and American artist's community and to live in a unique part of Mexico, where expatriate women are free to be themselves, speak their minds (except on the subject of Mexican politics which is against the law for non-citizens). A place where they will be accepted for who they are and contribute something to the greater good of all who live there. Unlike many Mexican ports and border towns, San Miguel is not overwhelmed by gang and drug violence. Its residents, for the most part, feel safe living there.

Since my family and I had begun making multiple annual sojourns to San Miguel, I'd never had reason to worry about our security. Our neighborhood was a peaceful place where my family and I felt safe coming and going at all times of day and night. With my neighbor Gracia and her family watching out for us and for the house when we weren't there, we had little reason to fear being victimized.

But in the early spring of 2006, our peaceful artist's colony—the darling of travel and lifestyle magazines—was making international news for something other than chic remodels of ancient haciendas.

It was a chilly morning in March and I was slowed to a near standstill trying to cross one of Seattle's many bridges on my way to work, when the Father-Knows-Best voice of NPR's Steve Inskeep poured from my car's radio with ominous news:

"Some Americans who thought they'd found a haven abroad now have to worry about an attacker. A serial rapist has been targeting foreign women in the town of San Miguel de Allende."

I then heard the familiar voices of my friend Patrice and other women I knew in San Miguel being interviewed. In the five months I'd been away, an attacker had raped four women. All were expatriates, all were English-speakers and all, except one, were over fifty. Just like me.

By the time I returned to town the following June with my daughter Hannah and two of her friends, fear and uncertainty had taken up residency in San Miguel. Like a pair of overbearing relatives who have overstayed their welcome, they were sucking the energy right out of our fair city.

The heat that year didn't help. The summer rains, which normally begin in mid-June, did not arrive on schedule. Landscapes languished in arid profusion. The jacaranda trees looked tired and thirsty and the brilliant magenta blossoms of the bougainvillea quickly faded to a tepid mauve. Everyone was testy, worn out by the relentless heat, the lack of a much-needed rainy season, and a preoccupation with the belief that the rapist was still living among us.

Two days after our arrival, I met with friends from the Sociedad Protectora Animales (S.P.A.) over *huevos rancheros* in the shaded courtyard of the Café de la Parroquia. We were working on a new fundraising plan for San Miguel's animal shelter. Over the clatter of plates and a gurgling fountain, I caught snippets from a conversation at the table next to ours.

"Isn't it awful?"

"I knew it was going to happen again."

"The ineptitude of the police is so infuriating!"

"I've heard they know who he is; they just don't *want* to catch him."

"I'm scared sick. I don't sleep at all when my husband is away."

When I asked my S.P.A. friends if they knew what the women at the next table were talking about, they told me that the rapist had struck again, the night before last. His latest victim was a well-known author and high-profile member of the expat community. Like the man's other victims, she was middle-aged and American. The attack had occurred two blocks from my friend Joyce's house, where the girls and I were staying since my house was rented for two weeks.

"When the first rape happened last October, it was unsettling," said Chris, the Canadian shelter volunteer who'd helped us to adopt our dog Nacho. "But now there have been four more attacks. Everybody's really getting wiggy." She said the rapist's predilection for middle-aged, Anglo women had every English-speaking woman in San Miguel living under a veil of anxiety, wondering who among them might be the man's next victim.

Over dinner at my friend Miriam's house the following night, she told me that the rapist's second victim was a close friend of hers, a yoga teacher I'd practiced with several times.

"He got in by climbing a ladder left at a construction site behind the house where she was staying," Miriam said. "With all the building going on in this town, no one is really safe."

I felt ill as she recounted details of the first four attacks: women held at knifepoint and raped repeatedly over several hours by a deranged assailant who, between violating his victims, insisted they drink wine and speak English with him.

At dawn the next morning I peeked into the stuffy bedroom where three beds were crammed in dormitory style. My daughter and her two friends, clad in tank tops and boxer shorts, were asleep and splayed across damp, rumpled sheets. The listless whirl of the ceiling fan's blades barely moved the room's thick air.

I climbed the steep concrete steps to the rooftop terrace in search of a fresh breeze and to sit for my morning meditation. A rosy haze blanketed the city below. A hot air balloon floated on a sultry breeze beyond the apricot spires of the Parroquia and the blue and white tiled dome of the San Francisco church. I sat down on a cushion and folded my legs Indian-style. I closed my eyes and began concentrating on my breath.

Minutes into my meditation, I heard a faint scrabbling on the other side of the stone wall I was leaning against. The noise became louder. Bits of scree peppered my scalp. I opened my eyes and saw a scrawny young man in a ragged t-shirt tumble over the wall. Like a feral cat, I sprang to my feet and eyed him suspiciously as he dusted himself off.

"*Con permiso*," he said, excusing himself. He explained that he was working on the construction site next door. He only wanted to attach a hose to the spigot on our roof.

His calc-covered blue jeans and worn leather work boots supported his story.

"*Esta bien*," I answered tentatively. But as I watched him grab the rope and rappel back down the twenty-foot wall, anxiety began spreading through me like an aggressive cancer.

After the morning's rooftop incident and the lurid reports I heard about the details of the rape, I began hyperventilating at the thought of being alone with three pubescent girls in a house with no locking inside doors and walls that opened to the sky—walls that strangers were climbing over.

I decided not to mention the guy on the roof to Hannah and her friends. I was relieved that they seemed unaware of the hysteria produced by the recent attack. That night I waited until the girls were asleep before rolling a giant potted ficus plant in front of their door to block access.

As I was shoving the pot into place, Hannah rolled over, propped a sleepy head up on her hand, and asked "Is that to keep out the rapist?"

"He isn't interested in us, sweet pea," I said, trying to shrug her off. "I'm just being paranoid."

Then I booby-trapped the door of my own room with precariously placed chairs and lamps, tucked a spear-like rod under my mattress and lay awake until three a.m. ruminating about the only time I'd felt more frightened in Mexico. My first trip to the beaches of Oaxaca.

April 1974. My boyfriend and I have gotten separated from our friends who have rented a cabaña we plan to share. But we think nothing of it. Instead of looking for them, we decide to roll our sleeping bags out on the lovely white sand beach and lie under a navy blue sky watching shooting stars zigzag across the night canopy. We've heard it's dangerous to sleep on the beach, so we bury our money and other valuables in the sand.

Sometime around midnight, the gentle slapping of the luminescent surf lulls us to sleep.

But not for long. We are suddenly kicked awake by two Mexican men wearing steel-toed boots and smelling like cheap Oaxacan mescal. They shine flashlights in our faces and aim a Lugar pistol and a semi-

automatic rifle at our heads.

"Get up," we're commanded in Spanish.

We do as we're told and are herded like animals, barefoot and wild with fear, through patches of creeping cactus. Our feet are shredded by the time we reach a coconut grove where a late-model Chevy pickup with a cedar-shingled camper is parked. An American, with a stringy blond ponytail and wearing a Mexican peasant shirt, sits on the tailgate of the truck. A single kerosene lantern lights the night.

The men with the guns tell us to stay put and disappear again. I assume the guy with the ponytail is in cahoots with the armed men since he seems unperturbed by their actions. Then he explains: "These guys are federales, the Mexican federal police. They get their kicks by rounding up hippies who sleep on the beach and shaking them down." Evidently it wasn't the first time he'd been shaken down.

Minutes later the men reemerge from the darkness with two more boys and a pretty, strawberry blonde from Chicago. They insist that the girl's visa is not valid and give her the choice of paying them four hundred pesos or going directly to the "police station" with them. The man with the ponytail interprets their demand for the Chicagoans who speak no Spanish. The boys shake their heads and insist they don't have the four hundred pesos. Then they try bargaining with the men, as if in a market.

"This isn't a business transaction, it's the law," says one of the federales.   He grabs the girl by the arms and leads her toward the beach. She shoots me a beseeching look, as if being female, I am the only one who understands.

"They'll probably just rape her and let her go," says the ponytail when the men and girl are out of hearing range.

I feel like I'm going to be sick. I know that poor girl will never make it to any police station. The men have the cover of night and the silence of Mexico to conceal their crime. A silent scream wells up in me as I watch them disappear into the darkness.

Then one of the boys from Chicago speaks up.

"Maybe we should have just given them the money," he says.

I want to punch the two of them for their stupidity. Instead I run to catch up with the drunken men and the girl. With the pistol trained

unsteadily on me, I beg the men in my childlike Spanish to let her go. I tell
them the boys have the money and that they will give it to them.

The next morning in San Miguel, I wandered over to the benches in the jardín where Americans gather daily. The square was abuzz with more details of the rape. Beneath the shadow of the Parroquia church, I heard anger and distrust spilling into every conversation.

The police's inability to capture the rapist was subverting the goodwill that normally exists between San Miguel's foreign community and its local bureaucrats. Like the stucco walls of many of the town's colonial mansions, it was beginning to crack. Even the carefully polished image of our handsome young mayor, Luis Villareal, had been tarnished. And everyone seemed to have a grievance.

American women were outraged by the lack of concern and sensitivity demonstrated by San Miguel's police force. Victims had suffered double humiliation when, after being raped, they were interviewed about the intimate details of their attacks in rooms open to the public. One woman was furious when she discovered she'd been the butt of jokes made by the police after reporting her rape.

Mexican women were angry too. They were furious about the attention the American victims received from the police and investigators, while their pleas for justice for Mexican rape victims had, for years, been ignored. They also claimed, which is well-documented by human rights groups, that Mexican police frequently blame the victims. Archaic laws regarding rape only served to inflame the outrage: the age of consent is twelve years old and incest has historically been considered a consensual act under Mexican law. Victims of incest were frequently punished as severely as the perpetrators.

On top of all that, a number of foreign residents were in a standoff with the chief investigator over his refusal to release a composite sketch of the rapist. Many local San Miguelenses supported his decision to withhold the rendering. The chief claimed it was an unreliable sketch, but there was probably more to it. There's ample evidence that white crime victims frequently have difficulty identifying non-white criminals. A false accusation would be a public relations disaster for the police chief and for our dashing young mayor, whose sights were set on a higher office.

The only heartening news was the rumor circulating that the F.B.I. was now involved. This sudden appreciation for the F.B.I. amused me: the bastion of oppression from our youth had now been transformed into the "good guys."

Worn out by the incessant negative chatter and too little sleep the night before, I decided to leave the jardín. I wandered past the town's newspaper hawker, and bought a copy of *Atención*, San Miguel's bilingual paper. Tucking it under my arm, I traversed the shady square and ambled down calle Reloj, past the Blue Door Bakery where the perfume of fresh-baked *bolillos* filled the air. I turned up calle Mesones, en route to gather the girls from an art class, and arrived at the Plaza Civica. There our town hero, Captain Allende, was guarding the newly planted landscape from his bronzed mount. Daylight had washed away the previous night's feeling of menace.

I studied the faces of the people around me: limbless and sightless beggars with outstretched hands; bow-legged ranchers in neatly pressed Levis; bespectacled, stern-looking nuns; weathered *vendedoras* pedaling over-ripe avocados. They were the faces of people preoccupied with the effort of eking out a living, making ends meet, keeping their families together, and serving God. No diabolical men bent on violating middle-aged, English-speaking women lurked among them.

Later, while lying in bed perusing the *Atención*, I was surprised to find an article by the writer who had been raped only a few days before. She described the events leading up to the attack. How she neglected to lock an inside door and woke up a few hours later with a knife at her throat. But something else she reported intrigued me.

After she was raped, the woman somehow summoned the courage to ask her violator to leave, knowing he had raped his previous victims multiple times, over many hours. When that failed, she began to pray. First in English, then in Spanish. As she invoked the Virgin, reciting several Hail Mary prayers in Spanish, her attacker became agitated and asked why she was praying. When she replied, "I am praying for you," he abruptly left.

"The prayers, or more likely the Virgin herself, drove him from my house," she said in the article. The *Atención* printed the full text of the prayer in both Spanish and English, and the victim implored the women of San Miguel to learn it.

I memorized the prayer and began reciting it with regularity, not really for the girls' and my protection but for a greater purpose. I drew comfort from the idea that maybe, through focused intention, we could accomplish what the police had not been able to in the last nine months.

It turned out I wasn't alone. By early July, I knew many women who said they were regularly reciting the *Ave Maria* prayer.

Within days of the attack, San Miguel de Allende was, again, crawling with police. More than fifty federal, state and local agents occupied the city. A restive hum filled the hot, humid air. The truckloads of uniformed men patrolling the streets and the *click* of steel-toed boots on cobblestone made it feel as if our city were under siege.

As with more notorious predators—Ted Bundy, the Boston Strangler, the Green River Killer—the odds finally caught up with the rapist of San Miguel. His ruse came to a swift end on July 5, 2006. Police surrounded and arrested him in an area near San Miguel's scenic overlook the same day Felipe Calderon, vowing to fight crime and take out the drug lords, was elected President of Mexico.

The F.B.I. had indeed intervened, identifying José Luis Álvarez Gonzales through a DNA match and providing police with a photo of him that was confirmed by one of the victims.

The paunchy, balding, fifty-eight-year-old Álvarez more closely resembled an aging computer programmer than the stereotype of the crazed rapist many of us had imagined. He'd done time in California and Texas for thefts and break-ins, and not surprisingly, was an experienced locksmith. He confessed to all five rapes and numerous burglaries too.

As word spread of his arrest, a collective sigh echoed through San Miguel's streets.

That evening, as if to contribute to the celebratory mood, the rains arrived bringing relief to the parched landscape. I breathed deeply for the first time in a week, removed the iron spear from under my mattress, and repeated one more grateful *Ave Maria*.

Patrice Gopo

Jamaica Boxes

I remember how my father took a dinner knife or a pair of scissors and sliced through the brown packing tape. With one quick motion, his knife opened the cardboard flaps of the Jamaica boxes and filled the room with the dry-ink scent of old newsprint. My sister and I had to wait a moment longer while my mother's ginger hands removed the crumpled newspapers protecting the contents of the boxes. As a child, I read past the stories and articles from what seemed like far-off places and saw the bounty of Jamaican curry powder, jerk seasoning, tamarind balls, beef patties and other staples and treats. All impossible to find in Alaska.

The tamarind balls were always for me since their tangy flavor held little appeal to the rest of my family. The sour dried fruit dusted with sugar created a sensation in my mouth reminiscent of the resulting steam when water drenches fire—two distinct flavors coexisting in one unique form. Sometimes I felt like a tamarind ball: Jamaican descended and American born. Not fully sweet and not fully sour but rather two distinct flavors coexisting in my unique form.

In school, I wanted to belong. I wanted to believe I was like everyone else, but I realized I wasn't.

Once, my third grade teacher led the class in a discussion about the types of foods we ate for dinner. I can't remember why. Perhaps to better help us understand nutrition or food variety or some other reasonable lesson.

"Patrice, tell us the meals your family has each week."

I knew this and so my response was quick without much thought, "Rice."

"And what else?"

"Well, chicken and vegetables. And rice."

66

"Mashed potatoes?"

"No. We don't eat that." With each answer I could hear murmurs coming from the desks grouped around the room.

"Baked potatoes?"

"Sometimes we have potatoes with the rice." My classmates giggled hinting at the odd combination of potatoes and rice.

"Spaghetti?"

"My mom makes us rice. Each day is rice. Except Sundays is special rice and Saturdays I don't eat because it's soup. We always eat Jamaican food." It seemed simple to me, but I realized my answers weren't the right ones. My answers didn't fit what my teacher was looking for. I wanted to tell her spaghetti and mashed potatoes, but I knew that wasn't true.

My mother's ability to ensure Jamaican or Jamaican inspired food at nearly every meal was actually a significant accomplishment given the location of our family. She carefully rationed ingredients and spices from distant places and tracked down what little Jamaican-like food she could find in our chilly land. Sometimes she went so far as to ask our local grocery store to put aside a bunch of green bananas. I can even recall the store manager phoning to let her know about an unusual shipment of plantains.

And so onto my plate flowed an extensive repertoire including slow-cooked oxtail, jerk chicken, and stewed peas with dumplings. All served with an abundant side of rice. While my parents adapted to their American surroundings, the food in our home hearkened back to the early years of their lives, the years when they first met each other in the breezy, salt-scented air of their island home.

Two months shy of her graduation from nursing school, my mother married my father during his visit to their home country of Jamaica. Several years earlier, he had moved to America and now worked in the outermost boundaries of the country. The wedding materialized in less than a week as my father had obligations to return to in Alaska. A reception hall found, a church booked, a dress sewn, a marriage started. Two months later, my mother immigrated to the farthest reaches of America. She brought trepidation about a frigid new land along with a mental cookbook that would later give her daughter yet another reason to feel out of place. Before I was even born, my parents' choices and experiences began to fill me with the ability to straddle many worlds as their journey impacted the contents of my own life.

As my nose inhaled the box of foreign yet familiar smells, as my hands held treasure from a distant land, I understood that more importantly than the patties, spices, tamarind balls, coconut milk and other foods, the Jamaica boxes brought connection. They linked me to a bigger world than I knew. The world of my mother. The world of my father. The world of my grandmother. While my family's presence in Alaska was something of a novelty, a Jamaica box made me imagine there were more people like us even if they were far away. Touching the contents of those boxes was touching the hands of distant people who wanted to be part of our lives. Even if the other children at school didn't fully understand me, there were mysterious, faceless people out there who did.

As the years passed, I gradually made peace with the snow that birthed me and the sun from which I descended. Time and maturity allowed me to recognize Alaska as a comforting cloak of community rather than the awkward fit of a coat that wasn't my size.

In time, I married a man from Zimbabwe, and we chose South Africa as our first home. Like my parents before me, I became an immigrant. For the first few months, my tears were my only visitor. They never politely tapped at the door, announcing their impending arrival. They never allowed me the option of letting them in. Instead they burst through the door, ripping off the hinges, forcing shirts to remain unfolded and pots of rice to simmer too long on the stove. My immobilized body lay on my bed, knees pressed against my chest, arms wrapped around my legs as choked hiccupy coughs escaped my throat. In this space, I communed with my tears. Some of it was pregnancy. Mostly it was remembering the beauty of the life I learned to love in Alaska and longing to create a new one.

I blamed the baby growing in my womb for my unexplainable need to linger over a plate of my mother's stewed peas. What else could justify my desire for a food that never even reached the end of my list of favorites? A whiff of the slow cooked, gently spiced beans simmering away in a mixture of coconut milk and tender ham pieces always brought a look of disappointment to my childhood face. And yet here I was, almost tasting the familiarity on the tip of my tongue. My lips salivated as if the now pleasant odors actually hovered in the air. Thinking of the familiar smell reminded me of a large table filled with people who loved me.

Both my cravings for food and feelings of isolation pulled me to the local market. My feet wandered through the store searching for coconut milk, trying to remember which type of beans, hoping someone might initiate a conversation with me. My voice could have asked for help, but my accent brought curious stares and misunderstood phrases, effectively rendering my speech silent. Instead my legs meandered up one aisle and down the next, trying to take note of every item I failed to recognize, trying to identify the ones that might be familiar. I mentally audited the store in a manner that would have made my accountant husband proud. This ritual filled portions of many of my days. It was a simple attempt to prepare what I longed for coupled with a hope that someone might engage in my world.

"Mom, I don't know what to do. I don't know who to make friends with. No one seems to want to be my friend. No one asks me to do things with them. No one invites me over." The cold plastic of the phone pressed against my right ear. While voicing my feelings brought slight relief, the phone call failed to give me the warmth of my mother's arms.

"I miss Pop Tarts. I want stewed peas." I didn't even eat Pop Tarts. How could a person miss what they didn't eat?

I heard my mother begin her answer with a familiar cliché, "Patrice, you come from a long line of strong women. You can do this. When I first came to Anchorage, the loneliness was real, but it has long passed." Oddly enough, the cliché brought me comfort.

As the phone conversation continued, my mother told me about her own immigrant tears over 30 years ago as she explained how to prepare Jamaican foods I never bothered to learn how to cook. I listened to her speak of continual grey in her heart despite the presence of sun and the changing seasons. Her words talked of the emptiness of snow-filled days where people's smiles hid behind the bulk of winter coats and scarves. Their lives disappeared into the warmth of their own homes, leaving my mother standing alone in the cold. She relayed deep experiences with longings for her home country and musings that perhaps no one would really miss her if she somehow disappeared in the midst of a blinding blizzard while the falling white wetness built towers across the landscape. Then maybe, just maybe, she would melt away and find herself back under the blazing heat where she belonged. As her words spilled out about her past, her journey epitomized the strength of a mighty tree refusing to bend or break under the weight of snow.

These revelations surprised me, as I never imagined my mother struggled in the ways I now did. My own focus on my childhood problems left me naively immune to my mother's challenges. Her stories gave me confidence to reach within myself and unearth lessons hoarded from a lifetime of navigating the balance beam of multiple worlds. As I waited for select familiar foods to arrive in the mail, I unfolded the layers of loneliness and isolation, revealing beneath them risk taking and fortitude. This simple act of self-examination empowered me to find the coconut milk and discover a substitute for the beans. I added thyme and pepper in guessed quantities. I mixed the flour and water and kneaded the sticky mixture into dumpling dough. The savory aromas filled our apartment, and I thought I was a child again watching my mother prepare the stewed peas. I found the courage to invite two people to share lunch with me.

While my America boxes began their slow journey across continents, from Alaska to South Africa, I began an equally long journey to form relationships. As I waited for the much-anticipated treats to arrive, new discoveries such as resiliency continued to emerge from deep parts of me packed away long ago. Each discovery gave me greater strength to forge new friendships. My boxes arrived around the same time my abdomen began to swell with the presence of new life, and my South Africa friendships began to take flight.

Pop Tarts, Lucky Charms, taco seasoning. It felt frivolous like gold stilettos and yet I felt known. In my mind, I could envision far-off family and friends thinking of what I was longing for, people who were thinking of me. Over a cup of hot rooibos tea, I gushed to a new friend about the boxes' arrival. Days collapsed into weeks and months as my isolated feelings dissipated like the hazy steam from my tea floating into the air. In their place, I sensed the small, subtle beginnings of community bursting forth. The world didn't feel nearly as lonely as it seemed.

After a few years of marriage, my husband and I decided it was time to leave South Africa and return to one of our countries. We chose to start a new life back in America. In many ways, I never quite felt American, and I relished my multi-cultural heritage. Back in my country the feelings were even more pronounced. Pieces of South Africa now flowed through my veins, and I longed for a cup of rooibos tea much like I longed for my tamarind balls and Pop Tarts.

As we drove through our new city in search of belonging and fresh beginnings, the bold colors and pattern of the South African flag caught my eye. The simple words on the storefront sign read, "South African Food Shop."

"Oh, let's go see!" I said. My husband was more than willing.

As we stepped inside, the spicy smell of biltong laced with the floral scent of rooibos tea wafted past my nose. I closed my eyes, and I could see the aisles of our local Cape Town market. For a brief moment, the tingling excitement of discovering the contents of a Jamaica box all those years ago overwhelmed me. I opened my eyes to the reality that my little family had been given one gigantic South Africa box. The world seemed just a little bit smaller.

JANE HAMMONS

DOG OR HUMAN

8:30 p.m.

"Is it dog or human?" the officer on the other end of the line asks.

"I didn't look that closely," I say. "What difference does it make?"

"Ma'am if a dog from our canine unit did his business there, we'll clean it up. But if it's the suspect's, well, it's yours."

"Why don't you come over here and make that determination?" There is a fifty-fifty chance, after all, that it belongs to the police department.

"Ma'am," he gives it one last try, "I don't have any equipment here."

"Equipment?" I imagine a complicated
    canine/human
        feces
    determination/removal
        machine.

He sighs. "Do you have a dustpan and a broom or some kind of shovel?"

"You bet." Mother of two boys, ex-wife of alcoholic-drug addict, I am well equipped to deal with shit.

The officer arrives in less than ten minutes. My children and I live only six blocks from the police station in Albany, California, a small town well known in the San Francisco Bay Area for good schools and top-notch community services. A national newsmagazine once published an article commending the Albany Police Department's community involvement. I appreciate this. I live here because I want to feel safe.

BACKTRACK 4:00 p.m.

My neighborhood streets are named after presidents: Buchanan, Taylor, Jackson, Fillmore, and Polk. On my way home from work, I stop for groceries then drive down Buchanan Street, past the police station, noticing that the entire street is lined with police officers. Police in cars. Police on foot. Dogs.

I turn onto Taylor Street. There are twice as many police on my street as on the others. Overhead two helicopters buzz. My usually quiet neighborhood looks like the President's parade route.

Don't let it be me, I pray, unable to put my real fear into words. It isn't that I expect to be busted like Sarah Jane Olson for a crime committed in a long ago life. I imagine that my ex-husband is in my house—he holds the children hostage: a gun at their heads—negotiating the terms of a life he longs for but can never have.

I don't watch a single news report about some pissed off, suicidal, drug-addicted, alcoholic, father holding his kids hostage before he shoots them and then turns the gun on himself without thinking about my children and their father. In such scenes SWAT teams gather; helicopters hover; police line the streets.

"Those people are not murderers at heart." My children's therapist tells me this just a few days earlier when I express my concerns about my sons' safety. I confess to clipping newspaper articles about fathers killing their children, cataloging the list of prescription drugs they take, charting abuses the fathers suffered as children, inventorying recent antisocial behavior and comparing them in each category to my children's father. "They are desperate men and in most cases truly believe that the only way to keep the family together is in death," she explains. This is not meant to reassure me. And it doesn't.

Not a single police officer approaches me. Each gives full attention to the house directly across the street. I don't bother creating a mental image of whatever act of desperation might have occurred there. It can't be worse than what I imagine possible in my own life. I'll be much happier offering condolences than receiving them. I go into my house, put away my groceries and leave again. I'm off to see my therapist, happy that it's not me.

KNOCK ON THE DOOR: 8:00 p.m.

It's only 8:00 o'clock, but I have decided to slip into pajamas—a baggy tee shirt and white cotton pants. When I go to answer the door, I'm not exactly in what anyone would recognize as pajamas. I'm just comfortable, relaxed in false security.

It's a police officer. My sons, ages 10 and 8, crowd into the doorway next to me. We've had occasion to call 911 when their father lived here. Passed out with cigarette in hand; couch on fire. Drug-induced trances: paralyzed on the toilet. Fires in the microwave; car driven through the garage. They've seen the police arrive with paramedics and firemen. But never just the police.

"Good evening, ma'am. I'm here to let you know that there was an incident at your house this afternoon."

"Incident?"

"Earlier this afternoon a suspect in a burglary was apprehended in your basement."

"Earlier this afternoon." I am picturing the suspect in my basement while I happily put away my groceries. "When?"

"I'm not sure exactly what time, ma'am. I just came on duty. But there was some damage to the property."

"Damage to the property." My children look worried. Not scared yet. On the reels that are spinning through their imaginations, they haven't gotten to the frame that depicts a stranger lurking in our basement.

I'm not doing much better: *incident*; *damage*; *this afternoon*. All I can do is repeat phrases.

"Just thought you would want to know," he says, backing away, relieved that this has been so easy. "Good evening, ma'am." He retreats to his car.

"There was a burglar in our house?" my oldest son asks.

"No." I try to explain what I don't understand. "In the basement."

The eight-year-old is confused. He knows everything in the basement is worthless. "Did he steal the washing machine?" he asks, perhaps understanding its value to me.

"I don't think so. I guess we better go down and see what the damage is."

"What do you mean *we*, white man." This is currently the ten-year-old's favorite expression.

"I need to see what happened," I tell them. "You can stay up here if you want." A little nervous now, they both follow me outside. Excluding the laundry chute, the basement has no inside entrance; it can only be entered from the backyard.

Over the door, on the inside of the basement, someone—police or suspect—hung an old mildewed curtain. I recognize it from the shelf where previous tenants left some of their belongings. The panes of glass in the basement door are broken. Unnecessarily. I never lock the basement. I open the door and switch on the light. Most of the broken glass is inside the basement. I tell the children to wait outside.   The dryer is pulled away from the wall. Perhaps it had been used to barricade the door. My children's clothes from the laundry bin are scattered about the floor. Maybe the suspect hid in there. Maybe he tried to crawl up the laundry chute, the only way out of the basement, excluding the curtained door. How many burglars were there? How many were suspected of being in the neighborhood? The questions I should have asked the officer occur to me all in a rush. Exactly who was apprehended in my basement?

Then I step in it.

"Shit," I say.

"You owe us a quarter." My eight-year-old reminds me of the penalty for using bad words.

"No," I protest. "There's really shit—poop—on the floor."

"Gross," my boys say together.

"Back in the house." I gag. They flee. I stop in the yard to hose off my sandal before I go inside and wash my hands and feet with antibacterial soap, put the clothes I wore to work back on, then call the police.

I dial the seven-digit number of the police station down the street, using the yellowed list of emergency numbers tacked above the phone. I know from experience that 911 calls cost $75.00. Shit in the basement is not a 911.

I identify myself as the resident of the house where a suspect was apprehended.

"How can we help you, ma'am?" the officer asks.

"There's broken glass and feces all over my basement floor."

"Glass and what?"

"Feces," I repeat.

"What?"

"Feces," I say again, remembering Gilda Radner's Roseanne Roseannadana "Endangered Feces" segment from *Saturday Night Live*.

"What?"

"Shit."

"Ma'am, I'm going to put you on hold while I get my supervisor. We'll see what we can do for you."

LATER THAT SAME EVENING: 8:45

"I have some good news, and I have some bad news," the officer jokes as I open the door. "The good news is that it wasn't your house the suspect was robbing. The bad news is that our dog didn't do his business there."

"You can only get to the basement from the backyard." I refuse to just let him get back to the station. "The broom and dustpan are down there already." I hope he will follow me. He asked me if I had the equipment. I have it. He's going to use it. No discussion.

I tell my kids that I'll be in the basement with the police officer. (Translate: I'll be safe.)

Then I turn on Cartoon Network (Translate: They'll be safe) and show the policeman to the basement.

"Looks like one of the officer's stepped in it." He chuckles, seeing my footprint in the feces.

"Looks like it." I don't tell him that it is my footprint. I'm afraid he might interpret that as a claim of some sort. I'd stepped in it; therefore, it belonged to me: dog or human.

We dance around the pile, trying to figure out the best approach. The broom and dustpan are useless. The officer takes a quick inventory of the other equipment in the basement: trowel, hoe, shovel.

"Can we rip up this linoleum?" He notes the damaged state of the linoleum strip that covers the cement floor between the washer and dryer.

"You bet." I get a garbage bag. We take up the linoleum and deposit the filthy load in the garbage can at the back of the house.

"Now you're sure there's nobody else in my basement?" I am only half-joking

He looks at me, uncertain he wants to answer this question. "One suspect is still at large. But, ma'am, there is no way he's on your property. Our canine unit would have found him."

"Check the laundry chute." I imagine a long snaky man stretched out in that space for hours, waiting for the moment to make his escape.

"Ma'am," he protests, "it's really unlikely."

"It's unlikely that a burglar would hide in my basement and shit on my floor." I snap.

"The three of them split up, went in different directions." Resentful now that I am not simply grateful for the help he has given me, he takes the shovel and runs it up the laundry chute. "He'd have to be pretty thin to fit up there."

"True. Do you have a description of the suspect who remains at large?"

"No," he grunts.

"I want you to check my house." I turn away from him. I don't want to see his reaction. Maybe he thinks me a fool. Maybe he's angry. But I don't back off. My children are upstairs, alone, watching

Scooby Doo.

"Ma'am, our canine unit . . . "

"Was in the basement," I finish his sentence, not knowing, really, whether or not a dog could have sensed a person on the level above him, not really caring.

Dutifully, the police officer takes out a large flashlight and together we go through the house, opening closets, shining large beams of light under the beds. No monsters there.

MIDNIGHT

Though I was tired earlier, I am too anxious to sleep now. I sit on my new couch watching *Court TV* reruns of *Homicide: Life on the Streets*, a program I am addicted to. Suddenly there is rapping at the window behind my head. My heart races as I imagine that the suspect has returned, perhaps for stolen goods or drugs hidden in my basement. I'm frozen in place as an entire scene plays out in my head: me bound and gagged; my children kidnapped; our house occupied by thieves and murderers. Now it's the doorbell. The loud repeated dingdonging gets me to my feet. It also wakes my sons.

"Who's here?" the youngest one screams from the hallway.

The older one runs to the kitchen to call 911. I squint through the peephole of the front door. "It's your father," I call from the living room. "You can go back to bed."

"He's not supposed to be here." The oldest becomes angry as his father continues to ring the doorbell. Schooled in the regulations of restraining orders, my son wants them followed to the letter.

"Can I have Cocoa Puffs?" the youngest one whines.
"Just a minute," I yell at the door while my sons each choose a box of cereal to take back to bed with them. When they have closed their bedroom door, I open the front door slightly, leaving the chain lock in place.

"My god," my ex-husband weeps hysterically. "I've been afraid something like this would happen." Earlier in the evening when he made his nightly call, the boys told him about the policeman's visit. I spoke to him briefly to assure him that the police had taken care of everything. "I'm moving into the basement," he cries. "To protect you."

"Good night," I say politely, having learned not to engage in the insanity. I close the door and turn out the porch light, wondering if it's scarier when the monster under the bed is a stranger or someone you know.

Though it's late, I call my mother for the second time this evening. She has heard the details of the break-in already, but I need to tell her about my ex's offer of protection. She bursts out laughing. "Well," she says, "at least you'd know what kind of shit was down there."

DRAGNET CAPTURES TWO

You won't find the write up of the incident in my basement in *The San Francisco Chronicle* or *The Oakland Tribune*. But in *The Journal*, a weekly newspaper devoted to the events in our small community, I read the account of the crime committed that day. The canine unit sent into my basement was one dog named Grando. Automatic weapons were found in the car the burglars abandoned. The suspect arrested on Fillmore Street, one block west of Taylor, has a record of armed robbery and assault. One suspect remains at large.

In the article, my home was described as "unoccupied." Not exactly an inaccurate word choice, but neither is it entirely true. In the dining room, the canary sang. In the basement, the suspect hung curtains.

I continue to fight the compulsion to collect Father-Shoots-Children-Then-Self news stories searching for clues that will help me avoid a future I sometimes still fear. I do what I can to be safe.

I buy a padlock for the basement door.

SUZANNE KAMATA

THE HEART FINDS A HOME

My Japanese husband doesn't understand my obsession with passports. I'd been nagging him over the past few months, ever since I realized our eleven-year-old twins' passports—both their American and Japanese ones—had expired.

"We need to get them renewed," I insisted, back in November.

"Not now," he said, citing the cost and inconvenience—the paperwork, the required trip to the consulate in Osaka, on another island, two and a half hours away by car. We'd have to take time off from work and excuse the kids from school.

"But what if we have to escape?" I asked.

This didn't seem like an odd question at the time, considering the tensions brewing in nearby North Korea. My husband was sure that there would be a war, and the newspaper headlines weren't encouraging. I had fantasies of whisking my family off to the relative safety of multicultural Hawaii, where no one would ever again tease my son about being "half," or maybe to socially-progressive Scandinavia, where I wouldn't be the only blonde in the neighborhood. If there was even a risk of something bad happening, then why bother hanging around? We had options, after all.

My husband, of course, doesn't think in the same way. He didn't come from another country, like I did. While I've moved around—from Michigan, where I was born, to South Carolina, where I graduated from high school and college, to France, where I studied for a semester, then on to Japan, where I came 23 years ago to teach English "for one year"—my husband has lived in Tokushima almost all of his life. (He went to college in Chiba, near Tokyo, before returning to his home town.) We now live in a house built by and formerly inhabited by my husband's parents. As the oldest—and only—son, he is the designated heir. His father's bones are interred in a cemetery a short walk from the house, and it's up to us and his sister, who also lives nearby, to tend the grave.

My husband didn't get a passport until he met me, at the age of twenty-four, and I invited him to visit my family in South Carolina.

Many people, I know, live their entire lives without passports and most don't have leaving in the backs of their minds, not like I did, even after living in Japan for over half of my life.

I've lived on the fringes of this country for over twenty years, never quite fitting in. People often shrink back at the sight of my blonde hair and blue eyes. They avoid sitting next to me on buses. On my end, I often feel ill at ease as well. Although I speak Japanese fluently, there are gaps in my vocabulary, and I commit cultural blunders on a daily basis. Because saving face is so important in Japan, it sometimes takes years for me to figure out that I'm making a mistake. I'd been living in this country for over a decade before I found out that it was rude of me to store my broom in the entryway. I'd been here even longer before I learned that I didn't know how to serve rice.

While helping serve lunch one day at my daughter's school, an outspoken mother told me that I was doing it wrong. "You should only heap rice in the bowl like that if you are preparing an offering to the dead," she scolded. Also, apparently, it's indelicate of me to answer the door in my flannel pajamas when the neighbors, early rising farmers, come calling at seven a.m. Sometimes the constant corrections wear me down and I think I'd rather live somewhere— anywhere—other than here.

And yet, when the U.S. State Department issued a traveler's advisory on March 17, 2011, warning Americans from coming to Japan, and urging Americans within the country to leave, it never occurred to me to pack my bags.

A week before, a friend in Osaka reported via Facebook that he was experiencing an earthquake—the largest he'd ever felt in Japan. I didn't think much of it. After all, there are 1500 earthquakes in this country every year, and I'd been here during the 1995 Kobe quake, which rocked me awake in my fourth floor apartment. I was terrified. My husband, who was more accustomed to quakes, still talks about how I stood on the bed like a crazy person. If the trembler in Osaka was the biggest ever, I would have felt it here. Or so I thought.

An hour later, when I went to pick up my daughter from school, the principal rushed out to my car to tell me that a tsunami warning had been issued. The wave was due to arrive about half an hour later. My daughter's teacher told me that it had already hit the northeastern coast of Japan, washing houses away.

I drove home along a road that runs almost parallel to the river, a road that tends to flood during typhoons, my eye on the water level. In my rearview mirror, I could see where the river empties into the Pacific Ocean. Was the water being sucked out to sea? I couldn't tell. Fire trucks were patrolling the riverside, blaring sirens, and warning people to get away from the water and seek shelter inland.

I tried to stay calm for the sake of my children, but I was relieved to get home, to hole up inside and shut the doors, believing that the levee would keep the water at bay. Then my daughter and I settled in front of the television to witness the damage wrought by what turned out to be the strongest earthquake ever recorded in Japan.

The tsunami, when it hit Tokushima Prefecture, could be measured in inches. However, all weekend long, we continued to be under a tsunami watch. While I downplayed the danger to my children, I knew that our house was close to water, just over the levee from a great river, and that the tsunami in Iwate had leapt over less. I knew that another quake could hit at any time, closer to us. And then there was news of a failing nuclear reactor, damaged by the tsunami.

As I write this, there are ongoing concerns about radiation poisoning and food safety, even here on the island of Shikoku. I've started to take precautions, checking the source of our produce, making sure it isn't from an irradiated zone, and I put together an earthquake emergency kit, but, to my great surprise, I don't want to run.

While disasters piled one upon another, I found myself digging in my heels. In the days following the tsunami, I blocked out all news from abroad. I didn't care what was happening outside of these islands. Even though Japan was no longer the super cool, high-flying economic power that had first attracted me, but quite literally broken, I found myself firmly tethered here. Maybe it was because the children holding their somber graduation ceremonies in evacuation centers so closely resembled the kids I'd taught for my first ten years in Japan. They looked like *my* kids. And the now homeless fishermen and farmers reminded me of the neighbors who bring us freshly harvested spinach and carrots every spring. They were like people I knew, the ones who'd attended my wedding ceremony and helped out when my children were in the hospital.

By this time I'd renewed my children's Japanese passports and flight was an option, but I only wanted to stay, to help others, and to teach my children how to care for their people. They had become, I realized, *my* people, too. Instead of imagining our lives in another country, I thought of my son and daughter in a future Japan, a Japan that I suddenly wanted to fight for.

The other day, a door-to-door salesman rang my bell. When I opened the door, he peered around me and said, "Isn't there anyone at home?" As if I were invisible, or temporary. As if I didn't belong.

"I'm here," I said. I might have added, "I am one of you, and I'm not going anywhere."

HEIDI KOELZ

THE SMALLEST TWIG

I notice first the work of different hands. The inscriptions are surprisingly clear, though it helps to be level with the windowpane to read them. Colorless, diamond-etched, they catch the light.

What prompted this charming act of vandalism one spring day at sundown? We know the date because Nathaniel and Sophia Hawthorne both carved it into the glass: April 3, 1843. What the newlyweds engraved on a window at the Old Manse is intimate, offhand—ephemeral as an evening.

Sophia started with wide, arcing script. (Did she struggle with the implement? Did she try the ring first on her finger or straight off hold it in her hand?)

"Man's accidents are GOD's purposes," she wrote and signed her name and the year.

Nathaniel followed, in larger letters:

Nath' Hawthorne
This is his study
1843

Then Sophia, in cramped writing:

The smallest twig
Leans clear against the sky

Nathaniel added that those lines were "composed by my wife and written with her diamond." But she had the final say:

Inscribed by my
husband at sunset

April 3rd 1843.
In the gold light. SAH.

It's not difficult to imagine the couple passing the ring back and forth, but how had they begun? Had Nathaniel urged his bride to test the hardness of her diamond? Or did he catch her scratching the glass in his study and decide to add his mark? Sophia's first words suggest that she felt pressed to say something of importance. Man's accidents, God's purposes: she might have jotted it on the scrap of paper at a stationer's to test a pen, a sentiment she could stand behind, but nothing personal. Or so I thought. When I began to read about her, I learned that Sophia might have had in mind a particular accident: that February, pregnant, she had slipped on the ice and miscarried.

In that light, Nathaniel's graffiti—not much more than "Nat was here"—makes him seem almost petulant, refusing to answer her, to move in thought beyond the act of writing. Or is it just that I expect something more from him, the author? Why should Sophia's words be more poetic?

Was she throwing him a challenge: What is worth cutting into the house itself, to read day after day? Something abiding, no? A twig, then—something so small, so fleeting, it catches time by the throat.

His next line—that "composed by my wife"—might be playful, or proud, but I hear a patronizing note. It's that word "composed," as though she had tried too hard.

No matter, I'll play your game, Sophia seems to say: "Inscribed by my husband." But she couldn't help appending one last line. The sunset drew her out again; that "gold light" caught her painter's eye. Hers was the vision of something enduring in a twig against the sky.

For Sophia Peabody Hawthorne was an artist too. Before she married, she had studied with the leading painters in New England; she had exhibited and sold her work—despite suffering from regular, crippling migraines. As a suitor, Nathaniel first came to know her through her writing—a collection of exuberant letters she had sent her family from Cuba—and later drew on it for his fictions.

By the time the couple settled in Concord, Nathaniel had made a name for himself in magazines, though payments for his stories lagged, pushing them into debt. Still, their common journal attests to a cozy life. Sophia delighted in the fields and flowers of their country home, and in entertaining guests, while Nathaniel—whose talent, she said, was "to observe & not be observed"—smiled shyly or retreated to his garden. Effervescent spring to Nathaniel's dark, still well, she had envisioned for them an artistic partnership. But while he wrote, prolifically, she became a mother of three; she continued to shield his solitude.

When Sophia was pregnant with their first daughter, Una, her husband urged her, for her health, to stop painting. The last oil canvass she completed depicted slumbering Endymion being awakened by the goddess of the moon.

Knowing this, how can we read the window writing, work of one evening preserved in glass? The Hawthornes' diary offers a fuller record of their marriage, but one that's been carefully redacted: Sophia took pen and scissors to it before it was published. The windowpane is public, fixing private thoughts in place. What a difference it must have made to carve words into a surface that couldn't be crumpled, torn, or tossed away.

Between them, the Hawthornes dated this pane of glass three times; they must have had posterity in mind. Did Nathaniel credit Sophia because, having signed already, he was wary of her "smallest twig" being mistaken for his? It was more than a decade later that he complained to his publisher about the "damned mob of scribbling women" that had ruined the reading public, but it's difficult, reading this, not to hear a similar sentiment.

What touches me in this exchange, which transpired when Sophia still painted in the breakfast room beneath Nathaniel's study, is that I can almost follow her conflicted feelings about being, or remaining, an artist.

For many visitors to the Old Manse, the study windows are the most striking part of the tour. The weight of the couple's arms still seems to lean into the work. It's unsettling to look out toward the river and see their writing suspended before the boathouse, to be reminded of how effortlessly objects, even those we casually deface, outlast us. But although Nathaniel Hawthorne gave that historic house the name we know it by today—"manse" inspired by the succession of ministers who had occupied it before them—the Hawthornes lived there for only three years. They were turned out, owing rent.

But for the stories in *Mosses from an Old Manse*, the farmhouse might be a footnote to the transcendentalist movement in Concord. Bronson Alcott and Margaret Fuller visited; Henry David Thoreau planted the garden out front; Ralph Waldo Emerson wrote his essay "Nature" there. Or the tour might focus on the property's colonial history. A couple of generations earlier, Emerson's grandfather, Reverend William, had watched the Revolutionary War begin at the North Bridge, barely beyond musket range. Emerson commemorated that "shot heard round the world" for the dedication of a monument erected in 1836, six years before Nathaniel and Sophia claimed at the Old Manse their conjugal pride of place. By then that wooden bridge had been swept down the Concord River, but the Hawthornes would have seen the obelisk on the near shore.

From the study now, looking out at the reconstructed bridge, a visitor can fail to notice a low stone wall that survives from the farm's early days. It's only thigh high, the kind of loose line of rocks, unburdened by mortar, that New Englanders take for granted. The nearby roads are dotted and dashed with granite that was dug from the land, piled to clear fields and keep good neighbors.

From such a wall, not far from Concord in a stretch of reclaimed forest, I set out late one February afternoon on a snowshoe hike. It's rare to meet others in the winter woods, though the air is the best of the year—easy to breathe. A good snow stays fresh beneath the trees long after the roadside pack turns grimy from passing cars. Even off the trails, with underbrush blanketed and branches bare, there are no vines to trip over, no impediments to sight. Traffic in the distance could be mistaken for a river's lull. Ice crunches underfoot.

In that concentrated quiet, I came upon a snowdrift swept into a suspiciously tidy square. I had stepped down into the hollow before I realized I was standing in a cellar hole. It wasn't much to look at: traces of a foundation, what used to be a house, a barn—impossible to tell. When I come across remains of settlements in other seasons, I usually pause, but I'm quick to move on. But having stumbled into that ruin, with only my own tracks to mar the scene, I stopped. In the gold light of the setting sun, I saw the marks of an individual's hands—that careful arrangement of stones, half covered in the midwinter cold. I couldn't match the work with a name, but I knew whoever built it had laid a foundation to last.

I thought of Sophia's "smallest twig," of what it meant to be a woman at a time that brooked no scribbling wife's ambition, but nevertheless to insist on recognizing some harmony of form, even— especially—in something so slight, so seemingly insignificant.

The apple trees behind the Old Manse can't be the same ones she studied from that window, but her inscription, her view, remains. And if she hadn't thought that fragile twig worth seeing, I never would have read about her life or learned that none other than Emerson had called her "a true artist" with "the beauty making eye."

SANDRA GAIL LAMBERT

ROLLING IN THE MUD

I've never touched the earth much. Water, yes. As a child, I'd unbuckle knee pads and thigh straps to lift legs out of their braces. My skin hissed as it pulled away from the brushed leather of thigh cuffs. With braces and crutches left in a jumble off to the side, I'd crawl into snow-fed lakes with sudden, immense depths or swim in pools until the world acquired a chlorine-rainbowed hue. My legs pushed though the water and expanded into their natural shape. The abeyance of gravity would smooth the indentations of straps and aluminum rods designed to untwist and make plumb. These days I slip out of a wheelchair and into Florida waters. Spring-fed rivers warm or cool depending on the season, and Atlantic waves toss me until the sea floor scrapes against my skin and water burns my lungs. Summer times, in the bathtub-warm and gentle Gulf, I lie on my back, glasses off, stare at the now blurred, impressionist sky, and float with no effort the way big women can.

But it's not often that I touch the earth directly. Sometimes my hands dig at the surface to plant or pull in my yard. More often it is less immediate: still connected, but once removed. A friend digs for me, her shovel hits a root, and I hear the thud of metal and see the sudden strain in her forearms. I search out the narrow reaches of blackwater creeks where leather fern spores bronze against my shoulders. My kayak noses into the high-tide openings in salt marshes until maiden cane tangles the paddle and black needle rush leans in to itch over my knuckles. Driving over the wash board ripple of a dirt road after rain can shake the topography of a landscape into my bones. And now and again, the rasp of littoral grasses at the edge of a lake sounds into the keel of my boat and feathers the backside of my thighs.

The La Chua Trail into Paynes Prairie is one of my places of least remove from the earth. Here I first saw a bald eagle, a lotus in bloom, a whooping crane. I've pushed my wheelchair past two hundred alligators lined along the trail, their heads following in slow motion, while I and friends make jokes about looking as little like poodles as possible. That year when low water levels attracted hundreds of wood storks, I went day after day to see the fluffed necks of the young ones, and it's not unusual for a water moccasin to raise a warning head out of the grass alongside one of my wheels. The Prairie is a reason I moved to Florida.

I first traveled the trail in a manual chair, then in a scooter, and now in a power wheelchair. When I hear the hiss of sand under my wheels, feel the sink and pull, I know to shift my weight and turn onto a clump of grass that congeals the surface and gives traction. I traveled this trail before there were signs or gates. I traveled it before the State built an observation deck with steps instead of a ramp. It blocks the piece of dry ground where I used to perch each winter to look over the marsh and watch thousands of sandhill cranes mix with occasional groups of white pelicans. And now a vista-destroying boardwalk snakes around Alachua Sink, but it is still a place of connection. I still travel here.

All the seasons on Paynes Prairie have touched me. The purple and yellow days are in the spring - swaths of marsh marigold and spikes of pickerel weed. You have to go in the summer to see the lotus and the June weight of air in my lungs is a comfort even as sweat slicks the vinyl of my arm rests and stings along my spine. September, still summer in Florida, is always a judgment call. Clouds, black and shot through with a metallic green, tower into the sky, and I brace against downdraft winds to watch the last sunlight at the edge of a storm. It races across the Prairie tinting the oranges from rust to tangerine, the yellows to neon. It is only when lightning strikes close that I can turn away. Full speed, leaning forward over the controls as if that will make the chair go faster, heedless of hips and back, I bounce over the trail to my van. If I've timed it right, I'm closing the doors before the first, fat raindrops turn into a voice-drowning rush against the metal roof. Once, in the season of government controlled burns, a sheer curtain line of fire came close, so thin that it barely blurred the view beyond, and it seemed possible to take a single step and be through it. The inner structure of the air changed as ions shifted and crackled the hairs along my arms. It was as if I were on another planet. Sometimes in the winter there are cold days that make my bones ache. Alligators burrow in the mud to stay warm, the low humidity blues the sky, and egret and ibis white glints against the eyes.

In the late nineties, the Prairie flooded. It wasn't like in 1873. Then the Alachua Sink that drains the Prairie blocked and stayed that way for almost twenty years until, in a sudden drop, the lake disappeared and left steamboats, waterfront tourist attractions, and thousands of fish stranded. For us, it flooded high and for long enough that water lapped over the outside lanes of the highway that cuts the Prairie in two, and alligators, desperate for any high ground, lay nose up to the traffic. There were daily reports. Would the road crumble apart? Float away? Crack? I wanted it to. I wanted to witness the Prairie become once again the Great Alachua Savanna. This did not happen.

But I started searching the road for a place to pull over, yank my kayak out from the back of the van, and slip into the water. I'd leave my empty wheelchair beside the road as a puzzle for the police or State Park rangers. All I had to do was get beyond bull horn range. It would be worth the ticket just to see what it was they charged me with. But I'm not quick and my van is not stealthy so I never tried. Of course, I wasn't the only one thinking this way, and eventually the State Park allowed guided kayak trips. I signed up.

When the day comes, I'm early so it's just Lars and me at the edge of the flood. The water is wonderfully disorienting. The big oak where I usually park my van and start my strolls is at the new shore line. Lars, the man who literally wrote the book on the Prairie, is unloading all the rental kayaks while I snap and click the gear into place on my own boat. He has to go unlock the gate for the rest of the people. Will I be okay? Yes, I say. And this is part of why I admire Lars—he believes me. He lets me be on my own. This type of respect is usually something I have to fight for, even threaten lawsuits over. Sometimes in groups Lars introduces me as an outdoorswoman. It's my favorite thing that I've ever been called.

He leaves. I'm alone on the Prairie. It is still rising, they say. There is no one else here. I stare at the water and think I see it creep along the trail. The gate is locked until Lars unlocks it and lets the rest of today's kayak tour in. I don't have long to be alone, but I do have this time. I won't wait. I drop out of my wheelchair and land on the very last of dry earth, at least for today. I scoot on my bottom, pull the kayak, scoot more, pull the kayak. Through my nylon pants, under my bare hands, the ground becomes first cooler, then wet.

This isn't a regular lake edge. No pennywort laps through stalks of arrowhead and bull rush anchored in muck. No buttressed trunks of cypress trees line the shore. This has been high ground for a hundred years. The spiderworts, star and pepper grasses, accustomed to sun-baked sand, are dying under the water but their roots hold firm in earth that is reluctant to become mud. Again, my arms lift the weight of my body and this time my palms press through sand into water. The path is becoming lake bottom. I pull the kayak to me and lean against it as a red-tailed hawk screams past. This used to be a dry meadow that provided mice and snakes. It will be again. This lake won't exist forever. These events that have led to me being alone, here, on the ground are as ephemeral. I listen for engines, but it's too soon to expect anyone.

I lie on my back, knees bent. A thin skin of water ripples down it. My legs flop to the side, my hip follows, and now my breasts are against the earth. My body mixes the wilted grasses with the soil. I roll again and my shoulder blades sink into the smoothness of dissolving plantain leaves. I spread my arms and rotting grasses wrap around them. A twist of my head and I'm at eye-level with everything I used to wheel over. Another roll further into the water and wet slides along my ribs and covers my wrists. And now I think about an alligator swimming and searching for dry land.

I reverse direction until my elbows scrape into hard sand and the stiff edges of hedge-nettle and Spanish needle. I lift onto my elbows and look around. I can see for a long ways. There are no alligators. I leave the myth of safety on high ground and roll back into the new mud. I stretch out flat, face up. Am I an agent of erosion? Am I joining water and land? My arms reach over my head until fingertips brush into the loosened fibers of earth and muscles pull in a stretch that I usually only feel in bed. It tugs at my flanks and below my belly where thighs and hips are in an unaccustomed straight line. The underside of both knees aches, a good ache, with extension. My head falls and creates a well of water that laps at my earlobes.

Lars' old van rattles over the gravel. I squirm to sitting, readjust my clothes, pull strands of brown grass off my shoulders, and push the kayak through wilting dog fennel to a floatable depth. I splash the less muddy water over my front to clean up a bit. Leaning on the kayak, I kneel over it and tumble and twist into the seat. My knees are the last part of me pressed into the watery earth of Paynes Prairie.

For hours we kayak through fields of lotus and alongside the sunken steps of the observation tower. Attached to the drowning branches of elderberry, gelatinous balls of frog eggs rock in the slow wake of our boats. I stop paddling. The others are ahead of me. I lean towards the bow to ease my back, and my face lowers over my knees and into the oily plant stains and heavy velvet smell of the shoreline. The kayak, responding to the shifts of my body, the wind, the pull of imperceptible currents, turns itself around. Behind us, where we've just traveled, alligators rise.

I'm home. It's evening. I've hosed the sand and slime off the boat, rinsed the paddle, and untangled rotting morning glory from around the bow line. My body is showered and smells only of oatmeal soap and chlorinated water. Now, I'm going to sprinkle baking soda over the laundry, but I hold the clothes against my nose one last time. The water will rise over where I was today and then fall away. What will the path look like when it emerges? Will there have been time for sagittaria to root and grow tall over the water? Will the purple, white, and yellow of bladderworts skim the surface to either side? As I roll over a barely dry trail, shifting away from the patches of mud that remain, will my front wheels dip and lift out of the lingering physical memory of my body? Perhaps lotus will have spread close to the path. I'll perch at the edge of my seat, anchor one arm around the backrest, and lean over the water that remains to reach the oval petals and touch into the swirl of orange-stalked stamens at their center. I close the washing machine lid and set the rinse water to hot.

Marjorie Maddox

Pennsylvania Round in Four Parts

I.

Before Pennsylvania, the world was flat, the distance between two horizons a straight view. In those other states, I walked a state-of-mind, linear but unliveable. Map coordinates located something less than inhale/exhale. Now place has something to do with oxygen horded in the limbs of hemlock and elm, with the way these mountains bulge with breath. Air blooms among such unbashful blues and greens, darts with the dragonfly, drinks with the white-tailed deer. Always, it winds with the creeks, then glides over Allegheny curves to rise up with the hawks. When the firefly blinks, it is not an SOS but a refrain from a mountain song so old you can hear the hills humming.

II.

The only light in the shotgun house is the steady blink of the TV. I've swept her job at the mill beneath the corners of a forty-year-old carpet, crammed his factory work in the closet they no longer open. But for years, I couldn't ignore the hum of what they didn't have, the absence they gave my husband in abundance. I can almost touch each wall with its peeling paper of orange watering cans as I hike between sheet-covered furniture lined up for the one clear view of a sitcom. Though I try to get comfortable, I can't. Even the air bunches up against itself between straight planes of plaster.

Outside the narrow windows, bricks block the coal-tinged breeze. Rusting lawn chairs clutter the neighbors' crumbling porches from which out-of-work, middle-aged men stare at each other and do nothing. Teens compete at squealing their makeshift hot rods down the thin strip of asphalt leftover between tightly parked pickups and hand-me-down four-doors. From the cracked sidewalk, barefoot girls in midriffs pause their hopscotch and wave.

I head instead to their backyard, where blooms border a six-by-four yard and spill over with geraniums and pansies, roses and Lazy Susans, tulips and marigolds. Humming birds nip nectar. Tomatoes bob from stalks tied-up with old panty hose. Lettuce proclaims victory over rabbits, and strawberries congratulate themselves for against-the-odds growth. My brown thumb, envious to the end, fingers joy.

III.

The doe and its fawn enter our backyard on the slant, kitty-corner themselves from rhododendron bush to magnolia. Theirs is a quiet joy, stepping just so from their hills into suburbia, the distance six hops of a skipped stone. They've forgotten to worry and remember this grass and the long limbs of our maple. They step easily between swing set and tool shed, detour around a half-finished game of croquet. Nurtured on grace, they politely turn their sleek necks to avoid our gaze. From behind glass, my children stare. They compare the soft sheen of the deer's fur to sketched likenesses in store-bought books. My husband warns them not to open the door, not to let the conditioned air out.

IV.

Beneath the tent flaps, my children and I breathe in the wild Pennsylvania air. The mountains, we say, are hugging the wind, the laurel so thick we could pick a thousand blooms. All evening we count the blinks of fireflies. We sense hawks circling the night clouds above our camp and bears obediently pausing between the zigzags of evergreens. We listen long into the dark until the drone of crickets leads us into dreams full of deer and ruffed grouse. Then we doze without worry, the curve of the world huddled about us as we breathe its crispness in.

In the chilled morning air, when we emerge from sleep and the tent door, it is—almost surprisingly—just our backyard on the outside, our hammock waiting in the half-light of dawn. We think we hear the doe and her fawn, but it is my husband up on the patio, already flipping blueberry pancakes on the griddle. The country-style bacon sizzles with joy when we join him, humming our campfire rounds

ANDREA MARCUSA

DATA PLACE

On the Internet @ 3 PM. Above the Rockies, in a 747, meetings in San Francisco miles behind, and ETA Kennedy Airport hours away. The Kelly green dot, plain and straight forward as a period, appears on the laptop screen signaling that the Skype internet picture phone is on.

Another minute and the Skype ring sounds above the din of the jet engine. I answer and see the fragile, flickering image of my Mike broadcast from North Africa. We chat about my flight and trip to the West Coast. He asks me if I can hear the muffled call to prayer that flows in through his window from a nearby mosque. I don't have the heart to tell him no, so instead I ask him what time it is and he says almost midnight.

Another Kelly green dot brightens. It's Dan, his brother, now connected. I type him an instant message asking about school, then look up at Mike on the screen and tell him I'm on with Dan, too.

"That's so cool," he says. "Ask him what the score is."

It's amazing how North Africa and the American baseball mix in Mike.

While I type, Mike says he'll be right back—his cell phone is ringing. Just as I've pressed the "send" button to ask the score, he returns to the screen, cell phone in hand. "Mom, it's Dad calling back from Paris." It seems that each of us has reached across space and time at exactly the same instant to this data place, a complex set of servers and code that we'll never see.

"Say hi for me and tell him I'll call when I land at JFK," I say.

Dan has typed back that the Red Sox are ahead by seven.

"Mom, he sends his loves and he'll land in New York around 4 PM tomorrow and to say hi to Dan for him," says Mike.

Four of us on three continents on earth, and me in the air, 30,000 feet up. Somehow we want to connect despite the separation, or maybe because of it, via computers, cell phones, keyboard, but still in the shorthand dialect of family, with phrases as familiar to us as kitchen table banter.

Dan writes in the medium of IM, Mike from the remotest point prefers the video phone and my husband is content on a Smart Phone. The messages zip back and forth, bouncing from satellite to earth and back up to me on a plane, which when I look down is now approaching the Great Plains. A bit about the baseball score and Rivera's close, something about midterms and bio-chem lab, and the weather in France (rainy), Morocco (hot), and New Hampshire (flurrying). It feels so familiar, yet by its nature and necessity so urgent, but also such an ordinary fact for our time.

I wait for Mike to say something or Dan to type and then I realize how it's hard to separate the emotional links from the high tech signals. I'm told that these connections enable us to reinforce, rather than replace, our bond. I know that I'd like nothing better than to all be together in the same room, in the same city, on the same continent, gathered around a meal and a ball game. But this nuclear family, like the universe, expands and stretches to ever distant reaches. We remain linked by all the complex emotions binding families together and connected via computer chips, pixels, bits of data and Wi-Fi. This connection is invisible but magnetic, despite how easily it can disconnect from the tiniest interference or turbulence. I want to tell them about this—the importance of it all and the fragility of what we have right now, in this instant. But I don't. Instead I hold the moment close to me, the feeling as beautiful and fleeting as the wisps of clouds I whiz past outside my window, that glow in the pink light of the setting sun.

Diane Lee Moomey

Solstice, again

The drive at dusk—halfway between San Gregorio and Half Moon Bay, I stop the car beside a nameless cliff. Water hangs lightly in the air, not quite rain. The engine clicks and crackles as metal cools, until finally the only sounds are of the surf on the beach far below and the surf of blood in my own ears. Though the sun is behind clouds, I spin the crystal suncatcher hanging from the rearview and get out.

Hush—that pause as earth rolls into darkness. Hush as "day" turns an invisible corner and becomes "night"; as "autumn" at this same moment is turning that same corner and becoming "winter." Sky low enough to taste, and that quality of air found here and now and at no other place or time: chill moisture rising with the smells of old dying things, of kelp and clams, of salt, of the occasional whiff of smoke from a chimney. Eroded hillsides are clad in shades of brown with occasional traces of leftover summer green. New grass has barely appeared; clay slopes still cling to last season's ragged blades as one might cling to a towel, slipping out of the shower.

I turn my back to the Pacific and face the highway, leaning against the still-warm hood, imagining lives for my companions on the road. *This* one passing three cars at once, is late for the last meeting of the day; *that* one with grocery bags heaped against the windows, is hurrying toward a home soon to be filled with the smells of food and the noise of small children; *this* one *not* hurrying, is driving thoughtfully just under the speed limit to a quiet empty home to spend the evening with books and music.

That one over there is also not hurrying, as I was not hurrying during all those months and years when Home was simply the drive from one "X" on the map to another. *That* one is one for whom "place" does not exist, for whom "home" is that contained within

Car: one with nowhere to stay, only waiting until the night is late enough that one parked vehicle with sleeping person may not be noticed.

I turn to face the Pacific again. The beach below is empty of visible life, as were the snowfields of the Canadian Shield at this very hour half a lifetime ago. As I imagined lives for my fellow travelers, so I imagine lives for my fellow fauna: for seals and gulls shoulder to shoulder on rock islands just out of sight; for starfish and anemone in crevices at the bottoms of tide pools, for hermit crabs trying to get comfortable in borrowed shells, for barnacles hooked tight to old boats and rock faces. I imagine lives for shrimp fishermen in boat-homes anchored far offshore, at this hour heating soup in warm galleys. I imagine all these having claimed Place, having sought, even fought for, that.

The almost-rain has turned to drops, and wind comes up again: not yet cold, but *I* will be when my cotton shirt is soaked through. I turn back to the car. Day's light is almost gone. The only color left in this dun afternoon is the yellow gleam in my windows: false flowers bought last month in a gleeful shopping spree and now filling the dashboard, the hatchback, and every side window this Ford possesses. I pat her hood, settle into the front seat, spin the suncatcher again, and think of turtles.

Not turtles *here*—I have never seen any *here*—but of Turtle for whom the seeds of Place are in the genes. Turtle is born with the first layer of Home already wrapped round her like a cloak. As, to my surprise, was I: searching has revealed not *Place found*, but *Seed found. Seed* is carefully watered and fed and gives birth to the self's home: the car home, the road home, the house-home, the place-on-earth.

The hurrying ones are gone now. The highway is slick and shining in my headlights as I pull out into the northbound lane to finish my drive. Not far now—a few miles, a right turn, a left, another right. A winding climb up the flanks of earth's dragon, to the very upper curve of her back, and parking in the place that is left open for me. I am welcomed here. Key in the lock, hand on the doorknob; I think of the Rumi poem about one who lives with half a loaf of bread in a house that fits around her like a nest, and needs nothing more.

Needs nothing more. This tiny place where my *things* are—my lights and plants, my paper and paints and music, the place where tea is, where fire will soon be, where the door can be shut tight against the wet and the cold—this is enough. I feel a rush of gratitude to all my midwives.

The gray-and-gray cat is twining herself round my ankles, calling loudly, reminding me it is high time indeed that I came home, time to go inside and take care of the most important business of the day. Before the door is fully open, she has snaked through the gap and waits beside her purple dish.

I wipe my feet, set down my bag, and close the door behind me.

CAROLE ROSENTHAL

THE WOODS (1953)

1

The woods behind the school were dark and green with a ribbon of creek running through them. The creek glittered like tarnished silver. The banks were steep, the water shallow. When the sun was high, patches of light shifted like breath on the high grass, and vines muffled contours of trees on the edge of a clearing. I never saw people in these woods, only signs of people, their cast-offs, crumpled cigarette packs, Old Golds, Lucky Strikes, their sodden wrappers, half-stomped into the dirt, cellophane gleaming. I spotted grape Nehi soda bottles, dented beer cans, a twisted argyle sock. I found a paper bag stuffed with used sanitary napkins floating half-in, half-out of the water, trembling in a rivulet on a ledge of stones. What was it? At first I didn't know.

I crept down to the creek, skidding in mud, clutching a broken tree branch to protect myself, and to poke at the sack. The sack tore, and a dark, slimy-looking pad slipped loose, and floated downstream. I didn't have a regular menstrual period yet, I didn't have any period yet, though I longed for one. Would I ever be like the other girls in the seventh grade who already had snappy code names for their cycles like *my monthly visitor is coming, or Herman is here*? My father said yes, but my mother kept mum on the subject. *Keeping mum* was a phrase of the times. "Mum" was also the name of the red-capped deodorant my mother hid, along with her own box of sanitary napkins, beneath the sink. She never talked to me about the working of my body, or her own–and she never would. Not that bodies embarrassed her. She freely assessed other women's bodies. "Flabby thighs" (women in swim suits at the pool), "prominent clavicles" (too skinny), and "trailer *tuckhes*" (one of my friends). On the contrary, as an artist, she gloried in studying flesh. But words embarrassed her. Words were too public for her, too powerful. She left the frank discussions to my father ("Daddy's modern," "Daddy's so smart!").

"It's natural," my father said. "In puberty you're going to start bleeding every month. Once menstruation begins, girls need to keep themselves very clean. You'll need to fold back the lips of your vagina to clean yourself when you bathe."

"How do *boys* clean themselves after they menstruate?" Stricken, but smart-alecky (*Vagina! Vagina!* my father was big on clinical names, not cutie-pie ones), I'd imitated his matter-of-fact tone.

He squinted at me, hard. "Boys don't menstruate."

"Why not?"

My question made him realize he'd left out an important anatomical point.

But I seemed to be naturally dirty, like a boy–"nasty," in the southern vernacular.

When Mr. Barnes, the school principal, made me line up in the school hallway each morning, waiting for him to sign my pink admittance slip to class because I was late, I was considered dirty in another way. "Evil-minded," he'd murmur to me, and I squirmed. "A bad reputation is the worst thing a girl can have."

My "bad reputation" arose when I talked too much in class, eager for attention. I talked about sex, anxious guesses and boastful lies, trying to encourage other kids who knew more to discuss this subject with me. I had various theories I asserted as fact. One was that boys' penises were flexible and moved autonomously, like a tongue, minimizing clumsy body thrust, hip bones clunking other bones. Some seventh grade girls bragged about their boyfriends in eighth grade or in high school, so I bragged I had an even older boyfriend who'd graduated from high school. To verify this, I cut my father's younger and handsomer head out of my parents' wedding picture and carried it in my wallet, leaving a hole in a tuxedo standing next to my mother and her beautiful bouquet in their wedding album. I was humiliated when Joe Honeycutt, a slow learner in my class, sent me a note asking me to meet him after school so he could "rape" me, and the popular boys intercepted it and laughed, and passed it around. "She's asking for it," the boys said.

I followed the path along the creek to the meadow. Even before I got out of the woods, I heard cars on the road, the spin of gravel that led directly to our house, and the occasional motorcycle. The motorcycle might belong to the high-schooler who thought I was "cute," his little sister told my little sister, exciting and frightening me.

A dog barked wildly, out of sight. Donna, my neighborhood friend, saw me and stiffened and glared, her skirt tight across her belly and hips, wrinkled from sitting in school, her arms crossed under her ample, still jiggly breasts. She was an eighth-grade repeat, a slack-mouthed, wide-hipped kid from New Jersey whose family sent her to live with her elderly aunt and uncle here because she'd gotten in trouble with her "uncles," young guys, she described them, guys who carried rubbers in their wallets.

Donna tilted her head, and her wavy brown hair swayed off to one side. "Why didn't you wait for me after school? You said you'd meet me under the tree."

"I forgot," I said.

Another lie. I wanted respite from my bad reputation, and from Donna, who was part of it it.

Mr. Barnes told my mother I went to the woods to meet boys, but he was wrong. When I wanted to see boys I'd walk home the long way, on the road that passed Ace Hardware, past the barber shop adjoining it with its swirling candy-striped pole, and past the penny-candy store where you could buy cigarettes. That's where older boys, suave drop-outs with their pegged pants and ducks'-ass hairdo with comb marks, slouched against lamp posts and smoked. The one I had a crush on would smile at me from the front page of the local paper when he was arrested as a cat burglar the following month.

But the point of my long moody rambles in the woods was to be alone. To get away from my school and from myself, that skinny, flat-chested package of fears, longings, and inexplicable compulsions that

105

had me labeled as a "behavior problem." Ashamed of my inexperience, of being younger than anyone else, of being Jewish in a setting where a classmate had feigned admiring my hair while stroking my head to check for horns– knowing that my shame for being Jewish was wrong, a *shondeh* for Jews everywhere–I was a baffled outsider in the new territory of adolescence and the Bible belt south, a "northerner" who didn't speak the local lingo ("I swan!" people around me declared as exclamation, interchangeable with "I swear!"). I often couldn't fathom them.

Hey, good-lookin'
What'cha got cookin'?
How's about cooking
Something up with me?

It was late spring, the air sticky and soft, and everybody was singing Hank Williams' songs. We'd lived in Virginia for almost a year. *If it doesn't work out, we can always move back, my parents had promised.* It's not working out! I shouted each night. But nobody paid attention.

I turned around. Someone was tossing pebbles in the road in front of us. Donna swiveled too. Two older boys strolled up the narrow strip of sidewalk behind, boys I recognized from outside Ace Hardware.

Donna called out, "Hey, you! Don't be bums. We don't want you following us! Walk faster," she commanded me, checking over her shoulder to make sure they were still there, yelling and giggling. "Go away! Get lost! Take a long walk on a short pier," and to me, breathless, "Hurry, hurry! They're catching up."

I began to run.

"Slow down," she hissed, alongside me for a moment and grabbing at my elbow.

Another pebble landed nearby. These boys weren't exactly chasing us, but they were closing in.

"Where y'all going?" the tall one asked, catching up with me and Donna. He had carved out cheekbones, long, slitty blue eyes, tight blond curls. This was the one who had been singing at us.

"We're going home!" Donna skewed her hip defiantly, bumping into him, and slanting her eyes. "Where are you going?"

"We're going to walk with you." The boy twiddled his cigarette, blew a smoke ring and then smiled sidelong with narrow lips.

"Maybe we're heartbreakers," Donna said, and giggled. "You don't always get what you want." She skipped a little ahead of him.

The blond boy stopped and ducked his head, looking serious. For a moment he spoke formally. "Let me introduce myself. My name is Bobby Batey, and I've seen you before. This"–he poked his thumb back to the brown-haired boy–"is Jimmy Searcy. He's a good old son, a gentleman, you'd probably like him real fine."

Jimmy Searcy caught up with us too. He was cute, lean and doggy-looking, wearing a striped tee-shirt, like a little boy, twisting his thumb in it, with liquid brown eyes and an air of clumsy enthusiasm. Later Donna would tell me that Jimmy was baby-ish, that Bobby Batey owned the good looks. To me, Bobby was mean-looking, his features too tight, as if he'd been skinned.

Jimmy asked me, "Hey, who is your teacher at school?"

"Mr. Koontz. He's new."

"What grade?"

"Seventh. This is his first year teaching. He was in the Marines."

Jimmy looked interested. "Is he tough? Does he whup people?"

I shook my head. There were boys who got paddled in the boiler room, but by Mr. Mashburn, the assistant principal who looked like Snooky Lansom on Your Hit Parade on TV, not by Mr. Koontz, who seemed bemused most of the time.

"I used to go to Alexander Park too. I like that school." I was struck that he was talking to me like a regular person, not someone making fun of you, or flirting, not like a boy. "Then I went to Craddock, but I dropped out to go to weldin' school so I could work in the shipyard along with my Daddy."

"*Weldin'* school?" I mimicked his accent.

Funny to me, strange, that grown southerners called their fathers "Daddy," like little kids.

"To learn how to weld boats. It's good work. You ever been on a battleship? Where do you come from?"

"Chicago," I said. "We moved here last year and we're moving back soon."

That was a lie. The lie I told to myself, the same lie my parents told when we moved down south, my desperate wish.

Donna Motley slipped in front of me, pushing, laughing, and fell into step with Jimmy, so I lagged to one side.

"You and Jimmy, huh?" Bobby Batey said to Donna. He scooped up another handful of pebbles from the road, and flung them past her. He started humming "Your Cheatin' Heart," singing the part about how it would make her "blue," and ending by crooning–"*Come walk with me, pretty baby, Baby Donna–Baby Donna–*" until Donna laughed and swept her hair back, and slackened her pace, letting him brush her body to catch up.

We got almost to my house at the corner, a gray-roofed house on the other side of the street with pink corrugated asbestos shingles, and I swerved abruptly away from them and trotted through the back, locking the door. Donna called out to me, Jimmy too, but I raced through the tiny kitchen and dining area to the living room in time to watch them through my screen door as they turned too at the end of the block, Donna strutting now towards her aunt's house with Bobby, almost arm in arm, Jimmy trailing. I saw them pass our yard with its two strips of cement for a driveway, high grass growing between. *See*-ment, the southerners pronounced it.

Just as they said Marilyn *Mon*-roe, with the accent on the first syllable. My father parked his Studebaker on the *see*-ment strips when he was home. I heard sudden, more frenzied barking, high-pitched. My own dog, Tawny–my sister's dog, really–threw himself against the screen, jumping up, wanting me to come out and play.

Jimmy Searcy heard him too. He'd spied me in the doorway peeking at him, and called to Tawny, "Here, boy, here, boy, here pup, here... *hooh, hooo, hoooo...*," crouching and extending his hand.

"Is that your dog?" He was on the other side of a wide lawn that had no flowers or shrubs, only a single sapling. "That hound sure looks like a coon dog. He could probably go after raccoons real fast. I bet he's a good hunter. I have a friend in Carolina with a coon dog just like that. If you ever want to get rid of him, let me know."

"He's ours," I yelled.

Jimmy bullhorned his hands. "I'm going to come by and see you sometime."

Tawny was still barking, locked out, pawing the screen and then dashing in circles as he followed Donna and Trixie, and the two guys.

My mother was asleep. Not even the barking or my yelling had woken her. She took naps in the afternoon, sprawled sideways on her bed, fully dressed, black hair loose, splayed across her cheek and the pillow, a bubble of saliva moistening her lower lip and drooling onto the chenille spread. Robbie was playing on the floor of our bedroom. Robbie and I had always shared a bedroom since she was born, but we hardly talked to each other.

2

It was the worst year of my life, worse than last year in Chicago when the baby died and my mother, sad, voiceless, slapped me hard every time I asked questions about it. For weeks, she stopped talking altogether. I worried back then that I'd caused the baby's death by sheer power of wishing, having previously instructed my parents, after Robbie turned out to be a disappointment to me, not to make any more children. From my mother's point of view, if she didn't speak facts and feelings out loud, maybe they would go away. For me, words held the opposite power: if I talked about things, naming them, I had the ability to control what happened, I could restore proportion to alarming events.

"Carole is slow to adjust," my father said. "She doesn't make adjustments easily, she's fallen under bad influences."

It was true, all of it. Especially the bad influences. Donna Motley had taught me how to masturbate using the projecting corners of desks and drawers, wearing towels around our waists for modesty so that we couldn't see each other. "My uncles showed me this," she bragged. I looked up and saw her panting red face and loose mouth and she looked somehow sticky to me, like she'd been eating grape jelly.

3

I watched Jimmy Searcy walk down the street by himself, back hunched. Bobby Batey must have stayed behind, alone with Donna. Jimmy kicked a stone when he crossed the road, then spotting me behind the screen, he cracked a smile. He waved and swung his arm in a giant arc. I ducked back from the door, embarrassed he'd caught me spying.

"Who's that?" my mother asked. "He's cute." She fluffed her hair and glanced at herself in the mirror. My mother liked boys, and she hoped that boys would like me too. She feared they wouldn't, which would reflect badly on her as a woman and mother. "Anyway, you're too young to date. Go change your school clothes and cut the lawn."

I ran to my bedroom. Often we fought, but that day she didn't want to be distracted by me, she was working on paintings she planned to show off in a local show. I changed into a backless halter and shorts, then examined myself in the mirror. I hoped boys in cars would honk their horns at me, admiring, when they drove by, seeing bare skin and not guessing from a distance how young or old I was. Safe anonymity. Twice that month I'd called boys who didn't know me and pretended to be someone else. In our yard the grass was high, scattered with dandelions and wild onions. Tawny leaped ahead, barking, joyous.

"Make that dog be quiet. Neighbors will complain."

Neighbors already complained because we kept our lawn too wild, ungroomed, with blades so high they tickled my legs, while they cropped their lawns like military haircuts, like the military housing these square boxes had been, built fifteen years earlier for families of returning sailors after the war. The power mower was broken, like much in our house. Daddy kept promising to fix it, but never did. The weeds were thick. I pushed the hand mower around the peach tree sapling I'd begged him to plant. It had blossoms, but it was still spindly, like me.

The smell of sliced wild onions layered the air.

"Ouch! Ow!" The hand mower slid away from me. I'd stepped on a pricker.

My mother yelled out the window, "Mowing in your bare feet? You're going to lose a toe."

I limped out of sight to the back, and dropped to the seat of our little red swing set. I watched Robbie through the tangle, dressed in her white pinafore from school, still clean, as played dolls by the sandbox. She'd lined up the dolls by size, big to small, and dressed the tiniest in pink hollyhock blossoms she'd stolen from behind her classroom.

A car whizzed by, a boy I couldn't recognize hanging out its side window. "Hey, Donut!" he shouted, mockingly. "Where's your hole?"

Boys were vicious. I flung myself down in thick weeds near the ditch. Mosquitoes bit me.

"Can I play?" I called to my little sister. I knew I was supposed to be too old to play dolls–I hid my dolls when friends came over, ashamed. "Please!" I begged Robbie, wanting to dip my dirty self in her spotlessness and silence. "Pretty, pretty please!"

Robbie didn't look up. She buried her doll in the sand.

My mother stomped out the back door, clothes-pins clamped on her blouse. "Where's Carole?" she asked. "She made me ruin a painting." Through grass blades I saw her raging. "I need Carole to hang the laundry."

"I'll hang the laundry," Robbie offered.

My mother laughed sharply. "You can't, Robbie. You're too little to reach the clothesline."

"I can stand on the kitchen stool."

"Carole!" my mother cried louder, ignoring Robbie, worried.

I didn't move.

Donna Motley burst out her back door, three houses down, hearing heard my name being called. She spotted me right away from her steps. "I see you hiding there, Carole, you titty-baby!"

"Where *is* Carole?" my mother asked Robbie. And louder, over her shoulder to Donna: "No need to be crude."

Was this growing up? I yearned to grow down, back to Chicago and being a child.

4

An adolescent, I was "in transition," my parents assured me.
I didn't know then that I'd always be in transition.

5

The next day Jimmy Searcy showed up at my door, his tee-shirt sticky with sap and sprinkled with twigs. He'd taken a shortcut. At the end of our two-block street which had no sidewalk, dense, viny wilderness pressed against high wire fencing. Nature, like human nature—like my own nature in particular—needed to be held back. KEEP OUT, KEEP OUT, read the signs posted on heavy metal. Our part of town, unpaved, seemed to have been randomly carved out of nature after the War, the yards impersonal, back-hoed and blank, unadorned by shrubbery.

My mother was out buying groceries. I wasn't supposed to let anyone in. I told that to Jimmy Searcy and he propped lazily outside against the short iron bannister on the porch. Chestnut hair flapped down his brow. When I slipped outside too, he gazed at me, lowering his head, loose-hinged, intent. I thought of him as a boy who tagged along on the fringes of other bolder boys' action. Like me with Donna. I eyed his little-kid outfit and rosy cheeks, relieved that he didn't make me bashful like Bobby Batey did or Ben Neese on his big red motorcycle.

"What do you want?"

"Hey, what's your pup's name? Where's your dog?"

"Tawny. He roams."

He jerked backwards, uncertain. Probably he'd never heard the name Tawny before or even of that color, so I explained to him that

112

the dog was named–by me–after the color of a lion's mane.

"Tawny." Jimmy studied me: I could have been a dazzling firefly, flickering my tail. "You're smart. You know a lot of words." He cupped his hands and shouted. "Tawny! Tawny! *Tawn–eeee!*"

I started. He tried to calm me. "He's a coon dog. You need to train him. Them pups like to travel."

"You can't train Tawny," I bragged. "Our dog roams everywhere and he's only eleven months old. He's big, he *scares* people." Tawny's ability to incite fear thrilled me. I believed that fact might interest Jimmy Searcy because he was a boy.

He nodded. "Coon dogs are real loyal."

Suddenly Tawny flew across the boulevard in front of traffic and bounded safely onto our gravel road. He leaped the front-facing ditch, pushing his nose hard into Jimmy's armpit. The dog's coat was sticky with wood-sap too.

Hooo! Jimmy yelped. "Good pup, *gooo–ood*, good boy!"

Tawny's paw caught Jimmy's tee-shirt.

"That's all right." Jimmy stuck a finger through the snag. "Want to sit in the grass? Why don't you teach this redbone hound some manners? Teach him to hunt."

"I don't like hunting."

"Then you're a strange girl to own a coon dog."

What did Jimmy want? He rolled with Tawny in the grass. "Old Floppy," he teased, pulling Tawny by the ears. He didn't tell me I was cute like the bag boy at the grocery store who'd led me to reply, snarling, "Get out of here!" because I didn't know if I was being made fun of and I didn't want to look like a fool. Jimmy didn't heckle me about not believing in hunting. Jimmy Searcy liked me.

"Carole has a boyfriend," Robbie would tell my mother later, helping unpack groceries and put them away. I pinched Robbie hard, twisting her skin.

6

During the year I'd known Donna Motley, I often regarded her

113

with fascinated alarm. She terrified me, but I admired her daring, the way she flaunted herself. One night, we angled behind the school together to go to the monthly Teen Club and a Hop for junior-high schoolers. We extended our hands to be stamped at the door of a large Quonset hangar. It was bright-lit inside. A jukebox caterwauled near a table of soft drinks. In my pink blouse with the collar up, and a charcoal gray skirt, I thought I looked sharp. Don't mess with me, my outfit bluffed. Pink and black–the tough kids' color combination. I pumped my head to music. In front of us, Hugh Mayo and blonde Becky Rice, the popular couple in my class, jitterbugged. I hoped some boy, any boy, would approach me. I'd practiced dancing with Robbie. Outside, a clump of older guys, the same dropouts wreathed in cigarette smoke who hung around Ace Hardware, repeatedly poked their faces through the door to check the action. Inside, younger boys hooted and punched each other's shoulders.

Donna dodged away from me, into the swirl. When I couldn't spot her anymore I stood on my toes. Soon I was ready to go home, the dance an ordeal. Some girls in my class started a lying rumor that I was the one who'd printed FUCK MR. BARNES in giant script in lipstick on the girls' bathroom stall. Plus, no one asked me to dance, not even another girl. Then, Donna appeared out of nowhere, winking at me, and wagged her bottom. *Be-bop,* she fluted. "Let's get out of here." She grabbed my wrist, and rushed me past chaperones–all teachers from school–and past the gauntlet of dropouts outside, still slumped against the outside wall. A couple of boys trailed, calling to Donna by name.

"Do you know them?"

"Don't they just wish."

She bounced away from a boy who'd moved in too close. Her laugh was giddy, a little shrill. He reached to tickle her.

"Keep back!" she cried.

Encouraged, other boys walked towards us.

Donna skipped away.

I followed, hesitating.

"This way! After her!" a guy with pocked cheeks and a slippery pompadour pointed at Donna. A few more boys hurtled forward, a scraggly line, pushing past me, heading for the woods and Donna, who was sprinting to escape. She screeched with laughter. The commotion of running seemed like a game.

"You can't catch me," Donna called, her voice pitched high with quivery bravado and dizzy excitement.

I ran too. It was fun, frenzied, almost like a game of crack the whip, as if we were all holding hands, a long line of hands, cracking back and forth and chasing, never letting go. A string of boys surged by me, and others jogged nearby. I liked action games, even as a little kid. I didn't want to be left out. But I was confused, these were boys I'd never seen before, boys who couldn't seem to tell which was me and which was Donna. One stopped in front of me. Hopping, panting wildly, Jimmy Searcy emerged unexpectedly from the darkness. He too pointed the way to Donna. That diverted the onrush. I tried to push past.

"What are you doing here?" I felt uneasy. "You're not my boyfriend."

"Go *that* way, go that way!" he shouted at any boy who stopped to look me over. "I know her! She's a *nice* girl!"

Jimmy pushed me back towards the Teen Club and tailed the others into the woods.

I almost started after them, afraid of being alone. Beyond, out of sight, I heard maniac whooping, cackling, then Donna's crazy screech. Maybe the boys had caught up with her? I skidded on gravel because I'd stopped fast. I slid forward, a tumble, scuffing knees and palms, landing with my cheek on soft grass.

Two eighth-grade girls walking by stopped to gaze down at me.

"Are you all right?" one said. I could tell right away she was the kind of southern girl who could insult you to your face and you wouldn't even know it until later because she never stopped smiling. "I declare," she said, "that is a nasty group of boys."

I dusted my knees, silence my best protection.

I followed the girls at a distance, by the light of the road. In front of the candy store, blinds were closed. Ordinarily, I would have cut through the woods. But I was skittish now and saw my own double shadow under the streetlights on Highland Park Boulevard and whipped my head, worried a boy was following me.

When the girls turned off, I sped up.

7

I opened my own front door. Everybody was laughing. The Colgate Comedy Hour was on television. Daddy sprawled on the nubby couch in his Jockey briefs, bare chested, my mother reclined in the curved orange fiberglass rocker, and Robbie slid deep in the leather butterfly chair, wearing pajamas. I blinked. My family suddenly looked strange, alien, to me inside our little house and so did our modern furniture that was very different from any of our neighbors'. Light shined from our black tripod lamp that resembled the stick figures of space monsters in the movie War of the Worlds. My father and brother and sister glanced at me, then back at Jerry Lewis. Jerry Lewis was pretending to be a monkey. The world buzzed outside, spiraling excitement, but inside its vibrations exhaled out of my body like a sigh.

I stood at the front doorway and pretended to wave good night to Donna, as if she had accompanied me home. I didn't want my parents to know I'd walked home alone. Or what had happened. I didn't understand it myself, it would have upset them. The next day at school I'd search Donna for clues when she wasn't looking—and check if she was walking funny. Donna sported a new blouse but she seemed the same to me, same high-pitched laugh, same wrinkled skirt. On my way home, I would spy Jimmy Searcy on the porch talking earnestly to my mother, head ducked. Not spotting me, he sauntered off.

"Such a sweet boy! So naive," my mother dimpled. He must have flattered her. She was beaming. "He told me he saved you last night from being raped." Am I remembering her words correctly? Probably not. She asked me no questions. I was grateful but

116

mortified. "That boy likes you," she said. "Next year he's going to attend Wheldon School." She had pretensions and pronounced it southern like he did, like a boys' private preparatory academy, instead of vocational training.

I remember the TV was blaring non-stop laughter that night before when I returned. And how I scoured the darkness outside from behind the flimsy screen door as I kept waving madly at someone invisible, or something enormous, too close to make out. In the woods, leaves tossed, *whoosh, whoosh*–too far away for me to hear–but in our yard a night breeze stirred, wafting the fragrance of wild onions, and rattling the spindly peach tree sapling. The world was alive, and I was too.

"Did you have a nice time?" my mother wondered. She was standing beside me. "Did anyone ask you to dance?"

ANGELIQUE STEVENS

EXPOSURE

The elements of a subject that speak to us are often scattered and can't be captured in one photo; we don't have the right to force them together, and to stage them would be cheating… which brings us to the need for photojournalism.
-Henri Cartier Bresson ("HCB on Photography" 76)

In Kompong Chnnang, two hours outside Phnom Penh, a Vietnamese woman paddled me through the largest floating village on the Tonle Sap River. I sat camera in hand, uncomfortably squat-kneed, on an old wooden longboat that threatened to topple us if I shifted. I peered inside one- and two-room shoebox houses. They were laid out in lanes like housing tracts but with rivers for roads and square holes for doors. Row after row, tin roofs covered palm leafed sides and patched wooden floors. Houses, maybe 30 by 30 feet, floated on the water. Anchored like boats at dock, but disconnected from any land or piers, they were little islands unto themselves, each one an open diorama of Khmer water life.

Inside, a full life visible and exposed: pots and pans hung from shanty ceilings, hammocks rocked toddlers, clothes draped over balconies and rooftops. Some showed little TVs facing children sitting on fold-out chairs. Others displayed men napping on makeshift beds of palm leaves. Women scrubbed dishes in little washbasins on floors, small children played games on broken plank boards. Dogs barked. Life was happening within each little house. We floated by taking note of the light, the shading, and the subject of each picture, waving and exchanging hellos to the children in Khmer and English.

Henri Cartier Bresson said that photography is all about that decisive moment when the photographer must decide within a fraction of a second the significance of an event unfolding. She must see the developing elements of a good picture—that physical moment where image meets poetry ("Decisive Moments" 46). This is what Nathan, our photography teacher, taught us in the two-day travel photography workshop I took while in Phnom Penh, Cambodia's capital city.

Three of us—all strangers—gathered on the first morning at Nathan's studio for a technical class before our afternoon field trip. We learned how to frame the subject. The principle subject should never be in the center of the frame but on the periphery in one of the thirds of the picture where one of the four imaginary lines intersect. The rules of aperture and shutter speed taught us that if we let more light in through aperture, then we would need a shorter shutter speed and vice versa. Nathan explained that travel photography is more complex because there are so many variables; the photographer has no control and the light rather than the eye is often the guide to the subject. The camera is essentially a light box; it's all about what the photographer is asking of the light.

On the water, we drifted through the village. I saw a young girl in a green shirt finger paddling toward us in a little aluminum washbasin. She was maybe nine and half swallowed up by her washbasin and floating unrealistically, like a doll in a bathtub bowl. I stared in awe before I realized this was a decisive moment. I looked over at Nathan on his longboat. He was already shooting, adjusting his shutter speed, choosing an angle, asking the light how to expose her.

I pointed my camera. She looked at me. I snapped the picture. Still too far away for my inadequate camera to focus, her image was blurred and clumsily appointed to the right third of the picture. There was nothing else in the frame to make up for the blur. Behind her stood two drab shanties—one boarded up and broken, the other rusted aluminum over dried-up palm. An ancient longboat docked next to the aluminum shanty overflowed with wood for cooking. In front of her, dirty brown water reflected an overcast sky. A horrible picture.

She paddled closer. I pointed and snapped again, my photo owning more detail but not finding the right lines and form. When we passed each other, she in her washbasin, me in my longboat, she was no longer paddling. She floated on the current dragging two fingers through the water looking back at me looking back at her. I snapped again.

Henri Cartier Bresson said, "Of all the means of expression, photography is the only one that fixes a precise moment in time. We play with the subjects that disappear; and when they're gone, it's impossible to bring them back to life. We can't alter our subject afterward" ("HCB on Photography" 76). This little girl floating down the river reminded me of childhood fantasies. Watching her finger-paddle her way toward me, I saw a miniature me pretending to float in a walnut shell on the gutter stream outside my apartment. When I was a child, my parents' fighting sent me out into the rain to sit curbside and watch the water carry debris along miniature rivers. I imagined little worlds on rivers. I placed pebbles in walnut shells and dropped them carefully onto the flood and wished myself beyond the gutter stream of my life—to some other chaos than the one I knew. I followed the shell as far as I could or until it fell through the storm drain.

I wondered if the little girl in green ever wished herself somewhere else, if she ever pretended for a minute that the trajectory of her life could be altered. I watched her as she reached the moldy step to her shanty. I snapped another picture. The image was underdeveloped. The light was too poor. She pulled herself up out of the bowl and onto the deck of her floating house. Then she set her bowl against the house to dry and sat on the edge watching us paddle through the rest of her village.

On our drive back to Phnom Penh that day, we asked our tuk tuk driver to stop at a rice paddy so we could take pictures of the planting. Ten workers stood in a perfect diagonal in a foot of water planting rice shoots in ten evenly spaced rows. Each body held a perfectly cut and tied bundle of bright green rice shoots. Each bundle might have held one hundred stalks. Those workers, both men and women, were in a small corner of a small square of hundreds of acres still yet to be planted. I couldn't imagine how long it would take to plant the rest of the empty fields. It was an image of incalculability.

We took our shoes off and walked out onto the raised divider between paddies. Cameras in hand we waved to the workers. They waved back. Aware of us, they smiled and laughed with each other. Then we started shooting. In various positions we each tried to capture the moment, carefully placing our subject in one of the thirds of the frame. Two of us waded into the muddy water; another stood on the divider. We must have been a spectacle to them.

One woman left the row to get another bundle from the massive pile waiting to be planted. After retrieving it, she stood for a moment shifting its weight in her arms, holding the bundle like a bouquet, her only suitor the scorching sun. Her head tilted up just enough for me to see that she was stunning underneath her wet muddy workers clothes. Under a hot afternoon sun, she wore long sleeves and long pants and a wide-brimmed hat wrapped around her face with a scarf. The small triangle of face left uncovered revealed flawless earth-colored skin, high cheekbones, and a strong nose. Her features were characteristic of American Indian faces so common on reservations like mine back home. She looked like she could have been my sister. I turned my camera to portrait and shot. The only other skin exposed was that of her calloused hands. In a country where skin-whitening cream can be found in locked cabinets in roadside gas stations, her dark skin was just another source of shame. Conscious of the cameras pointed at her, she smiled with embarrassment and tilted her head down.

Cartier Bresson says that "the photographer must respect the mood, become integrated into the environment, avoid all the tricks that destroy human truth, and also make the subject of the photo forget the camera and the person using it" ("HCB on Photography 76). If this is true, then I did it all wrong. I had superimposed myself so deeply into the scene, that it was forever altered by my presence. It was almost as if she stopped for a minute purposely to allow us to take her picture. Underneath that exterior of hard labor and a hard life, she was like a Khmer Cinderella. I crouched in the water in front of her so I could get the right angle. I wanted to expose her beauty. I wanted her to believe, like I once did, in a future that couldn't possibly be true. But she moved too soon, and my shutter speed was too low. I snapped three more times with my exhaustingly slow camera, but the moment was gone.

On the second day of our photography tour, we took a ferry up the Mekong River to Silk Island a few miles outside the chaos of Phnom Penh and far from the Killing Fields. We meandered along dirt roads lost to another era where houses stood atop stilts and cattle grazed on front yards. We stopped along the way to take pictures of a temple or a brightly colored house and children ran out to greet us. Nathan showed us, in each of our pictures, how the angle of the camera can change the way we look at things. He told us not to be afraid to alter our perspective. We squatted on the grass and looked up through our lenses at children in dirty hand-me-down pajamas.

Our first stop was a visit to a family Nathan had been visiting for years. Underneath the house on stilts, two women worked away, one on a silk loom, the other spinning cotton. The loom, like all the others underneath houses on that island, was a wooden contraption the size of a table. It had several broken pieces of board that served as spools for the different colors of thread. Sitting on a stool, the younger woman pushed back and forth the ancient bobbin that brings the cross thread. This beautiful piece of fabric would take her days to create and bring her pennies for her trouble.

The grandmother sat on a platform a few feet away spinning thread onto a spool. She emanated ease and simplicity. She sat on the hard wooden platform, both of her legs to her side, no pillows or mat underneath her. Her hair was gray and shaved close to her head. She wore loose knee-length pants and a light button-down tank, no shoes, no hat, no long shirts to cover her dark skin. Her movements were certain and effortless.

There was a metal bowl full of raw white cotton next to her and another huge bag on the ground near the platform. In front of her was a handmade wooden wheel connected to a spindle. She turned the handle of the wheel with her right hand. In her left, her fingers worked magic as the spindle pulled a seemingly endless string out of the rough wad of cotton she held. I snapped a picture, but it couldn't possibly express the illusion that I saw.

There were no rooms full of straw to spin into gold and no future of fairies or dreams of different worlds. There was only the magic of her art, the certainty of spinning cotton, and the enchantment of an island known for artisans whose ancient techniques survived even Pol Pot's genocidal terror.

I put the camera down and tried the cotton. I took a piece from the metal bowl and played with it between my fingers trying to coax out a string. It ripped apart in my hands. The old lady smiled at me. She put her work down and let go of her spindle. She took my hand into hers and placed my fingers around a small wad and pulled. I felt it slipping through my fingers, the fine thread used in textiles all over the world. She held my forefinger and thumb firmly on the cotton so I could gauge the precise amount of pressure needed to turn the cotton into string as it slipped through my fingers. I needed to reach that intersection where the pulling, the pressure, and the letting go would meet. I let her guide me. I didn't question what she had to conquer. I didn't wonder if she ever needed to escape. Instead, I sat still on the platform beside her. I closed my mind to the chaos of my own past, relaxed my arms and body, and I tried to find that place of ease she had already entered.

S. M. Volchok

Notes v. Noordermeerweg 9:8.97

There are wildflowers overtaking grass, this year, wildflowers surrounding even the surprise pumpkin patch on a slope between the front lawn and the road. There are bumblebees buzzing at each bloom. There are countless white butterflies, and numbers of orange butterflies. There is a red dove on the roof of the farmhouse, and a nest of sparrows under the eaves. There is a blue front door. There is a rose garden just beyond the entrance, bushes recently cut back, hacked down to the ground. There is ivy climbing up the bricks of the house, front and back. There are seven uncurtained picture windows downstairs. There are, upstairs, eight narrow, screenless windows, two of them thrown wide to the mid-summer's afternoon. There is a tiny casement window set into each gable, the kind one unlatches to swing open from an airless garret. There is a woman in an upper front bedroom window, gazing out at the road. There is a man on a tractor in the nearest field. There are flies walking all the exterior walls and windows of the farmhouse. There are endless spiders spinning endless webs, an infinity of invisible silk strung across every available corner, outdoors and in. There are thousands of tiny insects swarming thickly in sultry air. There are worms waiting under rocks in the dank stand of trees beyond the kitchen. There are slugs and snails on the concrete floor of the barn, on the wet clay paths through the fields. There is a dog, and three cats. There is a henhouse, with three ducks inside. There is a rooster strutting around and around the property. There is a white horse cropping yellowing grass in a side pasture. There are boxes for honeybees behind a narrow orchard of apple trees, plum trees, pear trees. There is a pre-fab, plastic greenhouse filled with wooden pallets and machinery that won't fit in the main barn. There are grapevines along one length of the greenhouse and overhead. There are blackbirds eating the ripening grapes. There are tomato plants along the other length, straggling but still bearing fruits. There are herbs, including *wiet*, infusing that single corner of the greenhouse with green. There are three bicycles, flung down wherever. There is a big German motorcycle in the garage, and a smaller Japanese one abandoned in the sawmill shed. There is a rusty-rouge Citroen camper permanently up on blocks between two hillocks. There are bright green doors on the faded red barn. There is an impressive pile of wet firewood stacked in the front yard between house and barn, and a mud-splattered white station wagon, never parked anywhere else. There is always traffic on the two-lane blacktop at the end of the short driveway, moving in both directions. There are mainly trucks and tractors, but there are also cars, motorbikes, and numberless bicycles. There are occasional pedestrians, older folks walking for exercise, looking for company. There are cows straggling back to their barns in the distance. There is noise from the many machines of the neighbor's agribusiness. There is stillness closer by. There are ditches on all sides of the land. There is a public water race beyond the woods on the far side of the road. There is, here, out of sight of passersby, a new, private, man-made pond. There are already water-lilies taking root, blossoming, pink, purple, white. There are reeds, grasses, and waving underwater green. There are several species of transplanted fish, still small, elusive, secretly growing in the darkness of the water's depths. There are a rotting hand-hewn picnic table and picnic benches dragged over for pond-side dinners. There is a backless bench in better shape further on. There are white leather armchairs (thrift shop) and white plastic armless chairs (garden store) scattered about the backyard. There are clouds covering a sky of no describable color. There is, for the moment, no rain, but neither is there is sun. There is distance and grayness and mist. There is the smell of freshly spread manure from the east. There is the smell of sea from the west. There is the swooping sound of a high-tech windmill from the south. There is the sound of caged birds chipping and chirping, from the neighbor's yard to the north. There is the sound of free birds from all directions. There is a sudden silence.

There is a hush. There is a waiting. There is a rush of wind through the trees. There is a branch cracking. There is a man on a tractor pulling into the drive, moving out of sight of the woman still sitting in the open window, moving toward the work yards behind the long barn. There is the sound of another tractor starting up in the distance. There is another. There is the sound of keys clicking, clicking, on a laptop keyboard. There is a car coming. There is no sun. There is rain, now, there is rain, suddenly; there is rain, rain, and more rain.

LORENA WILLIAMS

RELIC

I follow the tracks of a lone mule deer, a trail of perfect, white lungs stamped in snow during the animal's leisurely walk. My jog takes me along the ditch road past rolling hills of sagebrush, the windswept Oregon desert silent but for the *tee-dee, tee-dee* of pygmy nuthatches huddled together in the morning sun. The crunch of my shoes through crusty snow disturbs the tiny blue-gray birds into a chattering departure, only for them to alight on the very same branches just moments after I pass.

I didn't realize how badly I missed the country until arriving home last night, driving up the long gravel driveway to my parents' house at the northernmost edge of their twenty-acre farm. The manufactured home formed an island of light, a soft yellow glow cast from the windows. I turned off the Subaru, inviting the blackness to fold in, and listened to the cooling engine ping and tick. I stepped out into the snow and carried my bags to the house under Venus's winking eye. Dark pastures stretched away from the front yard, drawing from me a breath I had held for months. There, on the uncrowded desert plateau, I slept clear through the night.

I woke before the December sunrise, jet-lagged and disoriented, to my first morning in eastern Oregon after a year's absence. It took me a moment to realize I was no longer in Pittsburgh. I stretched diagonally across my sunken childhood bed then pushed Mom's handmade quilt aside. I dressed and left my parents' home, the land where I spent my first eighteen years, for a run along the ditch road as I've done a hundred times before. Outside I found 360 degrees of pink, blue, and orange horizon without a single building to interrupt it.

A quarter-mile into my run, I crunch slowly past the neighbor's farm. Along the north side of the ditch road yawns an irrigation canal only a quarter full and frozen. Tracks of birds, jackrabbits, mice, and mule deer crisscross between banks on the snow-covered ice. To the south in a pocket of sagebrush, three unmoving horses crowd together, their soft brown eyes watching as I shuffle past. I may be the first person they've seen in days.

I run harder, pressing deep into the desert that raised me, a landscape that I expect might save me now if only I can burrow deep enough. The road curves toward a shallow ravine cradling rusted heaps of car bodies, fenceposts, and other cast-offs. These twisted, broken relics rested here even in my earliest memories, but I haven't noticed them in years. Once, during a childhood walk with my mother, she pointed out the faded sky-blue fender and hood of a Plymouth Valiant, reminiscing about the 1964 push-button model she'd inherited from her Aunt Linnie.

The road separates from the water to curve up a steep bluff where bald tires and fractured concrete culverts pile higher each year. I stop at the hillcrest and survey the Lower Snake River Valley below. At my feet, the slope drops away into fields of corn stubble and grazing cattle. Farther east, wood smoke rises from the small town of Vale, still in the morning shadow of its namesake butte. Sixty miles southeast of Vale, 7,500-foot Shafer Butte hulks above Boise. Content with the reasonably unchanged vista—the cows, the distant tractor making its way up Graham Boulevard—I turn toward home and prepare to lie.

"No—I actually really like living in a city," I say through a mouthful of scrambled egg. "It's great being so close to everything, you know? I ride my bike pretty much everywhere."

My parents sit where they've always sat, Mom at the end of the table near the kitchen, Dad closest to the front door and thus his workshop. This morning they brim with questions about my first four months of graduate school in an eastern city.

"Yeah, how are things going since your good bike was stolen?" My mother's skepticism is thinly veiled.

"Well, the Craigslist bike isn't quite what my Specialized was, but it gets me around." I don't tell them that the bike has a bent wheel, just three gears, and that the chain binds every time I grind up Woodland Road. "I replaced the tires and the brake pads, and I need to find a longer seat post—"

"I worry about you riding around in traffic like that," she says in a concerned mother tone.

"I take the side streets, mostly. It's better than driving."

"All that goddamn traffic," my father adds.

I nod, not sure whether it's smart to agree.

"Have you been able to sleep okay with the new door? Has anyone else been robbed in the neighborhood?" Mom won't relent.

"No—"

"Have they found the son-of-a-bitch or any of your stuff?" My father can only be referring to the pistol that was stolen during the robbery—the Ruger Mark II that he had given me as a going away present.

"No, they haven't found anything, but it's okay. I sleep fine and the cops said it was just a fluke, that the neighborhood doesn't usually see that sort of crime."

I take another bite of eggs and hope for questions about school.

That afternoon I drive seven miles east to town. Vale, Oregon, one of the first stops along the Oregon Trail, is a one-square-mile farming community of 488 families, one grocery store, and the Starlight Café—an all-night truck stop whose parking lot barely corrals the horse trailers, dually pickups, and run-down Buicks. Snow-covered Vale Butte rises above the town, partly girdled by the lethargic lower Malheur River. French trappers originally dubbed this watershed the *Rivière au Malheur*, River of Misfortune, in the early nineteenth century after a hidden cache of pelts was discovered and repurposed by a band of Northern Paiute. The river is now heavily used to irrigate fields of onions, sugar beets, potatoes, and alfalfa.

There are no traffic lights in Vale, and the town center is simply the junction of the Central Oregon and John Day Highways. I turn north at that intersection and pull into Hair Affair, where Robin Fulwyler has cut my hair since childhood.

Trimming shears and comb in-hand, Robin shifts in tight Wranglers and Roper boots as we catch up. Her curly red hair and makeup keep up her agelessness, though she is intent on convincing me that I make her look old. I sit in a silver-and-black beautician's chair as she velcroes a black apron around my neck.

"You know, your dad ordered some shampoo from me, but your mother had already ordered a huge bottle for him for Christmas." She says this to my reflection in the mirror, pumping my spinning chair higher to trim the tips from my two feet of blonde hair.
Topics of discussion in Hair Affair predictably involve shampoo, but also cattle, crop prices, the new pump attendant at the Chevron, or weddings. "I didn't know what to tell your dad," she continues, "so I ordered it anyway. Now he has a lifetime's supply of Paul Mitchell!"

I laugh too hard and too long, appreciating small-town pleasures and real conversation. I look at Robin in the long mirror in front of us and stop laughing when I see a flash of confusion in her mascara-ringed eyes.

I pay and tip Robin—the two amounts combined still don't add up to what I might pay at Supercuts—and drive the dirt road over to Logan's Market where I should know better than to think I can make a quick beer run.

"Oh, Lo! You're back for Christmas?" Linda, the store manager, speeds around the service counter for a hug, her curly blonde hair smelling of stale cigarettes. She is the cashier to whom, twenty years ago, I confessed stealing a Ring Pop. Ten years later she offered me my first job as a stock girl.

"Your mom told me you were in graduate school in the east!" She pulls away from our embrace but keeps her hands on my shoulders.

"Yup. Yeah, I've been in Pittsburgh since—"

"Pittsburgh? Now why Pittsburgh?" Her head turns to the side, eyes dipping into a question. This is an expression I'm getting used to.

"Well, it's a good school, you know, and—"

"But you've been in Arizona for years."

"I love Arizona, especially the desert," I admit. "It was hard to leave, but I was ready to go to grad school after four years off."

"And now, *Pitts*burgh?"

My own reaction had been no different when I learned where my top-choice school would take me. Never having seen the city, my preconceptions were not uncommon—I expected a dark rustbelt hole in the ground where old behemoth cars crawled through grimy streets lined with smoke stacks and dilapidated factories. I knew virtually nothing about Pittsburgh; I had never even traveled east of the Rocky Mountains. The other half of the country might as well have been the setting of a historic fiction novel. To top it off, I'd never lived within 80 miles of a city. And now, *Pitts*burgh?

My lack of explanation leaves Linda perplexed, and I dash toward the beer cooler when another customer arrives. *Finally*, I think, *beer*. Though Vale is a community that most resembles those in Idaho or Utah, the fact is, I am from Oregon and the beer selection proves it. Sierra Nevada and Fat Tire, two quintessential Western beers, are overshadowed by their lesser-known pioneer cousins: Terminal Gravity's Breakfast Porter, Deschutes's Cinder Cone Red, and Ninkasi's Tricerahops Double IPA. I add two six-packs to my cart and head stealthily toward the produce section. Twenty more minutes pass before I make it to the parking lot, three more failed explanations for moving to Pittsburgh.

The sun on the snowy fields is dazzling. I drive the seven miles back to the farm, bags of beer, fruit, cereal, and vegetables riding perfectly upright on the road due west. Making the only turn into the driveway, I cruise slowly up the gravel road, the cows in the pasture glancing up at me. Smoke tilts sharply from the stovepipe and the leafless branches of the weeping willow in the front yard wave up and down in chorus. Ike and Happy, my parents' chocolate labs, rush halfway down the drive to meet me, then run alongside the car, smiling like labs do.

I unload the groceries and make coffee, sitting with my full mug before one of the three picture windows. Outside, the snow and wind and sun are unchanged. The willow continues to sway, its branches ticking against the roof. I close my eyes and feel the heat from the woodstove on my back.

My breakfast conversation and the trip to town have left me feeling irrationally defensive. I'm annoyed that people are judging my move to an Eastern city, even though I judge it too, every day. It would have been bad enough to move to a Western city, but to the *East*? The sense of superiority among Westerners is hardly news to me, but I've never seen the other end of it. I know that when a person heads East, those remaining are obligated to question her sanity.

Four months ago, in August of 2009, I left Arizona's heat inversions and emaciated prickly pear cactus and drove east for the first time. Vertical sandstone buttes and evergreen mountains gave way to rolling fields of corn and soybeans that unraveled for hundreds of miles. I drove into Oklahoma City in the dark, waking to a day filled with the dense hardwood forests I'd seen in photographs—swells of green veiled by thick fog in the early morning. I had never really considered the landscape of Missouri or Oklahoma, the verdant hills and extensive hardwood forests definitely came sooner than expected. Wasn't all of the Midwest like the Dakotas? I'd never been there, either, but somehow I thought that the arid landscapes extended farther east and south.

Hurtling through Indiana and Ohio, the scenery reverted back to yellow and green fields, an endless phalanx of corn soldiers. While the corn did not surprise me, the extensive deforestation did. More than two-thirds of the state's forests, I later learned, had been leveled for farming. The scene that replaced it was mind numbing. I sighed audibly when I crossed the Pennsylvania state line in the shade of trees.

During my first month in Pittsburgh, the region's humidity and monochrome landscape unhinged me a little, but it was the city itself that really shook me. Though I had considered city life in theory, *people were everywhere*—a reality, I soon realized, I was in no way prepared to face. My apartment building, the first I had ever lived in, vibrated like a sorority house, its eight units housing the ghosts of 1,000 tenants. If the constant noise subsided—the music student's grunge metal, the 19-year-old girls' shrill voices as they watched *The Real Housewives*, or the disturbed psychology student's 3 a.m. panic attack—there came the clicking of a Pomeranian's nails on the upstairs neighbor's hardwood floor while the manicured beast (Roxy) fretted over his missing parents. Yet with all those people around, I made not a single friend. I had felt more at home during trips to Mexico and Germany. At least in Europe I expected to feel like an outsider. Pittsburgh was in my own country, but it became very clear very fast that I did not speak the language.

During walks through Bloomfield, my new neighborhood, it seemed like the people who returned eye contact were either hitting on me or appraising me. *Is she wearing those cowboy boots ironically?* When I smiled at hipsters, they looked uncomfortable. When I smiled at older people, they looked reluctant to return the expression. A sort of perpetual paranoia set in, leaving me hyper-aware and untrusting. I became certain that any guy behind me on the sidewalk was a mugger and every driver a maniac who'd run me off the road to get home three seconds faster. I was not alone in my fear, though. My two cats—cats that had once dug holes in the floor near the entryway of my house in their attempts to escape—refused to go outdoors, hiding for weeks under boxes and in their crates.

Slowly, however, I lost the small-town urge to connect to every person walking past and I turned my music up to drown out the neighbors. But I still struggled to adjust to a city's daily rhythms. One night, during my first couple of weeks in Pittsburgh, I lay in my bed—just a few blankets on the floor—and began to fall asleep to the familiar song of coyotes. I opened my eyes—coyotes in the city? No, it was the sound of ambulance sirens. Two months later when my mother came to visit, she asked the same question.

"What am I hearing? Are those coyotes?" We laughed when I told her what it was. "At least you have something to remind you of the desert," she shrugged.

Between August and December I worked to adjust my lifestyle, trading wilderness for wooded parks, small mercantiles for chain stores, and a redneck bar with plywood walls and $1.50 drafts for a sports pub with glass inlay countertops, six flat-screen televisions, and $4.00 drafts. I bought and immediately lost my first umbrella and shivered through a rainy, bleak fall after realizing it would cost over $150 a month to heat my tiny cardboard apartment. I ground through traffic on my bike, learned that beer cannot be purchased in Pennsylvania grocery stores or gas stations, and caught my first public bus.

When I apologized to the driver for not knowing how to pay for or use city transit systems, he informed me that Pittsburgh was not a city. More specifically, it was not an *eastern* city.

"Pittsburgh," he told me, "is just a bunch of small towns grouped together. People here are friendly and hard-working, and are more likely to go to PNC Park for a ballgame than to a fancy restaurant." I heard variations of this speech from others locals, along with an assurance that "Pittsburgh is a clean, safe place to live."

I was starting to believe the accounts, too, when one afternoon in early October I came home to an unlocked apartment door, beyond which my living room lay, turned inside out. My desk sat stripped of the new Mac; the contents of its heavy drawers had been emptied onto the floor where every box and envelope lay torn open. Where my new, long-coveted specialized bicycle had stood were the scattered remains of dissected cupboards. The apartment had been robbed in broad daylight when all the other tenants sat in their living rooms doing homework and watching TV. No one had heard a thing.

"Things like this rarely happen in this neighborhood," the stern yet sympathetic police deputy said. After dusting every smooth, flat surface in my house for fingerprints, she and the investigator left me with tips to clean up the black dusting powder and the parting assurance that "Pittsburgh really doesn't have much crime."

The following weeks felt distended by sleeplessness as I replaced some stolen items, including my winter hats and gloves, and tried to push through the feeling of violation. I felt alone and scared, something new to me even though I did most things—including moving cross-country—by myself. More than once I sat on the couch at three a.m. cradling my Winchester .270 deer rifle (the only valuable that had gone overlooked). I would watch for the shadow of a body to block the crack of light between the new apartment door and its frame. The yellow sliver etched itself into my retinas, a visual tripwire linked to my trigger finger.

Christmas morning dawns blue and crisp. A fragile ice sheath envelopes the drooping braches of the willow. My parents will join me shortly, one on the couch and one in the rocking chair, and I will sit on the floor beside the tree to dole out gifts. The morning feels strange without my sister, Amara, beside me to reminisce about childhood Christmases. The most excitable, I always woke before her. But Amara was as fun to rouse as a coiled diamondback, so I usually focused on my parents. I would enter the kitchen on the tips of my toes and switch on the pre-filled coffee maker. On a tray, I arranged a small container of milk, a spoon, and two mugs. Once the coffee brewed, I carried the tray into my parents' bedroom. By the time Mom and Dad appeared in the kitchen for their second cups of coffee, Dad's with a shot of Carolans Irish Cream, Amara would shuffle out to join me beside the tree.

It has been at least four years since I came home for Christmas, and our old traditions seem far away. Amara now celebrates the holiday in her Missoula home with her boyfriend, and my other sister, 13 years my senior, is in Idaho with her husband and three kids. I feel like an imposter, a 27-year-old sitting by the tree like a child. A little sad, I fondle one of the homemade Christmas ornaments. I realize as I wait for my parents to join me that I ignored our family Christmas traditions throughout most of my twenties. In Arizona, I was surrounded by friends and by my girlfriend's family. It is only now, since I am alone in the East with no friends and no relationship that I come sulking back, head hung like a dog's. And as much as I feel compelled to burrow into this farm and this house for grounding, I know it is my childhood home, the place of nostalgia and weeklong visits. I cannot seek shelter here, only fleeting comfort.

I am still the one who made the first pot of coffee, but this time all three of us return to the kitchen for more. Thoughts of gifts vanish with the responsibility to break the ice that formed overnight in the dogs' water bowl. As if we all feel compelled to start an adult Christmas tradition, we fill the space, the absence of childhood anticipation, with pot after pot of coffee.

After exchanging gifts we leave the house, winding along the ditch road with the labs running single file in a tire track. A few minutes into our walk conversation gives way to comfortable silence. I crunch through the snow crust and high-step out of each footprint, determined to get some exercise before our big Christmas dinner. It hasn't snowed here in over a week, but the cycle of melting and refreezing has left patches of bare ground peeking out from thick scabs of snow. The road is a web of animal tracks that have melted through to earth, forming ice and dirt molds of dog, deer, jackrabbit, and coyote feet.

A couple of miles into the rolling hills behind our house I stop to admire a view I've never contemplated before. Snow-covered Cottonwood Mountain rises to the north, below which fields of corn stubble pierce through snow. Mid-afternoon, we return to the house where a neighbor has brought us a steaming homemade apple pie. Still disturbed by the morning's reflections, I stay outside in the biting wind as Dad disappears into his shop and Mom goes inside to start dinner. I nestle into my wool scarf, pull on my fingerless alpaca gloves, and walk across the snow-covered garden to the bone yard. The long row of our family's abandoned history curves around the half-acre garden, its contents jutting through the snow like toys set deep into the frosting of a birthday cake.

During our walk, I made an agreement with my parents to return home after spring semester to help clean up the farm. So come spring thaw, my father and I will haul the bone yard's relics to the landfill. This is a chore that many farmers, like my dad, put off until the rows of cast-off farm equipment and toys have grown unsightly. I am now interested in recording my family's thirty-year accumulation of junk in hopes that I can unearth a fragment of memory buried deep in the muck, hidden beneath the cracked aquariums and piles of splintered lumber, pooling inside the hollow walls of a dry-rotting tractor tire—a piece of home to take back with me to Pittsburgh. I open my black notebook and begin an inventory.

Bed frames. Bucket seat from a 1983 Datsun pickup. Cinder blocks. Box spring. Tree stumps. Rolls of rusting barbed wire. Shooting targets. Baling twine. Orange construction netting.

Six five-gallon buckets of rocks. As children, Amara and I collected obsidians, walking up and down our long gravel driveway in search of the marble-sized volcanic glass. We came home with hands full of obsidians and rinsed each one in the kitchen sink. Then, careful not to cut our fingers on their sharp, opaque edges, we dropped them into our red gumball machine. When our grandparents drove up from Los Angeles to visit each summer, Amara and I would haul the gumball machine to their RV and crank the dispenser dial for Grandpa at a quarter a turn.

T-posts. Space heater. Car tires. One rotten butternut squash on an old card table. Feeding troughs.

Burn barrels. Rusted through and filled with junk, they were, until just a few years ago, our family's only means of garbage disposal. Like all amenities, garbage service was slow to come to eastern Oregon. Here even party line telephones systems remained popular well into the 80s.

Aquarium. Pickup bed liner. Wood pallets. Steel pickup bumper. Tractor disc.

Aluminum siphon tubes. On a stifling August morning in the 80s, I walked with Dad to the quarter-mile long irrigation ditch that stretched away from our house. Dozens of curved aluminum siphon tubes were placed along the ditch in line with the irrigation furrows, ready to be primed to flood-irrigate the adjoining pasture. Dad decided that morning that I, a six or seven-year-old towheaded tomboy, was big enough to irrigate a field. First, he demonstrated. Cupping his palm over one end of the long tube and placing the other end in the ditch water, Dad pumped the tube until water exploded from under his cupped hand. The muddy water sprayed over both of us until Dad dropped the tube into the furrow where a stream of water appeared.

Confident, I picked up the next one and cupped my tiny hand over the mouth as well as I could. I shoved and pulled the tube back and forth in the water, imitating the motions Dad had made. Nothing happened. Repositioning my hand, I tried again with no luck.

"It's not working," I whined, dropping my hands dramatically to my side for effect. Dad took the tube and suctioned it firmly against my forearm.

"Now try," he urged. With just a few pumps of the tube, a shower of ditch water proved that I was, indeed, big enough to irrigate a field.

Barbecue. Steel desk. Dirt bike frame. Canning jars. Sheet metal. Wheel rims. Shovel handles. Two Camp stoves. Lawn chair frames.

Three Volkswagen vans. The vans have stood like sentries since 1985, lined up at the edge of the property. Paint chipped and faded, tires permanently deformed under the weight of the dilapidated frames, these relics were the original inhabitants of the bone yard. In the center, the brown '66 VW tilts, its passenger door wide open. The first to die, it hadn't budged for twenty-nine years. It belonged to Mom, who drove it until the spring of 1981 when she was T-boned by a black hearse pulling out of Vale Mortuary. The symbolic death of the '66 bus was followed by a prompt funeral procession to its permanent resting place.

Death by T-boning seemed contagious in the early 80s, as Dad discovered when he plowed his mustard yellow '71 into the side of a Pontiac one year later. The driver of the Pontiac, the partially blind grandmother of an Idaho senator, drove away while Dad called a friend for a tow. The van was left with a deformed front fender, shattered windshield, and broken headlight. Since its death, the VW has been adorned with a tow bar that Dad keeps out of the mud by storing it on the bus's roof.

The '65 bus, its baby blue face faded almost to white, escaped the T-boning curse. I was two years old when Mom stopped driving it, upgrading to Aunt Linnie's Plymouth Valiant. The bus had 210,000 miles on it, so Mom parked it in the bone yard (voluntarily) for Dad to rebuild the engine with parts from the two VW carcasses. As was a trend on our farm, 1985's good intentions gave way to an unrebuilt heap whose seats filled with boxes of canning jars, bags of Goodwill donations, hoes, rakes, buckets of rocks, books and, in the summer months, the occasional gopher snake.

Rabbit cages. Two-by-fours. Feed troughs. Jerry cans. Bicycles. Yellow, red, blue and purple bicycles. Road bikes. Mountain bikes. Kids' bikes. 21-speeds. Cruisers. Too many bikes.

Shivering, I head for the house. There is more to write down, but the wind has picked up and my fingers throb from the cold. I have unearthed stories, for sure, but these cannot save me. And save me from what? I have forgotten what it was I needed saving from—dejection? How I once thought the fond, but merely therapeutic, ties to home could magically undo my move to an Eastern city suddenly baffles me. My emotions swing toward disgust as I acknowledge the self-pity I've been wallowing in for months.

The evening sun, warm only in color, melts soft and buttery over the desert. Magpies hop through stalks of cheetgrass rising between cinder blocks and tires. I consider the time it will take to uproot the bone yard, the scars we will leave behind where our pasts once sunk deeper into the landscape with every spring thaw. But the symbolism of the rusting junk is already losing its grip on my psyche.

The dogs run far ahead, chasing after something I can't see. The only sound is my breathing and the crunch of my shoes on the stubborn snow crust that has covered the ground throughout my entire visit. I admire once more a horizon that goes unbroken by buildings or trees. Tomorrow I leave for Pittsburgh, and I am taking one more run along the ditch road before I go. I've had my fill of home, the open space that's at once liberating and suffocating. The sadness I felt at Christmas, the realization that this land is not a place to retreat to permanently, has given way to a feeling of relief. I'm no longer afraid to return to Pittsburgh, even if I know it's not the right place for me. It's only temporary and it's home for now, I decide.

In the distance, I see a coyote trotting deep into the sagebrush across the canal. She is in no hurry and pauses to look at me, then the dogs. The two labs sniff the ground frantically searching for the lost trail, but the coyote has already moved on.

POETRY

Janee J. Baugher

Leavanworth, Washington

Rainwater needling needles of ponderosa pine,
thrumming leaves of cottonwood.
The swallows have gone.
No hawks, eagles, or magpies either.
Javelins from clouds land circles
pockmarking the patio's sullen balustrade.
Lavender lupines shiver and shiver.
Balsamroots' saturated petals.
The Wenatchee River, its relentless surge over rock,
sprints through its wilderness.
My Labrador scurries out the door,
dashes down the flagstone stairs to the river,
jumps knee-deep into it. Head underwater,
she forces bubbles out her nose, scores a stick.
Unrepentant, she makes her mark
relocating objects, gnawing wood.
She's leaving a pattern on the universe
one branch, one swallow at a time.
The certainty of a changing world
pilots uncertainty in each animal's body.
To snag the fleeting, to relish the static –
apprehend river's howl and all that dwells on river's basin.
A vase of lupines, brown-eyed Susans, and lilacs on the table now.
The room slowly quits its light, falls tiredly grey.

Zeina Hashem Beck

Winged Carrots

You call them guardians,
these winged carrots
graffitied on the walls,
because you know
they take flight in your sleep,
land on rooftops, on clotheslines,
shield orphaned dreams
with their little black wings.

You call it *the sign*
because you have to look up
towards the sky to notice
it says "Rooms for Rent,"
it is white it rusts
from an old balcony,
the Arabic letters flake.

You call him Thyme
because he sweeps his bakery,
gathers the day, the *zaatar* dust,
always at the same hour.
"*Bonjour*," he chants,
no matter what the time is,
as if words could lift
the falling darkness.

You call it orange,
this elevator with painted walls,
because in a city where walls
yield, where rails rust,

where litter fills the streets
like abandoned punctuation,
it has managed to keep
its color.

You call it god, this sidewalk,
because you carry it with you everywhere:
in your pockets, your footsteps.
You've memorized its bends like a prayer,
its long silver-grey hair,
its cigarettes, its favorite
songs and curse words,
the holes in its shirts.

You call it evening
because of the way the rain
seeps through the streetlights,
carries some of their radiance, drips
on the green garbage bags,
on the bottles your neighbor lines outside.

You call it Beirut
because you have no other name
for the way trees and antennas tilt in the wind;
the wind always, the certainty of the wind.

ROSEBUD BEN-ONI

AT TEN I HAD THE LOOK OF LOCUST

At ten, I held the look of a locust and mothers of tarp and tin
    held closer their unborn in the streets of childpits.

At ten, the Americans came and built a factory for the women
    to work with solvents and a playground for their children.

In August I'd roost on the sheetmetal roof as a bad omen:
    that lazy locust should be devastating fields.

But nothing ever grew in the *colonia*. My devastation, unsimple:
    A pain to say when not plural, shameful place among pests.

I held the look of a locust, black-sunken eyes and long, thin limbs
    so mothers of melting plastic and plywood

scrambled for sawdust from the mouths of razor-wild men.
    Bloody nails wrote the mornings after in pencil lead.

I was unborn again, with look of locust, leather rebellious,
        spinning backwards, in constant omission,
            undid in twitching.

Twenty years later the factory is condemned, but the playground
    Stands with a sign in English: *WARNING:*
        Toxic waste, no playing.

Twenty years later my molted locust skins mark where we've been.
    They are paper-thin but untorn.
        I look through the fine webbing

    at yellow vapor of the never born,
        swinging windless,
            all limb.

JANE BLUE

ARCHITECTURE

My mother built things in her spare time.
She could have been an architect but she was a writer.
In 1954 she flew to Japan, the only woman on the junket.
My lanky, mannish mother. On Waikiki for refueling
a man took a glamor shot of her in a two-piece batik
bathing suit, pale journalist's skin, cat-eye glasses.
She looks like she needs a cigarette. In Tokyo
she stayed at Frank Lloyd Wright's Imperial Hotel.
Carbons sent back to San Francisco read "fabulous."
Carved pilasters of black lava stone, cantilevered terraces.
He was known for his prairie houses, clean roof lines,
repressed chimneys. Suppressed
grief written all over my mother's face on Waikiki.
Earlier in the century the architect opened an office in Japan.
At home his studio overlooking a pond in Wisconsin
burned and savaged, the arsonist hatcheted
Wright's lover and her children to death. His life
always hung in a balance between renown and tragedy.
Everyone's life hangs in some kind of balance.
The Imperial Hotel stood after the legendary earthquake
of 1923, phoenix in the razed city, swaying
on its floating foundations. In the carbons my mother
interviews Tonao Senda, 35, so lately
the enemy: "I looked up and I could see the B-29.
The firelight was shining on the underside of its wings.
It was beautiful," he said. Paragraph: "Tonao Senda
did not love the Americans." The Imperial Hotel
was demolished in 1968, as was my father. After two
weeks in Japan my mother, reinforced steel,
went on to Kyoto, Nara, Osaka and home.

M. L. Brown

Mother's Home Ritual for Quenching Fires

Unwind your garden hose   *Lady bird, lady bird*
    lay it across the insatiable lawn
        do not turn it on

Drink wine from a jar
    shake the dregs
        into your palm
            fly away home

Bathe in a tub without water
    walk into the kitchen with your eyes closed
        stare at the horizon
            your house is on fire

Build towers of ash on the walk
    the vacant swings
        the back seat of your car
            your children are gone

Borrow sugar from a neighbor
    let it melt in the driveway
        give away your matches
            all except one

Write the fire on your laundry list
    set it aflame
        watch the name curl into ash
            and that's Little Anne

Dine with firefighters
    wear a sundress with nothing underneath
       say a prayer to St. Barbara
                for she has crept under the warming pan

Steady your hand above a basin of water   *Lady bird, lady bird*
    pretend to read your fortune there
       pretend you are not thirsty.

LORRAINE CAPUTO

THE FISHERWOMEN OF TILAPITA

The noon sun reflects
    off the blue-grey sea
White-capped waves wash
    over the breasts of women
        holding red triangular nets
          by the sticks along two sides
They dip them into the water
    & lift them up again
        gracefully bringing the sides
          together, capturing their catch
Wet dresses cling to
    heavily muscled legs

Other women wait on shore
    with large tubs to gather the harvest

One runs down with hers on hip
Bare-bottomed   pot-bellied children
    toddle around
Their bare feet leave light
    impressions in the sand

In the near distance
        where the estuary meets the sea
    flocks of birds swoop & rest

Kristi Carter

Blue Ridge Androgyny

If you can the preserves, I'll break the logs for
winter. Until then, your warm knuckles will need
to button the vest of my three piece suit—
nevermind that we buried my father in the jacket
and the trousers. Nevermind my breasts flattened
under your suspenders.

Nevermind we could flatfoot to the thrum of my heart.
I don't have to remind my body: now,
my hand leads your waist instead.

Could you, would you, stitch your name into my collar?
That is to say, all this room in the crotch of
your pants I'm wearing even though my heart spills over.
That is to say, my milk for the baby even though you're
the one who sings him.

Can you see the raccoon watching us from the
pine branch? She must have seen us digging
through each others' bodies as she through
the pig trough, every night.

I'd like to tell her, our digging isn't really search.
We know what we find here, what we don't.
You, the sun in my mouth, and I, the eclipse
in your throat.

ANN CEFOLA

SUGARING

Note how he picks the water where she is.
If you watch, you can learn their language.
-birdwatcher on mating behavior
of Vermont's common mergansers

At the pancake house, I say *Blueberry*, you say *Cinnamon Sugar*.
Year after year at the wood table by the window. Today is different:
When we arrive, brown and white billows from the roof, our mouths

taste steam and we shout, *Maple!* running to trees that each wear
a metal basket like a postman's bag. Small gray boxes—edging
parking lot and following hill—empty: sticky liquid, collected, inside.

While we sit fingering menus, stealing napkins off tables, the sugared
water boils a floor below tended by a big man in a black T-shirt who
scoops impurities off the top, wood-fed fire flashing white between

open metal seams. Our waitress places plates before us, scoop of
      butter
sliding off each stack, and two tiny pitchers of the product you call
time consuming, I call *labor-intensive:* Forty gallons of stickiness

to make one that holds. Like that alchemy, you and I have roiled,
wildly timbering for fuel. Over two decades what invisible worker
      tended
our fires and filtered our fury? All that heat distilled to this gold now.

You drench; I drizzle. I push my half-empty pitcher across the table.
You say, *Are you sure?* Such sweetness tapped makes me lick my lips
yes.

SARAH A. CHAVEZ

THE MEXICAN AMERICAN PARADE

Used to happen downtown every year. The city closed
off the streets from Tuolumne and "M"
south to Tulare and west to Van Ness.
My dad took us, me and my light-skinned sister,
to watch the floats decorated with red and white
roses tucked into green foliage. The Fresno High
school band marched uniformly
while the auxiliary team kicked their dark legs
and threw their batons in between the flowered floats.
We ate street tacos and churros, drank Horchata
while people who looked more like my dad
than I did walked around rolling their Rs
and complaining *Está tan caliente*.
The only people caught wearing blousy peasant shirts
and full skirts trimmed at the base with colorful ribbons
were the teenage girls dancing the *baile folklorico*
at the end of the parade route on a small
wooden stage, where the rhythmic, hollow sound
of their *zapateadas* could be heard for blocks.
And afterward, those teenage girls took off
the costumes of their mothers and put their jeans
and bodysuits back on, teased out their gelled-back bangs,
and slid on dark lipstick before joining the crowd.
I begged for a souvenir, so before taking us
back to our mother's, my dad bought me
an eagle t-shirt from one of the street vendors.
He held the shirt flat against my shoulders
and when I looked down, I could see two eagles,
each ones' claws clutching fast to flags—
the one a red, white and green flag,

the other red, white and blue. The beaks
that stuck out from the eagles regal feathered
heads almost touched, mirror images of one another,
like reflections across water, across a border,
like brothers. The corners of the flags both dripped
the same color. It bled into a single pool
beneath their talons, filling the lower white space of the shirt.
Esto es usted, he said to me, pointing at the mixed red pool
y usted debería estar orgulloso.

Joanne M. Clarkson

In the Millinery Shop
For Esther

I enter, ringing tiny bells.
Three sisters lean over a work
bench of feathers, bows,
and blossoms in the shop
that was their living. They do
and don't expect me, lean closer
over patterns, inspecting
secret work.

I cannot turn my back any more than
I can wake. My hands are ivory,
my clothes in sepia, the stain
of old photos laid out in autumn light.

Ruth coughs and adds a daisy. She
outlived tuberculosis to die instead
in childbirth at the end of her 29th year.
Marguerite smiles, re-arranges blonde curls.

"Grandmother," I whisper to the middle
one, who is art, who lived out the terror
of her older sister's death and in envy
of how her younger sister mastered
every avenue of love. She traces

the faceless mannequin filling in
features, grooming shadow, making
every angle beautiful in a certain tilt
of brim. Under cover

of these rooms, she captured
futures, flirted with ecstasy and black
veiled despair. Women paid
for more than fashion. Tonight I

measure, snip and hand her satin
ribbon that she winds carefully
through straw shaping my
helix from the distance of
a dream.

CHRISTINA COOK

HOMING

Imagine the twisted white
summer-night-sweat sheets I stripped
off our bed the morning you left
were something so similar
to homing devices, geese threaded them through
the southbound sky
to patch a plan for their return.
Imagine summer's upturned barrel burning
as love is said to burn, rusty and hot
as the seat of the John Deere
still sitting where you let it run
out of gas the day your brother fell
through hoops to the silo floor.
Imagine my mind's corroded metal,
its gear-teeth biting but failing to catch
hold of a hope that the rye will ripen without you,
then picture the rhubarb growing so red
I had to make a wine of it
to return it to the earth. Picture our sheets
like prayer flags along the clothesline,
coupling with the wind.

NINA CORWIN

BORN A MIDGE DOLL

Freckles don't cut it, never did.
Might as well be invisible before Ken
and all his slobbering clones,
those beleaguered pups, their eager sights
trained on the silky tan of her, unblemished
Barbie myth they've swallowed
hog nose to fish tail.

See how the paint of me,
shoulder length flip, all pertness and cute,
puts up no contest alongside her lush tresses.
Even the perfect salute of these
molded plastic breasts flags no passersby,
as long as she's around. I could just spit.

Call me the clothes in the back of your closet.
Untouched, the faithful fashion standby,
leftover pills you have no further need of.
Expiration date overlooked. And this
is the lament of an understudy
for a terminally pink and healthy cast.

So I wait my wallflower turn, just poised
for the plucking. But there is no extra Ken,
no Ken without his Barbie. And I am but
an afterthought: beneath a thin veneer of smiles,
the privately surly, sexless member
of the Bridal Barbie entourage.

Virgin, not by virtue
but by cynical design, a mere accessory
most days. Though, frankly, in this slick
and seamless world, it's only such adversity
that gives me anything to say.
Beyond these freckles, hopefully
a texture worthy of a second glance.

I'd gladly trade these silly stretch pants
these curlers, this mocking mirror,
for a single chance to blow
this lousy shelf and find an author
with a more substantial script (at night I chant
these words to entertain myself).

But now, the Little Tyrant's got me
by the ankles. Shakes me
in the bully grip of her eight year old fist.
Protecting her future against invidious comparison,
she frowns and declares "Make no mistake,
this is a full dress reharsal."
I say the auditions were rigged from the start:
assembly line to director's chair.

Sometimes, I dream a perfect Barbie shroud,
a quick inside cut to the delicate molded wrist.
But her bloodlessness taunts me.
Always did.

Barbara Crooker

Question Mark and the Mysterians

I'm upstairs in my teenage bedroom, lights out,
listening to WABC, Cousin Brucie, under the covers,
my hair so tightly wound around wire rollers
the size of juice cans that it's impossible to sleep.
But how else can I get it to flow from the center part,
then flip at the ends in symmetrical s's? How can I
go to school, if my hair's not right? Who will I fall
in love with, who will take me to the prom, *who
wrote the book of love?* I lean out the window, no
streetlights here in the country, just Orion's cinch belt,
Cassiopeia's W, the same letter I wear on my chest
when I cheer for the team, *All for you, Red and Blue.*
I'm the only one who can do a flip and a cartwheel-
split. *In the jungle, the mighty jungle, the lion sleeps tonight...*
I wail along in my tinny voice, unable to imagine a village
in Africa, children squatting in the dust, but somehow
I tap into the small stream of longing that floats
off those high thin notes. Out there in the night sky,
the dusty river of the Milky Way is flowing, pulsing
toward the future, where s's flip to question marks,
little fish hooks, that bob and dip in the current,
go where it takes them.

BARBARA CROOKER

WILLOW WARE

I was the kind of girl who played alone, had tea parties
under hedges, where it was dark and cool and my father's
anger couldn't find me, using acorn caps for plates, moss
for a tablecloth, imagination and air for tea. When no storms
threatened, my mother would let me use the child-sized
blue willow china that *her* mother gave her, and I would stare
into the small cups, entering the story: the curved footbridge
where a cobalt willow wept by a tea house with a fancy roof,
two blue swallows winging overhead. In blue willowland,
no fighting was allowed. Once in a blue moon, a few clouds
floated by. Maybe we'll all go sailing. *Nel Blu di Pinto di blu.*

CAROL V. DAVIS

ROOTS

I keep returning
to the gnarly roots of things:

nuggets of words freed
from their appendages

In Russian
a verb depends on its prefix:

Choose carefully for with one
you can make it home on the

St Petersburg metro
before it halts at 1am to allow

the 500+ bridges to yawn open
so the hulking freighters can

slink into harbor
before the captain finishes the last dregs of vodka

Choose the other prefix and
you'll be gazing out of the rickety tram

that sighs at every turn of track
as it sways out of the city on a late fall afternoon

If you're lucky you'll make it
before sundown - the perfect time to forage

for mushrooms in the very forest where
the partisans hid, bits of song escaping over the treetops

It is cold by California standards
I burrow elbow deep in a cardboard box

grasping for that perfect
knot of bulb that promises a red tulip

come spring and so much more

Carol V. Davis

This Month in Michigan

Call it exile,

off a rural road named Main, on the edge
of a small lake that chants all night.

At the Dollar Store an empty-handed girl waiting
behind me in line, finally blurts: *Are you hiring?*

She's too young for such a hardened stare,
even with lids half-closed, turquoise petals.

The GM factory up Highway 91 out on strike again.
By the roadside the line workers' placards wobble like loose teeth.

This winter harsh enough to shred barns.
Come spring the rivers will swell till they topple their banks.

Still I seek refuge, optimistic
as those who plant before the last freeze.

An act of faith, as surely as the photos taped to the cash register;
amulets to protect the town's boys from harm in Iraq.

There is so much that threatens an early bloom:
neglect, disease, the before and the after.

EMARI DIGIORGIO

A WOMAN LOSES HER COUNTRY

She checks her pockets, dumps her purse,
sweeps under the stove. Nothing.

She goes without for a while,
but a woman needs a country. She tries
several others: a country greener
than her own. One with seams that last.

But this one's a little snug,
and she has trouble walking in it.

Another makes her feel fat. She wants
her old country back. In the paper,
"Missing—my dearest country. Last seen
six months ago in a dream. Raw sky,

blossom, black earth and clay. Familiar
as mother's face. Comes to 'Home.'"

Under the fluorescent lights of a 24-hour
bazaar, she studies a carousel of Olde Time
postcards: church ruins, a spillway, a group
of women washing clothes. She knows

their longing, leaves the milk and eggs
on the counter, disappears into the night.

SUSAN ELBE

EDEN IN THE REARVIEW MIRROR

Evening, and the river.
The longitudes inside you.

You reach in, pocketing a green furred stone.

Change the river,
you change too.

At first the world was yours but you owned nothing.
Sweet tarnished pears.
Dusty plums.

Now, only ache.
The apple's broken skin.
Small bitter bite.

You're sick from this fruit.
What you might need now.

The horizon in you starts to climb.
Up. Away.

Everything left behind
in dust—

      tiger lilies by the back fence,
      empty lawn chair on the porch,
      stuttering whirr of an old Singer.

The sheer silk of the river wrinkling
salmon-pink in last-ditch sunlight.

You're already gone.
The way a mountain's deckled edges disappear in rain.

CASA AZUL

*The house where Frida Kahlo
was born and died*

From the spectrum of ghosts, I painted
this house blue to guide my father
and mother to my door. They sit
with Diego and me in the yellow kitchen.
Papa's hands tremble
when he lights my cigarette.
Mama trails the scent
of incense from evening mass.

Papasito hides
behind his camera.
He records the portraits of our shadow
selves—the ones we want
the mirror to reflect. Papa reminds me,
"Do not smile. You seduce the camera."

At Mama's feet, the dogs
lick crumbs of pan dulce
from her fingers. She fusses
about the kitchen. From the strongbox
of her chest she pulls
a white handkerchief, bandages
my painting to soak up its blood.
Her rosary beads click, bones breaking.
She is tired of my gashes and scars.
When she returns to the spirit world,
I will reopen the wounds. They are
the palette from which I paint myself.

This house of cobalt
is the womb where I will die. For years
Death and I have played
at the game of *exquisite corpse*.
Before my first communion, Death drew
my withered leg. I counter,
sketching my heart. See
how it palpitates in my bare hands?

Rebecca Fish Ewan

Night Dive off San Miguel Island
After Adrienne Rich

Our fists opened to explosions of diatomic stars,
super nova bursts from our palms.

We began our descent—lighting an octopus dance,
inky with stage mist. Tentacles pulsated
off my hand. We drifted like flying flags—
one continuous wave weaving among coral-painted boulders
into a bite of salt.

Baby abalone shell tucked like a thermometer under my tongue;
I twirled the shell in my mouth, held it in my teeth, as if
I was a young seal displaying a new toy.

I can still see the silent migration of green sticks
illuminating our heads like neon haloes
as we explored the kelp forest...

Now I watch television, explain facts to my husband
while pointing towards Charlton Heston
diving a wreck:
"This film was made before high-pressure hoses—
see how the regulator comes directly off the tank."

Everything has changed.
I cling to that knowledge
to excuse what's become of me.

My husband nods at my information,
so useless in the desert.

I lick my lips for salt.

We drift off to sleep.

NANCY FLYNN

RUNAWAY

From the vinegar of a small town hell-bent to pickle its vulnerable, the tender ones bottled and stopped by the age of eighteen. From the tentacles belching fire up the grates, an open-jawed furnace to cinder every birthright, no matter if buckwheat, chestnut, pea. From the ration stamps of get along, coupons thumbed till worn, the pinching of pennies and cheeks. From the dizzy of a nosegay, bow-tied on birthdays, *eau de toilette* compliments of Jean Naté. From the lovelorn blasted, buried by dime store rumors, every dowry of resignation grateful for a run-down half of a double block. From a washboard pitted with ache, jutting from the unclear suds in a speckleware tub. From the busybody's clothesline inventory— what you are hanging, what you are not. From the alibi you're a beggar seeking refuge in a sonata, your sole audience a moth. To be the fickle consort of an inkwell, the one who'll spend decades disparaging comfort, her very hair knotty and unkempt.

COREY GINSBERG

HER HOUSE IS PEPTO-BISMOL PINK,
MY NEIGHBOR SAYS

Look at that asshole house on the corner. See that eyesore? Yeah, take a look at the cement box twat on that burnt-out lawn. Wonder who lives in the taint of this street. Bet it's some Barbie Doll icing hooker. Bet she collects flamingos and parades them on Valentine's Day. That house over there, it's tongue pink. It's a 1987 Boy George hypercolor nightmare. Good thing I've got on big aviator sunglasses. That's one slut of a dwelling. Makes my labia hurt thinking about it. Cirrosis of the senses. Could be the bastard stepchild of Mr. Bubble and Tinkerbell. Check out that shriveled soul of the captain of the cheerleading squad. I used to have Chuck Taylors that color—when I was six. Spit your gum out on that cotton candy sexpot. Gas station carnations, that hole is. There's a douchebag in my friend's frat who wears shirts that shade with the collar popped. That's some tacky kitsch bullshit festering on this swatch of land. We should call someone about it. Dear officer, arrest the foreskin of Miami. I've seen discharge from a unicorn more subtle than that house.

Lois Marie Harrod

The House of Signs

Remember the vacation house we used to rent—
the one with signs from porch to attic:
    DON'T OPEN THIS DOOR.
    ENTER HERE.
    SWITCH OFF THE FAN WHEN YOU EXIT THE
        BATH.
    IF IT RAINS LISTEN FOR THE SUMP.
    WHEN YOU FLIP THIS TOGGLE, THE FAN DOES
        NOT VENT OUTDOORS.
    DO NOT CHANGE CONTROLS ON THE DRYER.
    DON'T OVERFILL THE WASHING MACHINE.
    LIMIT LOAD TO FOUR BEACH TOWELS OR ONE
        SET OF BED LINEN.
    THE COFFEE-MAKER IS SLOW.
We used to laugh, saying anyone with such anxiety should never
rent.

Then one night we got a little drunk and moved
from room to room with magic markers, changing, editing—
    DON'T STOP IN THIS DOOR.
    CENTER HERE.
    FILCH THIS FLAN WHEN YOU SLEEP IN THE
        BAT ROOM.
    WHISTLE FOR THE PUMP.
    LIMIT LOAD TO FOUR BLEACHED OWLS.
    THE COFFEEMAKER IS ACADEMICALLY
        CHALLENGED.
making each sign more cock-eyed than it was.
Or did we just play the game on paper?
Make new signs to cover the old? Or did I only dream our doing?

We were always so careful not to shake up the world, weren't we?
But since you left, our own house is filling with warnings:
   If I open this door, you will still be here;
   if I switch on this light, you will be gone.
I have to be so careful.

BRANDI HOMAN

WHAT IT MEANS TO BE AN AMERICAN

It's a picnic. Buckets of beer, a bluegrass band, a shotgun
wedding. Casseroles in covered dishes, sparklers, fireflies.
Doritos and French fries. Cantaloupe squares and a waitress
humming in the background.

On pontoon boats, we want to waterski. We're all on ecstasy,
sour cream for a smooth tongue. Everything slides into the lake.
Our lifejackets are swollen, our cells blowin' up.
Our Mastercards work. Our teeth sparkle.

A Simpson sister tries to sing. Half of us are pregnant.
The other half are sterile. This is not a dystopia, so obviously
dystopic—our knives keep getting bigger.
None of us can stop eating.

LOUISA HOWEROW

ELEMENTS
Yiannis Moralis, "Two Friends," 1946,
National Art Gallery of Athens, Greece

In the gallery, I keep circling
back to the painting, arguing
against your assessment:
a conventional picture, two seated women.
Consider the date,
the colour of the younger woman's jumper
 civil-war red
 blood-in-the-streets red
 thousands-dead red.
How healing might come
from her soft red mouth.
The other woman understands
the temple of Athena needs rebuilding.
She's placed the tools within reach
 ruler, calipers, mallet
ordered Penteli marble.
Her hand in semi-benediction is drawing
the people in.
Consider the women's eyes and mine
 how we measure
 scars, light
the distance to redemption.

JULIE KANE

PURPLE MARTIN SUITE

*I have had several opportunities, at the period of their arrival, of seeing
prodigious flocks moving over [New Orleans] or its vicinity, at a considerable
height . . . I walked under one of them with ease for upwards of two miles, at
that rate on the 4th of February 1821, on the bank of the river below the city,
constantly looking up at the birds, to the great astonishment of many passengers,
who were bent on far different pursuits.*
— John James Audubon

1.

Any excuse, a holiday or death
will make them twirl umbrellas, shake their butts
to brass band music in the streets. I swear,
what *won't* these people make a party of?
So when my neighbor loaded beer on ice
and grabbed two folding chairs and said he meant
to go watch birds roost underneath a bridge,
it seemed no odder an excuse than Lent
to celebrate. We parked the pickup truck
by Entergy and slid down dirt banks under
girders where the Causeway Bridge meets land,
silenced by the rush-hour traffic's thunder
whizzing overhead. No sign, yet, of a bird:
I had to take my neighbor at his word.

2.

I had to take my neighbor at his word
that there would be a show, as birds arrived
in ones and twos and then in blue-black streams
to scribble meaninglessly on the sky,
thousands and thousands of them swarming; then,

as if an orchestra were tuning up,
the sun dipped under the horizon like
the fall of a baton, the "theater" hushed,
and suddenly the birds began to soar
in perfect loop-de-loops and barrel rolls,
whole squadrons of them flying synchronized
as vintage prop planes in an aircraft show,
till even those not mystically inclined
would swear they were connected mind to mind.

3.

As if they were connected mind to mind,
one group of them broke off and swooped en masse
below the Causeway, settling wing to wing
along steel girders; then a second pass,
a third, as any birds who hadn't found
a spot the last dive, flowed into the next,
the way a mother braids a daughter's hair
or villanelle picks up old lines of text.
When it was over it was way too dark
to tell their outlines from the sky or lake.
We stood and clapped as if we'd seen the Meters
reunited on a Jazz Fest stage,
joined beat to beat and holding in our breath
as night fell on that holiday from death.

Vasiliki Katsarou

Swan Boats, Boston Public Garden

In the slippery light of morning, the eye
swims in blooms, and mothers or others
wheel their charges beneath the statues
and the weeping willows

    scattered about
      poor prescient
   isolated   artists
      dot
    the footpaths

That cloying scent, pollen
tenderfoot
Anglo-Saxon pastel palette

So this will be my yearly visitation
to a site of excellence and toddler envy

that rarest destination
unchanged since Henry James,

     Swan Boats!

What could be more mesmerizing
than this glide
for one raised between pavements and sidewalks

Look, the Swan Boats have docked

on this island
that is childhood

*

Fickle sun
the sheen of the swan
not its preening

Left an Isabel
only to return a mother Merle

alas, even this season of mothers and children
is brief
this morning of life

my one son, almost grown,
to your two

This morning, Mother, you may pick up your brush
set up canvas
against this background

Prim and prissy New England
all checks and plaids

But what of our other home
island home of another life,
luminous, whorled
all shit and roses,
oranges fresh and rotten, sun-
bleached linens and ancient
embroideries?

In the flip and flash
of colored feather
where green meets black

and gold meets silver

You who lent me this stuff
only to squeeze it back out of me

Well, I am here
smeared across this canvas

brush and buttress
against the daily erosion
of the island

penultimate shade in the palette

poem beneath the tree

to skim the surface

to paint the sound of a bird's accelerated flight

Vandanna Khanna

Lemons: A Love Letter

Under dip and curve of ceiling fan,
under still-eyed stare of lizards
and hot hush of night, they are

what's left: small and tart,
wrapped in yesterday's *India Times*.
Stolen from your walled garden

in Old Delhi, their plucked
tenderness constant and sour.
Shuttled across miles of plants

rising thick and wild
from the edges of a map—
exiled to my hollow blue

kitchen, to garnish and sting
the curry. Thinking of it is
too much—sand and dialects

and time zones, too many
continents of half-sipped cups
of tea. Almost midnight and I

long for more substance,
for their weight to sag
and buckle in the basin

of my hennaed hands. And still,
their yellow fragility, sucked dry,
tastes as close to you as I can get.

VANDANNA KHANNA

IN THE KITCHEN

No one bothers me in here,
assuming I'm putting myself
to good use—fingers deep

in dough, massaging bread
into place, chanting names
from the cupboard like

a hymn: nutmeg and cinnamon,
rosemary and basil. I've avoided
this spot-lit stage: meat loosened

from bone, fish stewing in a pot.
All these spices push me
into the background, too many

to know their real names, just
by sense of what they might be:
masalas that make your nose run

all the way from the front door.
It's my mother who can eye
a pan and know what's missing,

measure by the feel of her hands.
Even in close up, she never misses
her mark, knows how everything

cooks at its own pace. In the kitchen,
she's all business, all Hindi,

teaching my hand how to memorize

the curve of a ripe mango,
the weight of coarse wheat.
But I'm no good in translation,

wasting hours in supermarket
aisles looking for the familiar,
for flavors that haunt the house

for days. Nothing's the same:
encased in shiny, American
packaging, neatly named, grim

under the florescent hum
of lights. My senses, my only
savior: the way my tongue

rings with it, turns to water.
Now I steal away time from sink
and stove, until my fingers cramp.

This is the only kneading I can do—
let words steep in their own juices
until they are sweet and heavy.

Fold them, one over the other.
Whip and whisk them until firm
and can stand on their own.

MOLLY SUTTON KIEFER

THE CAPE

My mother told me I would call it *beach brushing*,
that endless search of nicks in the sand.

I wanted a fine collection of shells
the color of welts, like the glass jar full

she kept in the master bathroom.
I'd count them in my palm, fertile plenty.

Instead, in the clefts left by slow waves,
we find chips of bone-white, the stuff

picked over by gulls and salted wanderers.
She spotted it first, the black hump

like a distorted helmet, and nudged it over,
ten legs spindling out. Already dead and fetid,

not the prize, the sand dollar I desired,
coin of a puzzle, but its armored foil,

the horseshoe crab. This living fossil
may have tumbled to shore to mate

in the spit of the sea, book gills keeping damp
the driest span, spiraling sand-circles to entice,

her partner climbing onto her back, scudding
into the tide. She didn't make it out, this one, her tender

insides exposed to the wind. My mother
scooped the arthropod into a sack, brought it

to the house, wanted to boil its guts
out, wanting the empty shell, but even dead,

thought too cruel, and instead,
forgot it drying on the clothesline.

MOLLY SUTTON KIEFER

CHROMOSOMAL GEOGRAPHY

When I am gone, my ashes will pound
into the creek, and there will be forgotten things:
this was where we found the snail together, where it
glommed onto your fingers, your tongue wild
and half-chewed. Or maybe you'll scatter me
in the garden, unknowingly in the corner
where the asparagus rose for three springs
and not in the fourth, leaving just the memory
of those ferny stalks. Maybe you'll fly me out
to Lake Dillon, let me silt down to the town
buried by water, and I'll ghost along abandoned
kitchens and gaze at the bench where I nursed you
and we learned of Virginia's earthquake. You could
burn me and tip me into the Inside Passage, among
spawned salmon and the fleet feet of black bears,
flush me into the Pacific, crowd against debris.
You didn't know me then, that honeymoon,
but you were there, your double X nestled against
other hopefuls. My body has been your map, your ruddy
grubby hands here and here. We lie in bed and I sway you
to sleep and this is where you name all the parts:
nose and *eye* and I notice I need to trim
those mooned fingernails. You show me your tongue
so I'll show you mine. Did you know the brain is the first
organ to wick away and the uterus is the last? I think of
these things, these places you've lived. I almost kept
those gallstones in a jar. Don't keep me in a jar.
I will love you from all places. You could pin

me to the ocean and swim, swim. I'll keep pace, print me
into your skin. You could name all the animals, you could
spawn, your X and your X, an alphabet born.

LITTLE GREEN STORE

It was Gainesville, Florida,
and I was five.
A group of us went down
the sandy road: Kay, Suzette,
and Billy Asbell, the boy
I loved. The sand was pink
and it made our feet pink
in their rubber thongs.
We had money for candy
from the little green store
and I was afraid to ask for what I wanted,
but I wanted to go.
We knew how to get there:
down the road this way,
then turn right
and you could see it!
A low square building,
green stucco, peeling to reveal
pink stucco underneath, as if
it were really made of sand.
And when we turned
I looked down at my feet
and they were my mother's feet
in her white sandals
pierced all over with tiny holes.
My toes were her toes, painted red.
And this was shocking
but I did not scream
because I was the grownup
walking just behind the children,

Billy and Kay and Suzette.
Suzette's red hair curved behind
the red rim of her left ear.
Billy and Kay held hands,
their dark heads tipped forward.
I can't remember ever getting there,
ever asking for what I wanted.
And sometimes the shoes change
to silver, to clear plastic, really,
filled with silver glitter,
shoes I got at the Serendipity Shop
in Nacogdoches, Texas,
with Terry Kennedy when I was nine
and my mother was in a room
drinking with adults,
and then it's clear
that was another day altogether
and I can never get back
to the little green store,
my pink hand tight with coins.

JJ Lynne

Terrarium

The bottles in the window tell me where you've been.
Brackish rims, opalescent bottoms, and dusty films—
empty except for a flush of white air,
splaying light like shattered fireflies on the kitchen's floor.
Stale, like your stagnant breath, they once knew the graze
of bubbling baths and chilled sweats that came when
the radiator kicked on, hissing horrid lullabies at 5 a.m.
See-through shrines rest on chipped
wooden panes—flexed shoulder blades.
Baby blue Russian jars, syrup-stained Canadian jugs,
and the emerald vial collected from my cluttered vanity,
my arsenal of scents and salves. The stolen gift.
Tokens from places you've never haunted
making memories out of glimmers and glass,
your shoes keep close to the doormat.
Building worlds out of phials in thin, open air,
as light as an anvil, as stiff as silk sheets, you are
planted and paralyzed in your familiar chair
reading books on Mars and alternate universes.

MARJORIE MADDOX

CARTOGRAPHY

Simple as a globe spinning
or a quick sketch of the country:
thick black lines as borders,
an ocean here, there,
maybe an interstate running through
and a few rivers, towns.

An entire state scratched on the back of an envelope,
rough, rough draft of an atlas. You trace me like this,
don't expect a dirt path in Kentucky,
freeways wrapped around Chicago, stretched to the East coast;
don't expect veins like roads, heel prints,
boundaries as strong or flimsy as fingernails, as lies.

I'm pinned to place like girders on a bridge,
steel become cold, colder,
like concrete stuck to earth in basements, construction sites.
Sometimes, tugged in and out of coves
in a current too much like a lover,
I float, half-eroded, mouth full of pebbles.

True, the shape of my face is in sand, mountains,
and I sleep to the click of an S.O.S., or not at all.
Because of you, I apply bruises to my cheeks like blush,
to my brow ash from the oldest volcano.
There is more to this than silhouette, than map.

What of your outlines?
An inch into Ohio you pinpoint cities. You're wrong.
This circle is the pond I first made love in,

the dot a patch of poison oak I wore,
a millimeter away: the line where train and Buick
ripped even the sky, severed then from after
while I watched, a car behind.

We draw and redraw maps to keep our footing,
define who and why we are:
thud of fist, jagged cry of a child,
whoosh of water taking in a body—here on paper.
These coastlines are fainter than breath, the barest stencil
of all we want to remember or cannot forget.

Lisa McCool-Grime

Salt

Once too much has been poured in, there's little
can be done. When will I learn

to take it one pinch at a time? Thank goodness
the onions are sweet

this season. Thank goodness the dandelions
have subsided. And yes

the mosquitoes are out in full-force, just one step
beyond the rectangle of air

that pants against the back door all afternoon
such a babel of pricks

to the leather of the upper arm. The bloodsuckers
swarm at the first out-breath

and drown in the soup which is too salty
for the tongue. For the cut, salt heals.

That's why I rub it into the wound.
Forget proverbs.

An apple a day does far less than an ancient grain
of the sea. Where

in all this great, gold kingdom, with its shafts
of durum and its sunflowers

going to seed beyond and beyond that
the missiles

named for the alphabet's sons
where, but in the kitchen

can I smell my mother?
One pinch at a time

she is that strong.

Karyna McGlynn

Don't Move Here

Being from Austin is a bit like being a unicorn
in a universe where people only care about unicorns
that also write screenplays.

When I try to self-promote
I feel like I'm selling long-distance plans
for no other reason than that my inner Hispanic boss
might give me an aggressive shoulder massage
and take me out for pizza.

I only end up uncorking the stinky chardonnay
of friendships I don't have the time to enjoy
but can't, for some reason, pour down the drain.

Chris, newly uncorked by my recent facebook blast,
tells me I can't write in my hometown, that my mind
gets muffled in the cotton of careless childhood
and whether my car is washed.

This is what shakes down on the lonely
inconsequential patios of this century.
My selfishness exacerbated by sunburn
and the belletristic myth that drives me
to dip my fingers in the Limoncello of Love!

Sometimes I use my dreams to spy on dead poets.
All my life I've been trying to catch the Brownings
boring each other. I want to bring them back
to my condo in Texas and watch them try to write a sonnet.

At Eeyore's Birthday you can still see men in shirts that say
"Welcome to Austin. Don't Move Here" and
"Keep Austin Weird" but you can no longer see them
as catalysts for a metaphor that stopped working
long before the economy collapsed on top of my poetry,
like a fat guy with a bum-knee at 80s night.

KARYNA McGLYNN

THE STORY OF THE PALACE

Let me tell you about how Princess Di died for me.
About how the news surged across the Atlantic,
gathered strange force as it swept over the Bible belt
and came hurtling down I-35 on the back of a semi,
how it slipped in through the tinted double doors
on a snatch of sunlight that briefly bared the dark
pulse of the Crystal Palace Gentleman's Club.

I had just offered a well-dressed man a lap dance,
and this is how he rebuffed me: with a polite but firm
"No, thank you. I'm waiting for big tits." like he was
waiting for the bus. How I must have looked: drinking
my sixth diet coke with extra cherries at a little lacquer
table across from an engineer who sat shyly stroking
red and black feathers at the open neck of my negligee.

This is how, at that exact moment, the news streaked
over the carpet's neon geometry, transmitted from stiletto
to stiletto in a crude game of telephone, and came for me
with almost a—how else to put this?—a wuthering, fanning
out like brushfire from dancer to dancer, how, finally
one of the older girls, Misty, in a turmoil of mascara
rushed my table, crushed herself into me and choked
the thing out: "Princess Di…She's been….*Shot!*"

I don't need to tell you how the news had been
perverted in its journey to Misty's mouth, but I
do need to tell you about how many times I've tried
to tell this story, how I can never make it sound
right, or convince anyone that it wasn't about me,

because however I tell it, there I am in a San Antonio
strip club, singularly unaffected amidst the anguish
of what I'd imagined were hardened women, who
now fled in various states of dance and undress
to huddle in the dressing room, how all the men
were left weirdly alone with their wallets, how girls
I'd never spoken to held me to their bare breasts
and just sobbed, and how the manager, against his
wishes, had to shut down the Palace and send
his inconsolable burlesque princesses home.

I hate this part because I have to tell you how
morbidly happy I was, because it meant I could go
lay out by the Mustang Motel pool, the sun blazing
gold on my toenails, the sky opening its feathery
aquamarine fan above me, gems of light swinging
their thin hips in the water. How, even as I told myself
I wasn't like them—my delusional fellow dancers
waiting for their fairytales to begin—I felt something
slip from my head and shatter. Somehow, sun-drunk,
I knew I'd been spared, body glittered in broken glass
while dodging the bullet's long and circuitous path.

CLAIRE MCGUIRE

POLLYANNA SMILES

Her prairie hair is grass gone to seed,
her voice vibrates on a fiddle string.
She taught you the meaning of homeward,
Americana Pollyanna, you tangle her name
in the cold northeastern stars.

She spills tall tales across the porch,
the air smells of thunder and cherry pie.
As a child she caught fireflies in jars
and has a scar in the shape of Alabama,
Pollyanna.

Tonight,
snow clouds roll through Chicago, the air is thin.
You stand in the window on a two hour layover
and look Homeward.

Pollyanna Mystica, a sky full of constellations
that you have already begun to forget:
watermelon seeds spit from the porch,
a spattering of insects on the windshield,
beautifully and infinitely random.

Freckles that trail down her knees and bare feet,
meandering paths you have followed before.
Pollyanna Diana, a fat moon smiles down on
the Kentucky dirt, rutted and red
where she will lay down her tired bones.

Jennifer Militello

There Remain New Branches

I can imagine such a place: like a flute, it comes apart.
Streets loosen like tobacco. There are animal skins.

It comes across, the way bodies' crying reaches us
and crawls inside. It is beyond the mirrored room

of my sister's eye. It has such a dark iris no light
comes through, and the shed light of rain becomes

a neutral sound. Here, we remember what it's like
to remember. Naming parts of the body, we find

they are familiar. Dreams never make the transfer
to days, and the gladioli are wilting.

Welcome to changing everything. Welcome to starving
out of sleep. By morning, weariness will have replaced

the jawbone of a thinned and willful sky.
This illness is savage. These clouds, they are scythes.

JENNIFER MOFFETT

LOST

Midway across the Queensboro Bridge
We realized they were still on the plane—
Hi8 video tapes in a coat pocket
The cabin by now sterilized and vacuous,
And we decided not to turn around
To instead rush home, unpack.

I imagined a stranger watching the footage
Of me sleeping (something he liked to film),
Silent vineyards and hills,
Narrow roads latticed with shadows,
A low, pregnant sun glittering across a lake

Or the scene we'd already previewed
In Tuscany: me on a balcony
Pulling kittens from the terra cotta roof
As the mother cat circled my feet.

I'd looked gaunt in the movie,
Fragile, bare feet burning
On sun-baked tile. Led by the faint
Sound of disembodied mewing
That no one else could hear.

This part not captured on film: me following the mother cat
Alone, slinking and pausing in unison
Into dense woods rising behind the villa.
Barefoot still, I lost her in a place
I knew she'd never leave, even for her babies

Jenn Marie Nunes

The Land Where Plums Abound

In botany, a **pome**.
(after the Latin word for fruit: pōmum) a type
of fruit produced by flowering plants in the
subfamily Maloideae of the family Rosaceae.

apples: youth, fertility – results in a six year pregnancy – to throw an
apple is to declare one's love & to catch it is to accept (greek –
hera/athena/aphrodite – causes the trojan war)

In botany, a **poem**.
(the language organs stitched by pattern. constructs the
wondering. what is the relationship of someone to the mythology
they make up

A pome is an accessory fruit composed of one
or more   cross-sectional slices of my body
        surrounded by accessory tissue. The lady
glands   interpreted by some specialists as an
extension of the receptacle   into town. Imagine
such ownership. Imagine the remains you grew up in. The
entrance & exit   then referred to as   girl
parts. The map of the town coded with stockpiles of food
&weaponry corresponding to the mounds & holes on my body
        the most edible part of this fruit.
Like any good symbol there are layers of meaning. It is difficult
to just say   some other fruit types look
very much like the skin flesh &core
respectively   without sounding overly dramatic. I do
want to clarify   a pome may be fleshy &
difficult to distinguish   my ripening case from the
town. It is acceptable to gut grade build &rebuild a r o u n d
the seed   my ingrown correspond to what
is commonly called the core.   The shriveled
r e m a i n s   relabeled public. Progress   c a n
sometimes be seen at the end   or a
movement toward homogenization   and the ovary
is therefore often described as inferior in
these flowers.

Rachael Peckham

Aunt Moreen's Confession

She was a victim of incest. It was nearly on her death bed that she confided this. –in a letter from my grandmother

There, in back of the sugar house. That first time, I was caught by the arm in a game of what else, hide-and-seek. Clothes-lined. I weighed nothing but I was good at slipping out of any hold. I thought it was just a round of that, but then fingers pinched my lips—*shh, Mi.* Just like that. My feet flexing, gouging the dirt. Inside my head I could hear a buzzing. Later, they accused me of crying *no one found me.* Don't be so sore, they said, it's just a game. And I could barely walk the path to the house and up the stairs and into bed. Pretending to sleep through breakfast, *just sticking my chores on 'em. Can't you see, Ma?* She couldn't. She and Daddy had their own trouble, working the orchard. Always wheat to thrash, more sap to boil, oaks to cut, *nothing gets done without some doing.* And there I was, chasing after brothers like a boy herself, making her mama mumble words like *you* and *watch.* I hid my soiled things in the bottom of the burn barrel. And even if they'd been found, they'd never get a second look. Not then. Somebody was always lighting clothes and bed sheets, making long kite tails of cottony smoke after the influenza scare and school was closed, when I had to stay home and keep up this game of hide-and-seek and *hush-up-now.* But look, they said, how much she misses school, a born teacher. Guess I could've gone some other way but I had no more fight in me, nothing left of me in that orchard, to everybody's wonder. *Poor Moreen,* picked clean behind the burn barrel she pushed over one morning, torching one whole acre in a drought no less. Oh, they knew. Shuffling me from different wards, springing for a special nurse and then a blood transfusion, oh yes—*this* I knew, mixing blood with blood. You can shock me silent and put yours inside, take it all out and

208

give it back again because I'm Moreen, with all its meanings—
wished-for child, bitterness of the sea.

JANEEN RASTALL

INTERPRETING DREAMS

She daydreams in Polish.
Decades tumbled
since she whispered to her sisters,
the party line thrumming
with secrets spilt in their native tongue.
Sinking down in her wheelchair seat,
slipping in and out of sleep
she transliterates the nursing home.
Polkas replace Sinatra on the intercom.
Stacks of *krem* topple next to her coffee cup.
The hairdresser vies with the dryer,
gossiping in a lowland dialect.
Sajak spins a Cyrillic wheel,
announces prizes with a thick accent.
Even the nurse's name tag
has gained an extra *k* and *z*.
She smiles through her sleep,
her translation finally complete.

MARTHE REED

WINTER CANON: SOUTH LOUISIANA

Bare branches draw a pale refusal, irritable beneath an absent
sun: charter of stillness, an opening overhead in the dissolution
of leaves. In the absent canopy, black and white warblers,
flashing brilliance of, prints like small hands (augere, to increase:
litany of imprecision.) A negotiation with place

Language rustles, dry in the wind where cold etches yellowed
grass. Empties the air. Composition of wet clay and oak. Roots
assume a quiet determination. A space shaped by the persistence
of rain, or raccoons. Small hands worked into the earth, their
tracery a sentence forming at the edge of memory.

Leaves and their absence, recollection a process of accretion or
sedimentation. Bare trees efface the distinction between sky and
horizon. In their refusal to abide by the darkness of winter, vines
cling, asserting a motion forward as well as back. Twining. Light-
washed trunks of water oaks and ashes. Motion

Forward: augment, a vowel or a lengthening of the vowel. Winter
refuses to participate. Canon piecing together stillness and
motion, cold and the directed movement of low pressures along a
gradient. Warblers and the flashing brilliance of. Language
pushed along a current of memory.

In the absence of memory, language insinuates itself. Introduces
another pressure. Permission, augere. Moving tangentially to the
source, water erodes its passage. Creek bed washing away earth,
revealing the twisting architecture of oak roots. Bayou a
crosshatched flightway, language and memory.

Jennifer Saunders

How to Learn German: Verbs

From between two parked cars
a man will step out
into the Bernese street.
You will hear *thunk*
like a branch falling in the snow
and will look up in time to see
the back wheels of a forklift
from the nearby construction site
rumble over him.

You will fumble the emergency call,
will dial the wrong number,
will stumble over umlauts
as you stammer you need an ambulance,
a man has been,
    has been,
        has been,
a man has been –
but the German verb
will not come.

An ambulance will arrive.
Paramedics will work
on the man in the street,
but not for very long.

You will tell yourself
it was not your fault.
You will tell yourself
other people called too.

You will tell yourself
one of them dialed correctly,
one of them spoke clearly,
one of them
    knew
        the damn verb.
You will go home
and pour yourself a drink.

You will conjugate
the verb *überfahren*:
to run over.
You will learn by heart
the verb *sterben*:
to die.

KELLY SCARFF

THE SMALLEST ORCHID, PUERTO RICO, 2009

You found it just as the rain started.
It's cupped pink body barely visible
under rain-soaked parkas
and fogged eye-glasses.

You told your mother that night
as you bathed her one remaining leg.
"I've looked for sixty-five years,
and that's the smallest one I've seen."
The sores from her wheelchair
have grown past her hips
and latched onto the loose skin
around her stomach.
You will have to re-wrap the gauze, again.
She will apologize
for not having dinner ready,
for not remembering to boil the rice
or season the chicken,
for forgetting to crack the coconuts
that have fallen across the lawn.

She hasn't cooked in years,
but you don't tell her that.
In her mind she still has all that life to go,
in her mind she is that smallest orchid,
stretching her cupped body upward
toward the rain.

Marissa Schwalm

Bridges

Four hundred and forty-six bridges
etch themselves across Pittsburgh,
jagged stitches holding
together a city where three rivers meet
skyscrapers, mountains, and the grey soot
memory of industrialization.

I remember my first bridge:
being birthed out of the cave
of an endless tunnel to meet
yellow steel, dark water underneath,
the city skyline, houses built
into slopes.
Snow floated down.
City lights flickered on,
I became a new city.

Three years in I learn the language,
how to translate the mumbling
stream of sentences with dropped consonants.
My toothless neighbor across the street asks
if I heard about the man who got shot
in the face two doors down. I tell him
I was taking a nap and woke to the gunshot,
watched from my window as the ambulance
came to scoop bits of his face off the sidewalk.
He wipes the back of his hand
across his sweating scalp,
asks if I've been to that new restaurant in the Strip
when I say no he shrugs,

You can't get there from here.

When we move again, even your truck doesn't want to go.
Massachusetts is prissy with a stupid accent,
words that don't make sense.
Two days before we leave
the platinum truck secures its tires
down in the gravel driveway,
refuses to move.

You kick the bumper with your steel toes,
punch the gas cover so it never shuts again.
Our dogs cower by bushes in the backyard,
and my mother is somewhere back in New York
trying to warn me of something unspeakable.

Too late I will learn of things hidden in that truck
under the seats, in the glove box, even under
the plastic hugging the stick shift.
That truck that we had to hitch up on a tow
to get it out of the 'Burgh, dragging it's beat up
exterior all the way to our sixth and final home.

Two states later all I see are bridges.
Bridges leading to places I once knew
long and heavy with steel, shaking
with burden.
Bridges to places downstream,
across a river, on a glowing hill,
somewhere I can't get to from here.

DANIELLE SELLERS

PEACH TREE, LATE SUMMER

At the nursery, I ask my daughter,
who's two and a half, to choose a sapling.
She trips through the spindly trunks in
black plastic buckets, pulls leaves off
to study them. She even chews them,
spits and wipes her mouth with the back
of her hand. Proclaims, finally, *Apple twee.*

But we're in Mississippi where apples won't grow.
Our love affair with winter is short-lived.
It often blankets our brown river
valley with a dusting of overnight snow,
a delight given then taken back too soon.
Heat muscles in when it shouldn't.

I purchase a peach, because she says
the leaves are shaped like green bananas,
like green half moons, like green sickles,
and because she was born in Georgia
the only place we were ever
a complete family, though she has no
memory of it, and I envy that.

Digging through clay in mid-September
is like putting a shovel to concrete.
Not young anymore, my knees grind.
The old tennis elbow acts up.
We wet the ground. She holds the garden hose,
and drinks from it though no one's ever
taught her how. I replace the useless

orange clay with store-bought soil.
We plant the tree, old as she is
but twice as tall, and tamp the earth.

Her first lesson in disappointment.
That what we want is often never
what we can have. Even
second-best takes leverage, sweat,
muscle and bone work. Where we end
doesn't look much different
than where we began. A tree
is still a tree, in the ground or in a pot,
and peach will never taste clean like apple.

PAULA SERGI

CRUMBS

Like you, I would've walked for miles
down the gravel road along the creek
by my childhood home
to nibble a cornice of rooftop,
lick icing mortar, risk
catching my tongue on a crevice
of crystallized sugar

and waited for the slice,
that flat taste of blood to flow.

Or followed Alice and the mushrooms—
that's a sweet road, too,
falling like soft bread,
squished down, then stretching
again, filling her white tights
a fat sausage, as if that—
adding all the scraps—
would be the way back home.

Imagine the flat of your hand
on that old crone's backside,
the bruise a dehydrated plum from your pushing
and shoving her into the little box of hell.
Even old, lean bones show direction
when they land like the hands of a compass.

So if home is a place to imagine,
if size isn't really the point,
then the porridge is equally salty
from either bowl, mama's or dad's.

DIANE SEUSS

DON'T FILL THE OUTLINE

the hound left behind with a hound. You know how good it can be, holding an empty leash. When the fire station burned it was a relief. No red truck to shine, no bell to clang, no hose to wind up or unwind. Admit you know how pretty it was when Ellie gave birth to a moon out on Born Street behind the hog market, that kid without a face, its head just a bare bulb, a circle, silvery, like a hand mirror. You know when a tooth falls out, the gap gives your tongue something to do, that when the mushroom factory left town there was no more manure in the wind all summer. Remember when Simplicity shut its doors, how outlaw dress patterns went blowing down the alleys and fluttered like paper birds in the limbs of trees?

Jen Siraganian

A House on the Seam

Outside, the garden bursts with snapdragons
and olive trees. The walls still clutch their scars,
fine fissures from bullets, gray plaster bleeds

with graffiti. Behind the lemon trees
(where UN guards steal fruits by the bushel),
a house is sewn into a country's seam.

A Jerusalem address that shifts each decade,
Jordan, No Man's Land, now Israel.
My father hasn't lived in it since '56,

and when my grandmother died, her best friend
(a missionary who knew about the orphanage,
the 13 miscarriages, and what really happened

during the Genocide) moved in. She shows me
my father's bedroom, assures me it hasn't changed—
a twin bed, a wooden desk by the window,

a sink and toilet behind a beige screen in the corner.
I notice the walls. So deep, they stretch the length
of my arm. When she heads to the kitchen

to heat water for tea, I press my shoulder blade
against the window's frame and reach outward
until fingers brush bars beyond the opened glass.

SARAH J. SLOAT

EUROPA

Johannes,
Your green apples leave me bitter.
I damn-near drowned in your puppet village,
sniffing out the buckets of sun,
my Chinese lantern rinsed with twilight.
I know the substantives you speak of,
but cannot spit them forth without a dollop
of schnapps under my tongue. Johannes,

the swain's waistcoat does not suit me.
I'm struck speechless in your forests -
such a grooming, and the tools you use
to foster this epidemic of hazelnuts.
I never intended to wander this far
into the Abendland. Johannes,

you have been a loyal tinsmith,
a diligent tinker at the great machine.
It's touching how at midnight you spit
upon the rag to furbish. But the machinery
is busted; it no longer runs on tungsten.
The bolts have flown, rolling off
as if accidentally into what
we'll call the occident.

SARAH J. SLOAT

GOOD WIFE OF HUNAN

You knew I'd been up all night startling the wok
and I'd been up for ages grooming the dog star
of ticks, throwing a tarp over all that barking
for the sake of the neighbors and cosmic harmony.
Clearly I'd been up with my measuring stick
by the river, which chilled my toe bones and triggered
that crying-jag phone call to my mother two monasteries
west of here, my mother who was glad to have girls.
Spring petals fell like snow into the year of the monkey.
Snow fell like snow into the year of the cat.
And it seemed I'd be up startling the wok
for generations and it seemed I was going to live
to see 10,000 or at least the day you dropped dead
drunk from the jug of plum wine and I'd shown
the barking star who's master.

JENNIFER TAPPENDEN

INVITATION TO MS. BRIGIT PEGEEN KELLY
After Elizabeth Bishop

Bring your stolen boy with his steaming white skin
and black hair like feathers
of a swan, bring the swan, too,
if it will come.
           I have a garden, a garden old
as yours and ringed in a fence of rusted iron arrows.
Its gates are carved pillars of limestone, smoothed by rain
but warm, today, in the budding sun. Your horse,
with his giant marble hooves, will find good forage,
if he will come.
           In every bush
there is the promise of birdsong, of burning
that will not be contained, that will
bud among the ashes of the understory.
           There is even a stair
that leads to nothing, its steps a perfect set
of granite ledges for sitting, for a picnic
among the hyacinths and their acolytes, the bees.
If you will come,
           my garden will be real
as the waving flag of your hair as you ride
in on the statue of your horse, the black swan
in the bend of your arm and the black haired boy
behind you, his arms around your waist. All of this is
only true if you are here.
           Please come.

JUDITH TERZI

TSUNAMI
starting with a line by Sappho

Who is the one with violets in her lap?
After the earth shook, she rang the bell
to warn the town to run. The women who sell
wool, their skeins spread out like garlands of tulips
and lilies, fled, but what about their shawls,
caps and gloves piled in the beds of trucks?
The sea grabbed boats of fishermen like a shark,
tossed roofs and furniture, churches and schools
in its wild walls. The rage complete, it displaced
their planks onto black sand, into forests and streets.
Violet is the light of mourning, *luz divina*,
luz of healing, *luz* of valor for Martina.
She is the one with violets; she knits wreaths
for the silt of the río Maule and shredded lace.

Meghan Tutolo

Monday Night in South Greensburg

What shuts me up is the stillness of Broad St,
a main road of back-home bars & bus stops.
The neighbor dog eats through the fence,
its splinter tongue feels freedom like the white wood—
to want a place it's never been.

In my room, the globe hasn't spun for days,
the phone disconnected on a black bookcase. Still,
I can't sleep in this silence, just the choke
of the furnace, just words on a page in my head.
The beams of wood sigh under the lone lamp.

Ocala, Florida: where the grass feels plastic,
and the hard juts of green are palm trees.
Somewhere in Ocala, there are golf tournaments, and
suited men who will iron your ties in the backroom
of some country club for twenty-dollar bills.

The maps eat walls, plaster chips under the weight
of paper & scotch-tape and the singular sound of starred cities—
where I'm not:
Las Vegas is a straight shot, just take 70 all the way.
To think of something that hot, to think of ice cream melting.
Here, grass is wet and the first sign of winter is a smoke in my
         breath.

The elderly migrate to Florida, 79 & 77, routes
that wiggle through Appalachia, mauve sedans on parade—
as in funeral processions without the yellow flags.
I am scared to get old, that I'll be here forever.
The skin on my face already feels looser.

DONNA VORREYER

FLYING BLIND

We have watched the gritty films
of first attempts, strange machines
leaping apoplectic from the solid earth

to land with the sudden thud of failure.
Yet history saw fit to lift the wings at
Kitty Hawk and lead us here. We know

the science, but we must believe in luck
to trust the pilot with our fate, to tuck
the small pillow beneath our heads, to

lock the tiny tray in the upright position
and lean back, somehow certain of how
it succeeds, how the recycled air mingles

the atoms of strangers into breath, how
our ears fill and mute the *maybes* of
the coming miles, how we buckle in

for hours over the wild Atlantic, tethered
to the sky by some unseen cord, how we
take for granted it will not fray or break.

ABIGAIL WYATT

DOZY MARY
(A Long-term Resident of South Ockendon Hopital c.1970)

That Dozy Mary is forty-two
is somehow hard to believe.
Yes, they tell me, this is her home
and all the world she knows.
She's happy here; she likes to help;
without her we really couldn't cope:
Dozy Mary's carried and fetched
for close on thirty years.

And, yes, it's true that Dozy Mary
survives from day to day;
out of the space inside her head,
she has learned to be of use.
More than able, she shoulders the wheel
on these grey yawning wards;
with a dull knife she scrapes the scraps
of meals we would not eat
from squat tables purged of spills
and stripped of their smears of joy.
Then, soft-shoe-shuffling, she follows behind
the trolley that lurches and squeaks
to mop and shine with patient pride
a world awash with floors.
Her broad bottom's ponderous weight
sways in quick-slow time
as Dozy Mary waltzes and sings:
Lah, lah, lah.

But Dozy Mary once was glad;
she had her hour of grace.
A midnight heaven's starlit scope
fell beyond measure in her hair.
Now it's cut close, that sullen bob,
but it' sheen is mystery still.
It's easy to see how it might have been
in another life unlived.

I'm a good girl, I am, Mary says,
and a child's tears prick her eyes.
What wickedness then once kissed her neck
and fell between pale, high mounds?
I'm a good girl, I am.
She starts and stares
and, sometimes, picks at her nails.
Dozy Mary is forty-two;
they tell me this is her home.

FICTION

Tantra Bensko

Nude Snow Ballet

1

I dance naked ballet in the two foot Indiana snow, my feet sinking in past the crunching crust, seared to glass and shine. The sun reflects on the surface like the blindness of standing up too quickly upon hearing the news that you have not died. When you wake to find out you must have years to go, have not been sleepshot again, as you are most nights, by the raccoons that walk along the stone wall outside your window, banging as you sleep, knocking over cats, each other, hunkering, scampering up the tree together, looking back embarrassed, as they disappear into the leaves and start shaking them in regular rhythm. Bang bang bang.

My skin is not as white as snow, but white enough to feel embarrassment breathing in and out through its pores. The one boy I like in school joked, saying I must drink a lot of milk. I thought he meant because I was palethin, so I spent all Summer dancing naked by the creek, in the clearing, to be darker next time I see him, or see *anyone* but my parents, in the Fall. But he was joking about my new monstrous breasts, gigantic things that live with me, and go where ever I go. Wasn't he?

My nipples hard against the cold, shine in the sun, but I don't care. I care about Swan Lake in my head. The creek beneath me frozen solid. The white feathers of snow I stir up as I lift my legs, leap sideways, twirl, while singing silent. Rarely does the creek solidify enough to dance across it safely, to our land on the other side, the extra land, special, that no one goes to but me. I leapslide, angle down, one leg out straight before me, the other bent low, ending up at the edge of the otherland.

I scramble up its little crunchy hill, the surface melting in the sun

233

in tiny rivulets with almost colors. I've mapped our land, naming everything, from the prisms of water reflecting on a tiny bridge, to the stones like colored eggs, and the giant nests for dreams, the places where summer nettles line my naked skin with red. Here, on the secret side of the creek, this is the part where words are banned.

2

The otherland area of the rolled up, crunchywhite map contains no words, only suggestive shapes, insignias, insinuations, associations, darkness, mold, erased drawings, scratches, crumbles. The map of the land a large scroll, and that wordless part eventually rounds off the edge of it, which is torn raggedly, unevenly, and burned with the sun focused through a magnifying glass.

3

Snow cream: raw milk, vanilla, xylitol, snow piled on the arms of a palethin naked dancer, her back, her hair everywhere, as she stops time by negating the automatic tendency to think in words. This is not easily done. Stir silence with a paddle, pat with the edge of it, mold with your hands, but don't put too much pressure, or you will melt it. A nice crust on it from the melting, if you blow on it afterwards, is nice for special occasions. Statuedancer might stir one day, might not. In the spring, try sprinkling early blooming flower petals on her outstretched dripping arms. Crocuses are good. Enjoy.

EMILY CAPETTINI

SAPPHO'S DINER

"Everyone's always trying to turn me into a lesbian," Sophie complains around a cigarette. "It's really annoying. Just because I hate my husband doesn't mean I have it in for all men, you know?"

I nod, pad and pen poised to take her order. Poppy seed salad, I remember, extra charge for adding grilled chicken. After that, it'll be three orders of waffles piled with the summer fruit medley and then the house special. Sophie's a seasonable regular, only comes in during the warm months, but racks up a bill large enough to feed a family of eight. Rest of the time, she's stuck with the husband, she grumbles. Boring. Never talks. She told me that once on the day she ordered white sangria instead of lemonade. "Have to go back to the bastard today. That's the agreement. It's a living hell. Bring me another glass, would you, love?"

She'd stumbled out a few hours later into a waiting limo as I was mopping up her fourth glass of sangria. "The *hearse*," Sophie howled.

"She's going to have a hell of a hangover tomorrow," Dinah said, locking the doors behind her with a relieved grin.

I'd nodded and looked at the slices of apple and orange floating in the mop water, saying nothing. Doesn't do to complain, my mom always said. Just keep working and don't get too invested in other people's business.

"Poppy seed salad," Sophie says, snapping me back into the present with off-white words that dissolve above our heads. The no-smoking sign over her head is yellowed with her two-pack habit, but I've long stopped telling her she can't smoke in here. All it does is halve my tip, and I need every meager piece of that.

"Add some chicken, would you? Not that fried shit. Grilled." Sophie flicks her cigarette into the bowl vase lounging on the table, eyeing the flower blossoms floating there with some distaste. They float better without their stems or leaves. Severed heads, nothing to hold them steady or keep them in one place. Envy flickers through me, and I shift, feeling the extra pens in the front of my apron slide against my leg.

"No dressing, either," Sophie continues, "can't stand the preservatives."

Tobacco escapes from the damp cigarette paper and the bowl of flowers grins at me.

"Yes, ma'am, coming right up," I say, flipping my pad shut and turning to go put her usual order in. The cooks never remember what she wants.

"And tell that dyke in the orange turtleneck and mary janes to stop staring!"

The answering, patient smile feels tight against my teeth, but I nod anyway. I turn, heading for the relative safety of the counter. *Dyke*, the word whispers along the back of my neck, digging under my skin. My legs ache with it, and I swallow the memory before it can force its way up my throat. Don't get invested.

Dinah's there at the counter, watching me closely.

"What's with your neck, Annie? Bug bite?"

"Nothing," I answer, clutching my hand into a fist. It's there, that word; I can feel it sinking in. I want to scratch. "It's nothing. Just Sophie, you know. She's smoking again—and we're going to have replace the arrangement on the table."

Dinah snorts. "I hate her. She must enjoy torturing the poor diner waitresses. That monkshood wasn't easy to find, you know."

"That's fancier than usual," I comment, unable to resist digging a finger into my neck, hooking the capital D under my left ear. It comes free. The rest of the letters break apart, flotsam. "Wait, are you trying to poison her?"

"No. But if she eats the arrangement, it's not really my fault."

"I thought regular cliental kept the place afloat."

"Just because she single-handedly brings in enough money in a week to pay our utility bill doesn't mean I have to like her." Dinah glances over. "You're bleeding."

"Oh," I say, touching my neck.

"Bug bite?" she asks again.

"Must be," I reply, tugging the lie gently into place.

Dinah hands me a paper towel and a bandage. I wash the flotsam off my neck and then my hands when I'm done. I rip off Sophie's order, sliding it over the metal counter to the cook. Dinah's giving me that funny look again, like I'm a platypus on two legs, taking orders, so I try and back track. "Sophie'll get bored again."

"Suppose so," says Dinah. She nods back out at my section. "Who's the girl in the turtleneck and what's she done to Sophie?"

I shrug, my "who cares," half-hearted as I round the counter to go take another order.

"Jinkies," says Orange Turtleneck when I reach her, nodding at Sophie. "What the hell's her problem?"

"Doesn't get out much," I reply. "Chain smoking makes her jittery, too. Can I get you something to drink?"

"Oh, I'll just have a water." She peers at the crumpled menu. "So, what's good here?"

"That depends. Any dietary restrictions?"

"Nope."

"Pancakes are your safest bet, though not the breakfast special. Just the pancakes. I'm not sure if we have any sides to go with them. Our supplier is a bit unreliable. Sort of a mystery, really."

She perks up at that, but deflates quickly after a glance at the empty chair across from her. She hands over the menu. "Guess I'll have the pancakes, then."

"I'll get those started for you right away."

"Take your time. I've got nowhere else to be."

I leave. Dinah kicks a crate out for me to sit on when I return to her side. The orders will be out in about ten minutes and the diner's empty, except for my two tables and a third person tucked away at the other end of the place, already eating. One of Dinah's tables.

"You know how long she's been coming in?" Dinah asks, though it's not really a question. "A crappy couple of years in about a month or so. Since the place opened."

"Oh."

"Seems to think that's earned her a place of honor at the same table for the last few years."

I shrug. "That's what I heard when I took over that section."

"So, just how long have you been here?" Dinah never remembers. She's no good with time, she tells me, always getting away from her.

"Seems like forever."

"Ever thought of moving on?"

"Sure, sometimes," I say, thinking of what it would be like to be rootless like the flowers Dinah trims neatly every morning for the tables. Tied to nothing, blown about by the wind.

We have this conversation every shift, but nothing changes in it. Sometimes, Dinah snorts instead of rolling her eyes or skips Sophie altogether to ask a question that is soaked in *why the hell are you throwing your life away with this job?* The answer she expects is one I can't give right now. The dead conversation turns and spins, but stays, like lily pads on the river that used to run behind my home.

"Can't move on, though," I add, "too much to do here."

"If you say so," Dinah answers and hands me Sophie's order. "You know what I always tell you."

"Don't work too hard. Get out and enjoy yourself sometimes."

Dinah outranks me in the diner hierarchy, but doesn't hesitate to remind me that I help keep the place running smoothly. It's part of the motivation behind getting me to take a day off. I need it, Dinah says, after working at this dysfunctional train wreck.

Sophie mutters a thanks when I bring over her order; her gaze follows the movement of my elbow, skimming up along my shoulder and coming to rest on my neck. I shake off the attention, check for blood, just in case. Pancakes get delivered next, and Dinah's shift ends. She's gone before I can remind her, *punch your timecard.* Marcie clocks in, on the dot, and I send her out to greet the newest customers. Friendly, customer-oriented, goes the mantra. Spin and turn, roots to keep you steady in the undertow.

Sophie leaves 15% for me. It's mid-summer, and her tips won't increase until winter is closer. Orange Turtleneck rounds up to 21%. I stuff the bills and mess of change into my apron and jingle for the rest of the afternoon.

"You worked a double shift today, and I saw your name on the schedule for the same in a few days," Marcie says just before the dinner shift when I sit on a crate again to rest my legs. "What are you saving for?"

"Nothing," I tell her, "just saving. I need the money."

It's not a lie, but it's not the whole truth, either.

"You could just take off one day," she says, an unintentional impression of Dinah. Marcie doesn't wait to hear another one of my vague excuses that holds water worse than the rust-bottom gutters clinging to the top of this little corner diner. Instead, she goes to greet the customer that's just taken a seat in her section.

I haven't got any better excuses than that; they're all vague and uncommitted. It's easier that way, really. With no lies spun and woven around me, I don't have to stick to a pattern. I've got enough keeping me here without creating more lily pads and rust-bottom gutters.

That night, I walk home on sore legs, glad of the distraction the exhaustion brings. Keeps me from thinking too hard about this place. The city around me looks like any other, I suppose, but I've never explored. The buildings around me are shut up tight, blank-faced.

Sometimes, I wander from my normal route—home to the diner, diner to home, grocery store to home, home to grocery store—but I always end up back on the familiar sidewalks. I guess there aren't that many roads around, and I don't know the city well enough. My legs ache again when I try to wander too far—not the diner-legs soreness, but something in my bones, phantom fractures.

The memories are never far behind the memory-pain of injuries long past. "I don't know you," they say, a whispered accompaniment, "I don't know why you've chosen to be this, this way."

They're clearer tonight. I remember monkshood outside my window then, the unhappy bow of a stalk in full bloom.

The run-down façade of the building next to my apartment—two blocks down, a straight shot from the diner—scowls at me as I pass.

You've chosen this.

When I tried to leave, turned my back on monkshood stalks, I didn't get far. Now I'm here, undecided, alone. I fall asleep to that thought and don't dream, but my eyes are still heavy when I pry myself out of my bed in the morning.

"How long have you been here?" Sophie demands when I walk over to take her order.

"Pardon?"

She looks me over, messy ponytail to tennis shoes I've had since I was seventeen. My skin prickles—Sophie sees *me* this time. "You. You're always here."

"I work here."

"For this long?"

"Yes. Now what can I get you?"

"No one works here this long. They take what they need and go. *You* know my order. No one's ever known my order. I've seen you bring me things before I ask for them." Sophie fumbles through her purse for her lighter. "You've stayed."

I open my mouth to ask again for her order, but instead, "I have my reasons," tumbles out.

Sophie looks amused. "I bet you do. I bet most of 'em have to do with the fuckers you left behind."

I press my thumb against the end of the pen. It creaks and cracks, like glass, like bone.

"Listen. You're only hurting yourself, you know, with this bullshit."

"What the hell would you know about it?" I snap. "What the hell do any of you know about repetition and routine?"

Sophie gets to her feet. Her breath is sour from her night that likely didn't end until last call. "What do I know about being stuck, stalled out in one place?"

"The same damn food, conversation, and table, every single day," I continue, and the next breath I take loosens something in my chest. "Every day," I say again, as if it will crack something in the prison walls around me, the boundaries and boxes I let myself be pushed in

240

to.

"I know plenty about it, sweetheart. I'm *living* it. Now do yourself a goddamned favor and *get out* before you become like the rest."

"What—why do you care?"

"You don't belong here with the rest of these people. They're static, been here too long, far away from their real lives to be anything but decoration now. If you stay here, you're going to be one of them."

"Then why do you always come back?" I find myself asking.

There is iron in the look Sophie gives me. I stand still while she looks over me, through me, to where the old confessions and spoken secrets fester inside. Flotsam that never drifted away.

"Here." She thrusts a small package wrapped in brown paper at me.   "Don't look back, Arianne."

I stare after Sophie as she leaves. My nametag says Annie. No one calls me by my full name here. It always seemed too elegant of a name for a girl who preferred jeans, t-shirts, and tennis shoes. Too grown-up.

"What happened?" Dinah asks, coming up beside me. "Did she *leave? Before* eating our entire stock of waffles and ruining my arrangements?"

The package is heavy in my hands.

Don't look back.

"Annie?"

"Yeah," I nod, but don't meet her eyes. "Yeah, she did. I think I had better take my break."

I head out the back entrance. The alley is splashed with early morning sunlight and empty. I sit down on the old folding chair I've left out there, and it squeals at my sudden weight. I look up, over the rooftops, to what's keeping me here. I can see it now, wedged between the blank-faced buildings that had scared me off before. It's a plain-looking wall—dull-colored, drywall, no holes or marks. I try to see where the top is, but I have to turn away from the sun beating down on me.

I don't know how far it goes, the wall. I know it's been what's blocking me, keeping me on the straight paths to the diner and grocery store. Neatly packaged in this place. I know Dinah can't see it, like I couldn't before; she looked at me blankly once when I mentioned my hesitance to wander.

"Why would you want to explore?" she had asked. I didn't have an answer for the anxiety that trembled through me at a constant low rumble.

But there's the wall, plain white.

I rub my sweating palms on my jeans that smell like yesterday's pie special. The paper bag still clutched in my hand crunches against my leg. When I open it, I find a ball of yarn, red and not very large. Sophie's tips have certainly decreased in value, I decide, letting the yarn roll off my fingers. It bounces a few times on the concrete and rolls away, unraveling, heading for the wall.

In this strange labyrinth how shall I turn, murmurs an old memory, a line of verse. *Leave all, and take the thread.*

Don't look back, adds Sophie's caution.

I untie my apron, folding it and leaving it on one of the crates. I pick up the end of the red string and follow it forward, weaving it between my fingers as I gather more of it. The world behind me falls away, and I am rootless, drifting downstream.

CAROL CARPENTER

THE MAPMAKER

When Rayna Travis Gullavor gets a notion into her head, it sticks like a grain of sand caught in an oyster shell, a gritty irritant calcifying, growing and transforming itself into a hard, round pearl. It nestles there, her third eye, the eye she can't close.

Rayna sees things. Lately, she feels her watchful eye moving back and forth, up and down, pupil dilated, open wide, vigilant, waiting for something big to happen.

The little things she sees are piling up. Things like Uncle Henry driving all the way to Cranston, the next town west, to buy new Jockey bikini shorts, a whole dozen that he keeps in a toolbox in the trunk of his 10-year-old Chevrolet Impala and washes twice a month at the Easy Ways Laundromat over in Brownstown, just south of Raintree. Things like the little boy down the street writing math formulas on the inside of his forearm before the semester exam or Jennifer at the Cranberry Cafe fudging the amount of her tips at tax time, or even Eddie, her husband, whose leg will end up in a cast when he slips off the roof next year.

"What did you see today?" Eddie asks jokingly every night before he falls asleep.

And Rayna tells him, only him, like she's done since seventh grade. Funny things, silly things. She sees them before they happen. But lately she's afraid to tell him everything.

Still, Eddie's response is always the same, "Rayna, you're a woman to be reckoned with."

"I am, indeed," she always replies. And when she gets right down to it, she thinks of herself as a woman of action, a woman who gets things done.

Like she tells Eddie, she can't help it if she sees things. Is it her fault that sometimes she doesn't see the whole thing? Besides, how's

243

she supposed to know when something is just a brick instead of the whole house? Okay, so Uncle Henry's Jockey bikini shorts were part of the strategy for getting Jennifer's attention. It worked didn't it? They used the tip money she didn't give the IRS so both of them could run off to Miami and fry their flesh in the Florida sun while the rest of us froze back here in Raintree. It's not as if Aunt Mabel cared much about Uncle Henry's bikini shorts or Jennifer for that matter, she just hated to miss out on going to Miami.

Rayna wouldn't mind going to Miami herself, with Eddie, of course. She's spent all 55 years of her life in Raintree, Michigan, right near the tip of the rabbit's ear. Or, more accurately, within a 33-mile radius of Raintree since she likes to grocery shop at the Farmer Jack over in Brownstown (but she always makes sure not to go grocery shopping when Uncle Henry is at the laundromat).

"Don't like my eggs runny," Eddie reminds her, the same way he does every morning. "And don't skimp on the salt."

"Bad for your blood pressure." Rayna scoops eggs onto his plate, wishing he would listen to Dr. Metpath about his cholesterol. "Ever thought about going to Miami, Eddie?"

"Nah, might run into Uncle Henry and Jennifer." Eddie pours ketchup on his eggs, stirring them around until they're covered with red. Next the salt, specks of white like tiny stars. "Reminds me, is my uniform pressed for the parade tomorrow?"

"In 37 years, have I ever forgotten?" She can't wait to see him march by in the Memorial Day Parade, handsome as ever, just a bit more of him than when he came back from San Antonia, wearing that very same uniform, stepping off the Greyhound bus, full of places he saw and she didn't.

"Darn fly." He waves it away from his eggs. "Hope they're not out full force for the picnic. You know, Aunt Edna refuses to eat potato salad anymore." He points his egg-loaded fork at the fly. "Hasn't eaten a bit since last Memorial Day."

"Remember how she had a big chunk of potato halfway to her mouth before she spotted the fly stuck to the potato with mayonnaise?" Rayna laughs, smoothing her green dress over her belly, a well-fed woman. "Who knows how many she already swallowed."

"That's one you should of seen coming," Eddie chides Rayna.

"Sure you didn't call those flies? You never did like Aunt Edna."

"Eddie Gullavor, you know darn well I can't conjure up whatever I want." Rayna stares across the table at him, her thumb scratching at the green Formica table top as if she can get below its shiny plastic surface, right down to the thing itself. "If I could do that, I'd see us in Miami. Yep, Miami. Probably on a yacht."

She runs her tongue over her teeth, licking away the salty taste, lifts her hair from the nape of her neck as she starts humming then singing full voice, buoyantly, "Oh spacious skies ... from sea to shining sea."

Eddie takes up the chorus, an echo: "From sea to shining sea."

His voice breaks reaching for the high note. "So what's the difference between a sea and an ocean?"

He sets down his fork, watches Rayna's hand turned palm up, fingers moving as if she's sifting a fistful of sand. "Rayna, stop it." He leans across the table and catches her hand in his.

"Let's do it, Eddie. If not Miami, then San Francisco or Seattle or anyplace near the ocean." A pause. "You know some people think life started in the ocean.

One at a time, his words shoot out like hard steel balls in a pinball game. "You're not yourself. This has got to stop right now."

Rayna waits for his words to bounce off corners, hit the target and settle into her pockets, weigh her down. She can't explain. It's as if she can hold Miami in the corner of her eye, a speck of dust at first, then a house and lately even whole city blocks evolve, and she walks those streets.

"We've never seen the ocean. Just think, we can go right to the edge. We can walk along the land and drop away. She shows him the book on Miami she got yesterday from the Bookmobile. The map at the back opens into her hands.

"Ever feel the ocean between your toes?" She wiggles her toes inside her shoes, against the curved leather that binds her feet.

"Drug dealers, sand, palm trees and retirees. That's all Miami is." Eddie slips on his work jacket, his name embroidered across the back under the Mobil logo, a walking advertisement. "Something wrong with Raintree all of a sudden?"

"Wait," but she can't stop the accident. His jacket swings loose and catches on the orange juice carton, knocking it to the floor.

"You're late. Go ahead. I'll get this."

Rayna squirts Joy liquid detergent into the dishcloth and kneels down on the linoleum. The orange juice puddles, the shape of the Grand Canyon, a canyon too wide to jump across.

She can see straight down, all the way to the canyon floor, and feels dizzy. She stands up, sways and keels over, forehead smack in the middle of the orange juice. Hard enough to knock her out. The fly feeds off the orange sweetness, a slight buzzing beside her ear when she opens her eyes.

She comes to slowly, not sure where she is. Then she remembers. She dabs at her dress with her dishcloth, wipes her face, then the beige linoleum. A faint outline remains, two streaks for the canyon's edges. The rest of the morning she works in the garden, clearing away dead leaves, turning soil. She fertilizes the lawn, a holiday ritual: Memorial Day, Fourth of July, and Labor Day. Days of fireworks and sparklers.

On Memorial Day, Rayna and Naomi stand shoulder to shoulder, as they've done year after year, watching the parade on North Central Avenue. "Here comes Eddie," Rayna says, waving her flag at him and the small group of veterans who left Raintree and returned to stay: after World War II, after Korea, after Vietnam, after the Persian Gulf, after Iraq.

"Still the world's not safe," Naomi sighs, tugging her bra strap back on her shoulder and tightening it, fingers moving deftly under her flowered dress.

"I know," Rayna says, hugging Naomi and pulling her back from the curb just before Charlie Dawson got so busy waving and looking back at Miss Raintree that he lost control of the red convertible on loan from Courtesy Chevrolet, ran right over the curb where Naomi had been standing a second before, tires crushing the cooler and the picnic lunch Naomi packed that morning.

"Nothing's safe anymore," Naomi says, aimlessly lifting the flattened cooler with her foot and letting it drop again onto the concrete sidewalk. "Not even in Raintree. Can't do a darn thing about it either. Just got to take it.

"Maybe we can. Do something about it, I mean." After all, hadn't she just saved Naomi's life? Well maybe not her life but at least kept her from the bruises and broken arm she would have had. It's the sign she's been waiting for, round as a pearl plucked from an oyster, full of light.

That night in bed, Rayna tips her head back against Eddie's shoulder, knowing what she must do, waiting for Eddie's ragged snores to tell her when she can dress again without waking him.
On her way out, she picks up the books on Miami, the maps where she traced different routes. So many ways to get there. On the familiar Michigan back roads, she drives slowly, watching for deer and raccoons as she rounds corners, flicking the headlights to bright.

Rayna pulls into the first rest area and parks under one of the lights. She studies the pull-out map in the library book she showed Eddie, tracing with her finger the wiggly lines that lead to Miami. She has folded and refolded the map so many times, the creases are starting to tear. But she locates the interstate, a junction where U.S. 23 connects in Briarwood.

She stops again in Mettalwood to check where she is. No traffic this time of night, or actually, this early in the morning. Darkness all around her. She flicks on the dome light and pulls out the map. Can't even find Briarwood now. Looks like Briarwood has worn off in the crease, too much folding and refolding of the map, or maybe it was never there.

Nonsense, Rayna tells herself. Briarwood was there. So where did it go? She knows she's not lost. Briarwood is lost. Maybe getting lost will scare the town enough to clean itself up so she's not always hearing about it on the evening news.

Rayna rests her eyes. Behind her eyelids, she pictures Briarwood.

As it was before she came. Now the void, the empty space where it should be. Rapid blinks. Her third eye, focusing, capturing the image, turning it upside down, holding it there.

No different than one of those souvenir plastic towns inside a snow globe. Briarwood. Turn it over, shake it and set it on a table and fake snow floats down, covering the town in white flakes suspended in fluid. An embryonic sac. Shake out the guns, the knives, the anger, the greed. Break the water: let it rain torrents until the streets are clean. She looks again, her vision clear.

Briarwood, the sign says, population 15,434. Rayna rolls down her window to watch the children walking to school, listens to them as they pass, faces clean and moist as if they've just stepped from their morning showers. They carry books clutched in their arms. She knows that they will learn someday about their birth, about how the waters broke before they were born.

She opens her map. She finds Briarwood, back on the crease, bold letters as if the name is freshly typed. She licks off the smudge of ink on her finger and passes through Briarwood. She picks up the interstate with no problem.

She stops at a Mobil station and pumps her own gas. Eddie will never stop any place but Mobil, even when they get really low on fuel. Spreading out the map on the counter, she asks the man who gives her change the name of a town she has accidentally put a hole through with her ballpoint pen. "No town there," he says, pointing to his map pinned above the cash register. But Rayna knows differently. When she arrives at the hole in the map, she stops the car then pulls off to the side of the road. Nothing there but cattails, furry brown spikes reaching up, rooted in the marshland beside the road.

Rayna opens her car door and steps out onto the road. She pictures the town, the cafe where she will eat lunch, the houses, the people. Gradually the town emerges like an oil painting, layer upon layer until it's complete: Flagsville, Ohio.

She opens her map. The hole is gone, covered with a black dot and the name, Flagsville. She climbs back into her car, and drives up and down the streets, watching through her windshield the town she has created.

When she spots the jewelry store, she parks her car and goes inside, the small bell over the door summoning the jeweler from the back room.

"You look like a woman who knows what she wants, the jeweler says, rubbing the bald spot on the top of his head.

"I do indeed." Rayna buys pearls, the real kind, not freshwater pearls or cultivated pearls but pried-from-oysters-by-a-fisherman, pearls round and perfect, lustrous white pearls to clasp a single strand around her neck.

"Staying in town long?" The jeweler counts the money she hands him, the $20 bills she's saved over the years and kept hidden in her sewing box, under the quilting squares.

"Just passing through. On business." Rayna smiles and repeats, "Yes, on business. I make maps. You know, trace in the new routes and bypasses. All the changes."

Rayna Travis Gullavor wears these pearls warm against her skin. Sometimes she fingers them as she drives. She sees Eddie pumping gas and cooking eggs, sees him spread out across the whole bed at night. For Eddie, Naomi bakes sourdough bread, cans the strawberries he picks and goes on television shows asking Rayna to come home. But Rayna cannot go home.

Not until Rayna drives through all the towns, until she sees the way to Miami is safe for any traveler, until she walks out into the ocean and waves crest, wash over her body, pick her up and float her out past lifeguards, out to where saltwater buoys her up and the pearls burst from their string and dissolve to sand—until then, she must travel alone.

BETH KEEFAUVER

LIZARD GIRL

after "Swamp Boy" by Rick Bass

There was this girl we used to torment in middle school. We called her Lizard Girl. We meaning the girls I used to hang out with. It was a long time ago. I never really did anything. I mean, I was there when we hid her clothes while she was taking a shower after gym class, and invited her to a slumber party at a fake address, and prank called her house at three a.m. in the voice of Freddy Krueger. But I never really thought of any of it, just went along. I let it all happen. A red-haired skinny girl with freckles who wore army green cargo pants and a yellow bandana tied around her forehead. She was new. She did not belong.

I was lucky enough to be one of the popular girls. We were gorgeous, worshipped, feared. We lived in the same neighborhood, grew up together. We're not friends anymore.

We followed Lizard Girl home from school. We left just enough distance to show she was not one of us, but linger close enough for her to hear every venomous word we spewed. Sometimes we yanked her red hair. She wore it pulled into two low pigtails that clung relentlessly to her scalp, despite our repeated attempts to rip them out by the roots. I don't know what it was about those flaming, frizzy curls that so infuriated us. Maybe because they were so different than our smoothly combed locks, twisted into tight French braids and tied in neat black or white bows.

Every day, we followed the red hair out of the school like it was a torch in the night. We followed her down the sidewalk, past the peach farm that lay between our neighborhood and the school, past the humming tractors with their spinning blue pesticide sprayers that enshrouded the orchards in a perpetual mist. We followed her into our neighborhood, under the arching branches of sycamore trees and down the hill toward the creek, where the air is thick with the smell of moist earth. Here, where the road ended at a vacant lot overgrown with honeysuckle and jewel-weed, Lizard Girl would make her passage. And this is how obsessed we became—we even followed her into the woods, ripping our candy colored tights on patches of blackberry thorns and digging our shiny black heels deep into mud. She knew we were there. She never looked back.

When she reached the vacant lot, she stopped to pull the yellow honeysuckle blooms from their vines, then curled her lips around the tips to suck the sweet nectar from their soft tubes. Sometimes she sucked from five, seven of them in a cluster. She reached into the thorny brambles to pick wild blackberries at the peak of their ripeness, then scrunched up her face when the sour juices burst on her tongue. When she pulled away, the thorns left thin scarlet threads the whole length of her arms. She skipped down the bank to the creek, waving her arms like red flags.

We tracked her like a pack of hounds trailing a fox. At the vacant lot, we stopped and watched.

She crouched down on a large rock at the edge of the rushing water, the ripples reflecting on her freckled face. She reached into the creek, slowly and deliberately, and wrapped the ends of her fingers around the rough edges of limestone slabs, rose quartz, chunks of granite. She lifted the rocks gingerly, just enough to peer under. She would do this for what seemed like an hour. Then she'd strike, the sunlight flashing in the spray, and slowly rise from the water gripping a writhing giant salamander the color of moss and flame.

Eastern Hellbender: Cryptobranchus alleganiensis. Third largest species of salamander in the world. Vernacular name from early settlers who thought it was a creature from hell, bent on returning.

We watched her with fascination, horror, contempt. She ran her hands along the hellbender's back, under the belly, down to the tip of its whipping tail. She stroked its head, pulled the slimy face against the curve of her chin. She talked to the animal: "So hyper today!" "Did you eat some yummy tadpoles?" "Mommy will put you back to bed." And she set the creature in the water, watching as it vanished under rocks.

After she released the salamander—or turtle, or frog, or whatever other disgusting creature she would catch, love, and let go—Lizard Girl opened her backpack and pulled out all kinds of beakers and tubes and magnifying glasses and things, like she had raided the cabinets in chemistry class. She filled one of the tubes with water and plugged it with a cork. Then she walked downstream, bending down and every now and then to fill another tube. Sometimes, she held the tube up to the sun, looking at the tiny organisms and shining particles spiraling around like stars in a distant galaxy. She reached in her backpack for a vegetable strainer and dipped it into a muddy, stagnant part of the creek. When she pulled the strainer out, water the color of weak coffee streamed through the holes. She stirred her fingers in the slimy leaves. Sometimes she found strange creatures, hybrids of worms and insects, like pocket-sized versions of the things out of the Alien movies. She collected these, too, in other tubes.

After she had filled the containers with some part of the creek, she gently packed her specimens inside her backpack. She was careful to hold it upright as she slid each arm through the straps and safely onto her back. Then she walked into the woods, following the creek. As she walked, she collected things. Blue jay feathers. Acorn caps. Fern fronds. Chipmunk skulls. Tiny jewel-toned stones made smooth and round by the endless rush of creekwater. She stuffed these things inside the zippered pockets and button flaps of her cargo pants. Then she trudged home on the wooded trail that followed the water line behind our neighborhood, moving like a packhorse carrying a heavy weight.

Some days we just watched. Other days—oh, we were wicked. We were brimming with invincibility and crazed with viciousness. We circled her like a hawk seeking a weaker animal. The bloodstreaked arms and wet, muddy pants incited us to savagery.

One of us would hurl the first insult. Any words that would pierce or punch.

"Hey, Lizard Girl. Hey, Lezzie."

"Your mama think you're a boy?"

"Come play with the pretty girls."

Once, we even jumped on Lizard Girl, pulled her down to the ground. Each of us held an arm or a leg until she was pinned. One of us grabbed her backpack. Lizard Girl thrashed and squirmed, trying to free herself from our grip to protect the precious contents inside, shaking her head back and forth and pleading for us to let her go. Then one of us, the cruelest, not me, the one with blonde hair curled into perfect ringlets, who wore half of a broken heart engraved with the letters Be/Fri on a thin gold chain, she, the cruelest, held the backpack in the air.

"What's Lizard Girl hiding from her friends today?"

She, the cruel one, slowly unzipped Lizard Girl's backpack and turned it upside down. Lizard Girl's eyes widened as the cruel one picked up each container, flipped the cork with her thumb, and spilled the water onto the ground beside Lizard Girl's head. Water splattered the dirt, leaving flecks of sand and stone on her face. The tiny mud-dwellers squirmed in the sun's fierce heat. Blood drained from Lizard Girl's cheeks as she watched the earth absorb her day's work.

Then the cruelest kneeled down beside Lizard Girl's face. She opened her black patent leather purse and pulled out a silver tube of lipstick the shape of a bullet. She turned the tube slowly, just under Lizard Girl's chin, until the blood red tip emerged.

"Hey, Lezzie, want to be a pretty girl? We'll have to fix you up."

Lizard Girl thrashed, trying to free herself from our grip, the way a songbird, after going limp in the clench of a hawk's talon, furiously beats its wings before death. The cruelest dug her painted nails into Lizard Girl's jaw and placed the red tip on her lips. Slowly, she drew on the lips, circling them over and over until the absurd smile of a clown belied Lizard Girl's grimacing, tear-streaked face. Then the cruel one pulled Lizard Girl's T-shirt out of her shorts and wrote LEZZIE across her stomach, the belly button dotting the "i".

Then we, all the other girls, grabbed fistfuls of that frizzy red hair. The cruel one watched with a smirk, replaced her lipstick into her patent leather bag. Laughing like wild hyenas, we dragged her down toward the creek, through thorns, over rocks, and rolled her down the bank into the frigid water. Then we turned our backs and ran, our cackles echoing in the forest.

*

Lizard Girl lived next door. We, my parents and I, lived at the edge of the neighborhood that was built when Arcadia Farms sold part of their orchards to a private developer. Ours was the last house at the back entrance with stacked stone pillars and a wrought iron gate that read "Meadowbrook Orchard: A Private Community." The gate opened when my mother or father pushed a button on a black plastic cartridge clipped to the visors of their luxury SUVs. Outside the gate, the smooth black pavement turned rocky and gray.

Lizard Girl lived on that side. Before they moved in, we could not see her house from mine. Then, the summer before seventh grade, Lizard Girl and her mother rang our doorbell. My mother made me go to the door. I remember because it was the first time she had spoken to me that day, a Saturday; she was reading a novel over a glass of wine as her mud mask dried in the sun room. I pushed my eye against the peephole. There they stood with a basket spilling over with tomatoes, squash, cucumbers, bell peppers, strawberries, carrots, arugula. They were strange women, the girl with her red pigtails and bulging pockets, and her mother, a tall woman with smiling eyes and long, wavy gray hair parted in the middle. The girl carried a green velvet pouch with multicolored beads sewn in the shape of a lizard. The mother wore a long broomstick skirt with intricate designs scrawled over it, like some ancient language I did not understand.

The doorbell rang again. My mother yelled. I stared through the hole.

After they left, I opened the door. The note read, "From your new neighbors. Enjoy the bounty of summer!" They had signed their names. I put the basket on the kitchen island. In the sunbeam, I noticed some of the vegetables were caked with small patches of dirt. A wormhole snaked through the bright yellow squash. When my mother came in for dinner, I was reading some teen magazine over the last slice of a frozen pizza. My father was still playing golf.

"What's this?"

"From the new neighbors."

"Lovely," she said as she dumped the vegetables into the trash compacter. "How did they get through the gate?" My mother was always suspicious of a gift that had not been bought.

Soon after they moved in, Lizard Girl and her mother cleared out the kudzu vines and privet bushes that hid their small board-and-batten house from ours. Whenever I'd go swimming, Lizard Girl would be in the backyard, looking in. Before my parents hosted a party for the firm, they hired a landscaper to build a tall fence with wide cedar planks and decorative trim and an elaborate trellis at the gate. The wisteria vines he planted eventually grew over the trellis and into Lizard Girl's yard.

Chinese wisteria: Wisteria sinensis. A prolific climbing vine with ornate purple or white blooms. Invasive in North America; spreads rapidly to the detriment of native species.

Sometimes, if I was bored, if my mother was off at a luncheon or getting a pedicure and my dad was at the firm, which was most of the time, I watched Lizard Girl through a crack in the fence. Their yard was like nothing I had ever seen, so different than the trim, impossibly green lawns in the Community, with their sculpted boxwoods and formal arrangements of Asian perennials. Lizard Girl's yard was lush, wild, teeming with life. Strange objects hung from the branches of trees—crystals and bones and feathers—the kinds of things Lizard Girl stowed in her pockets each day. A stone path led from the back stoop into a vegetable garden dense with thick stalks and twisting vines and broad leaves, bearing fruit of every color. The path spiraled through the garden, into an arbor under a thick tangle of grape vines, and ended at a fire ring with a small circle of stones and a split log bench.

At the very back of the yard, along the creek that bordered the forest, Lizard Girl kept an elaborate system of cages. She had all kinds of animals in these cages—a brown rabbit with five bunnies, a baby raccoon, a snapping turtle, and a crow with a broken wing. She fed them by hand. She talked to them as she pushed through the wires bits of vegetable rinds that she carried in a moldy wicker basket. Along the creek, hemlocks, rhododendrons, and poplars darkened the hillside behind their house. From where I stood, it was hard to tell where their yard ended and the forest began.

Now, of course, that forest is gone. Now, there are more houses like ours, but bigger. Now the smooth black asphalt runs by Lizard Girl's yard and beyond, for miles, a four lane artery of concrete with its network of capillaries through the entire west side of town. I mention her house as if it still stands. But Lizard Girl's home, her gardens and stone paths and cages of animals, are gone. Gone, too, are the endless rows of peach trees and the pesticide-spraying tractors, and the school where she was forced daily to face her tormentors. All were leveled for the Community's expansion. Eminent domain.

I haven't been back in a long time. I'm in Atlanta, in marketing. I spend hours staring at a computer screen, pushing keys, answering my cell phone, Skyping with clients. Or they send me in commercial jets thirty-five thousand miles above the earth at five hundred miles per hour, to other tall buildings in other cities where I stare at screens and answer calls and Skype clients. The people, these places are all so eerily similar from the air, from the insides of buildings.

Sometimes, when they send me northeast, I fly over the Community. From the air, the sprawling roads and new homes look like a computer circuit board. Sometimes, from above, I follow the creek to my house. I think about what the place might look like if Lizard Girl and her mother had been allowed to stay—an island of fecundity contained by a network of ChemLawn patches and strips of asphalt. I think, too, about my parents, if they had not divorced, if my father had not lost his practice and moved to Florida to sell time shares, if my mother was not a chain smoker addicted to her shrink, if they had grown old there together. But what does it matter? All that happened is erased, stories locked into the land by an asphalt grid.

*

We followed Lizard Girl from the wild heat of late summer into the soothing breeziness of autumn. The falling leaves tamed us. We watched from a distance. In winter we hibernated—made a few prank calls, hid her coat at school so she'd have to walk home in the bitter cold. But in spring the madness returned.

As soon as the other girls realized she lived next door—it was not something I advertised, it was not something I wanted them to know —my house became the watchtower. When the daffodils and tulips popped their vibrant heads out of the cold earth and into the late March sun, Lizard Girl began tending her elaborate system of cages in the backyard. The leaves had not yet fully emerged on the trees, and we had a clear shot from my bedroom window.

The days we followed her home, the days our hatred made us inexorably patient, we spied on her for hours. Our spying, which we only did when we were bored, when there was absolutely nothing at all else to do, revealed that Lizard Girl kept a collection of frogs and toads in the larger cage, which was at the back, closest to the creek. After she got home from school, if we hadn't snatched her backpack and dumped out her specimens, she fed the sci-fi creatures she caught to the frogs. She pulled out dried patches of earth and replaced them with fresh, moist earth from the creekside. She removed a black plastic tray of slimy water and filled it with new water from a gallon jug. Sometimes she added new frogs.

Green Frogs: Rana clamitans melanota. Following metamorphosis, juveniles often disperse from their natal ponds to neighboring ponds. Movements of up to three miles have been documented.

First, we used binoculars to look in on Lizard Girl when she worked at the frog cage. Then we moved in, closer, so we could see inside. Lizard Girl had recreated their native riparian environment, complete with moss and stone. But something was wrong these frogs. Some had only one eye, or two eyes on the same side of the head. Others had one or two limbs not fully formed. The freakiest one had an arm growing from the back of its head. When this frog jumped or lashed its tongue, the dumb limb flinched and the sticky fingers flung open and closed into a loose fist as if in slow motion.

This grotesque scene—the deformed frogs, the bones and feathers hanging from trees, the wild, un-mowed lawn—ignited our fear. Now we knew she was a witch. And at any moment, if we were found out, she could use her dark magic against us.

*

By summer, when school was out and the sun burned hot and the leaves obscured our view, we hid in the garden behind her house, safely concealed from the kitchen window by towering corn stalks and dense tomato plants. In the evenings, after she and her mother plucked Cherokee purple tomatoes and yellow peppers from their stalks, dug up sweet potatoes and green onions from the dark earth, we crouched below the windowsill and peered in. With soiled hands, they sat together at the kitchen table and talked and laughed while pulling long silver blades through the flesh of each vegetable, splitting open their gorgeous insides. Lizard Girl stood at the stove, looking into the pan as her mother tossed and stirred. Sometimes, she reached in the cabinet for dried herbs in small, unlabeled glass jars. When they sat down at the table, they held hands and closed their eyes. Lizard Girl ate slowly. With each bite, her jaw moved with the deliberate precision of a praying mantis.

After dinner, they watched a show about a small town in Alaska. Lizard Girl and her mother would curl up on the sofa underneath a handmade patchwork quilt. One of the main characters was a woman pilot with brown hair cropped short who lived alone in a log cabin and carried a rifle on the back of her pickup. Whenever the pilot appeared, Lizard Girl bolted up, moving her face closer to the blue glow of the screen.

From the cool side of the glass, we bored our eyes into that room, trying to crack through the pane with our absolute contempt. I say contempt, but I mean fear. A house without a father was unnatural, alien to us. Maybe evil. Back then, before college, before our parents divorced, we all had fathers.

*

Late one night, after the girls went back to their own houses in the Community, I woke with an excruciating headache. The full moon shone on my bedroom floor in elongated silver panels. I climbed out of my window onto the roof and let the silky light envelop me. The neighborhood, which I had known since I was three or four, looked foreign. The rooftops reflected the empty sky. The air was thick with silence. Each breath made me dizzy. I tried to stand but had no balance.

I heard a sound from Lizard Girl's yard. A steady rhythm, several rhythms at once, like the syncopation of beating hearts.

It was barely audible at first, then gradually became louder, until I felt it in my chest. I closed my eyes. In the rhythm, my head stopped spinning. In the rhythm, I absorbed the night air through my skin. I felt everything I had ever experienced gather under my ribs, felt my body extend out into the night in one motion, one moment, one pulse. How do I describe it? It was a feeling I never had before, nor ever would again.

Lizard Girl knew a secret. She knew something I was missing, we were all missing. And for that reason, I should have protected her.

But I didn't.

*

The cruelest had an idea. It would have to happen from my house. I would have to host a slumber party to execute the plan. In my room, we waited until the last orange glow disappeared from the window of Lizard Girl's home. We wore rubber gloves and all black. We slipped downstairs and out.

We filled a galvanized bucket with water from the pool. The water sloshed onto our bare ankles as we marched toward the creek, around the fence and into the darkness of Lizard Girl's domain.

We worked quickly. We scooped up the frogs and threw them into the bucket. At the fire ring, we piled broken sticks and pine needles and crisp leaves and held a match to the pile. As the fire grew, we lay three logs in the triangle formation we learned in Girl Scouts, to maximize heat and flame. We set the bucket on the fire. We boiled the frogs alive.

*

Sometimes I think back. At night, after work, from my window high above the city—whatever city, wherever I am—I watch red and white lights pulse between buildings, like luminescent blood cells tracing the bones of some upturned animal. I think of the last time I felt alive.

We were just being kids. Normal adolescent girls. We did not do anything anyone else would not have done, had Lizard Girl moved into a different neighborhood. Sometimes I just wish I could talk to someone who knew me then, you know?

The next morning, we watched Lizard Girl for a long time, long enough for my coffee to get cold, long enough for Casey Kasem to go from number thrity-five to fourteen. And yet that scene—Lizard Girl skipping down to her cages with a basket full of vegetable rinds to find her frogs floating in a cold, milky broth—is not what I remember most vividly.

It is this: sneaking back into the house as it began to rain, trying to suppress our girlish laughter as we tiptoed up the hardwood stairs, holding our mouths with one hand and, with the other, reaching out for a friend's arm or shoulder for balance as we navigated the dark hallway to my bedroom door. We fell onto my bed and braided one another's hair, tried on push-up bras and painted our toenails, watched Pretty in Pink and gossiped about French kisses and blow jobs until the darkest hours of the night. I remember falling asleep that way, in the flickering blue glow, with Avery's neck spooned in Morgan's arm, Kali's head on Haleigh's belly, my fingers twirling

Eugenia's perfect blonde curls, her breasts soft and warm against my arm, the beat of her heart coaxing me to sleep. We were entwined like the frogs whose limp bodies floated to the center of the swirling water as the flames died down, reaching for one another as they drifted toward the end of pain, though I did not draw the connection then.

We're not friends anymore.

CHRISTINE KLOCEK-LIM

CIPHER

Some people swore the house was haunted was scribbled on the south wall of her room in black marker. She didn't know who'd done it, didn't know why those words. Satire? Irony? She thought to complain, but— No. They'd think she'd done it, her depression finally slipping its cage. Instead, she dragged her thin mattress to the corner where the streetlight's glare wouldn't bother her and fell asleep. She dreamed of vowels. In the morning the first thing she saw were the words *Some people swore the house was made of glass* scribed in red on the yellow wall near the windows (the rest a mind-numbing beige). It looked like someone had carved incisions in a daffodil. She pressed her eyes with her hands. The words just drifted inside her head. She tried rolling on the floor, forcing her shoulders and heels against the hard wood as though the pain would help. Thank God the ceiling was still virginal: nothing to mar the comfort of cracked plaster.

Downstairs Jeff stood at the counter, hair a mess. He wouldn't meet her eyes.

"Where is everyone?" She grabbed a cup and stole a half-eaten donut from the table, pretending she didn't know exactly why his shirt was torn. Her fingers itched.

"Dunno." He turned his back and stuffed a scrap of paper under the sack of dried beans Fran had bought, the ones no one knew how to cook.

"Don't try to hide it." Her voice came out sharp but she didn't care. "I know she heard us."

Jeff glanced at her then scurried from the kitchen, crumbs falling from his clothes. She remembered yelling at him yesterday, how good it felt to finally let go. He'd left his phone on the counter but she ignored it, knowing the note was more important. She eased the beans off the paper but didn't touch it. The faint black print blurred as she read the words. Her stomach cramped. Remorse? Maybe.

She left the half-eaten donut on the table, knowing one of the others would eat it and went back to her room. The morning sun split the floor into patchwork and there were more words near the door: *Some people swore the house was broken*. She laughed and laughed, the sound of it striking the walls, bouncing back at her until she cried. She dropped to her knees as the madness took hold. It felt like home. She drifted to sleep on the floor, hair tangled and falling into small cracks between the boards.

When she woke the moon (so much bigger than it ought to be) let in enough light for her to see a single sentence tattooed on the ceiling: *Some people swore the house was theirs*. She nodded, hearing voices: Jeff's conciliatory murmur softening Fran's sharp fury, and suddenly she knew what she really wanted. She took up her marker and pressed it to her throat. Nothing was ever the same again after that.

SHARANYA MANIVANNAN

NINE POSTCARDS FROM THE PONDICHERRY BORDER

Sometimes I think of you and wonder if you really happened
– Aamer Hussein, *Nine Postcards from Sanlucar de Barrameda*

1

Each time I leave here, and leave I must, I number these things among those which I leave behind: waking in the quiet cool before sunlight, coffee on the round red table, the tendril of basil at the center of the open courtyard, the pepper vines curled around the trees at the porch steps, and at night, that mesmeric canopy of stars.

There are parts of the world that imprint themselves on our souls, and we carry them with us ever after. Then there are places where the soul itself chooses to stay, riveting down a piece of itself, tethering us so that no matter where we journey beyond that point, we are only orbiting.

So whenever I leave, and leave I must, I number my soul too among the things I miss. I come back here, transfixed, possessed, as if under a spell. I have long conceded that this is witch country. Its hold on me is almost ancestral, as though somewhere in this burnt umber earth lies a cosmic umbilical cord.

I would write to you in secret, in some civilized way, if I had such a way. But you have erased my coordinates from your maps, expunged all record of me, forgotten my name. Yet you own nothing of me, not even that which you took away. So I circle and circle back here, to this house of red bricks with its roof open to the light, this strange southern enclave, and like this, I try to reclaim all I have lost, all I have left behind.

Of course, you and I both know that this territory I have staked hardly belongs to me. I live elsewhere, in the city, a city I constantly attempt to abandon but cannot, wilting there like a plant that cannot tolerate new soil. In the long months that turn, before I know it, into the longer years, I cry out for something that feels intuitive, indigenous. And then I come here.

When I am away I close my eyes and see the entrance of this house, understanding at last why my grandmother spoke so often of a porch in her final days, as though to set eyes again upon that doorway of a home long departed would be enough. When I first came here, I was heavy with recent death. How was I to know that my grief would only widen and deepen, take spate? The things I carry, the things I cannot leave behind no matter how I try. I haven't had a night without disquietude since.

But I am here now, and sleep comes easy. Or perhaps I don't need sleep at all. It seems that the nights begin when the stars start to spark up, and end long after they evanesce, but the small hours between then and the new day are sating enough. Do you know I can hear you dreaming on some days, in another hemisphere? I raise fat rice and fried bittergourd to my mouth with my fingers and consume your sleeping diagrams with it, the afternoon around me heavy with the slumber of the distant and the lazy. The dreaming and the dead are with me everywhere I go. But here, more than any place else, they come and sit beside me. I finish my meal, fix a drink, read a little, and I wait here, threading bracelets from fallen leaves and bougainvillea, for whoever comes first: lost loves, ancestors, or those who wake from naps and amble over, well rested, ready to enliven the evening with their rumors, their vendettas, their perfectly ordinary lives.

3

When I first met the drummer, he came across to me the way he comes across to everyone else—moody, lonely, never sober, never sane. A fixture of the environment, a plain fact, and one so easy to dismiss. But then, there was that night when he was playing the ghatam, with me sitting on the djembe beside him, when he suddenly turned to me and said, "It's like you. You're so cool—you can take *anything*. Except for a compliment." This is how we became friends.

One of the dogs comes by, sniffing at my feet. In my hands, his fur is thick and smelly. He is full of fleas, and has eyes the color of mud after rain. Another unlikely friend. I was weeping one day, when you were here and yet so far, in the thicket just beyond the property, and he had come and sat by me. Not a whine, not a bark, not a single demand. Just sat by me, silently. And that's when I knew he had called a truce: I had been afraid of him at first, and like all animals, he had reacted only to what I put out. I think over that time now and wonder how I could have been led that far astray, my intuition deluded on such a profound level, so that I loved what I should have feared, and feared that which could love me.

With the dog, I walk back to the thicket now. There's nothing much to see there. Sometimes, grazing cows, their dung steaming and fly-studded in the heat. Sometimes, a snake. Nothing that will do me harm unless I invite it to.

4

The gardener whose name I don't know chops some aloe vera straight from the ground for me, his sickle cleaving the leaves so the sap drips onto my fingers as I walk back to the house. I put it in my hair to soften it; I will wash it out later tonight, before the party. My mother is allergic to aloe vera, but I am not. I have full lips, and she does not. I was once the ugly child of an exceptionally lovely woman, and I carry around the fragile vanity of those who are never secure in their beauty, never quite believe what their baby feathers molted to reveal.

She calls every few days, briefly. I do not ever call her.

I want to say that I don't think you know how lovely you are. But maybe you do. You behave like someone who has never had to ask himself if he deserves what he wants. How simply you plucked me, like a flower for your pocket or your hat. How simply I waltzed into your arms, and not seeing your thorns, took your sap to my lips.

For my hair, I have asked the woman who does the laundry to bring me night-blooming jasmine. I want the scent of it lingering after every greeting kiss there will be this evening. I know that in this village and out in the world there are people who believe that it was I who did the bewitching. Only you and I know it isn't true; like all instinctive creatures I was only reacting to what you posed to me. Still, I don't discourage the notion. After my bath, I will perfume my wrists and loop little bells around my ankles.

5

This house sits between two worlds: the Tamil village and the international commune. It is both and it is neither. It is of no world at all but its own.

In the morning we will have breakfast in Quillapalayam, the drummer and I. He has a new bike, a big one, but I like his old green one. It's reliable, closer to the ground, quieter. More and more, I am beginning to trust things that move slowly, that stick around. We will order omelets and coffee in that shop along the main road. I will inevitably be distracted by some trinket or top—you cannot find things this pretty in the city I live in, and yet in this tiny settlement, you can—and we will talk about the party. He may be in a bad mood. I may not be hungry, as I sometimes become after intense nights. We may be silent, but it will never be taken for a slight. He and I are direct people. We have sharp tongues and soft hearts.

If he has an errand to run we will leave Auroville and head into Pondicherry town, where we will have lunch afterwards. Pork at Rendezvous, perhaps, or seafood at Hotel du Parc, where we can sit on the elevated terrace that trembles each time someone walks across it. We will ride up and down the beach twice—where the water breaks on stone reinforcements put in place after the tsunami of

2004 and a single pier juts out with no purpose—make one stop to buy more wine, and then head back. It will be a Sunday, and this quiet town will be quieter still (except for tourists from the city in which I live, whom you can always tell by their bad driving and drunken antics). Knowing the drummer (and I think I do) he may swing around by the shops where men sitting by the windows gawk at us—a wizened man and a little woman on a bike—and taunt them, waving and yelling, "Look at all the monkeys!" Knowing him, he may even swing around to do it twice.

6

Basho in the 17th century: "Those who remain behind watch the shadow of a traveler's back disappear." Do you ever think of the love you walked away from? I myself have learnt to love your absence, your aftermath, everything tinged with a brief and bittersweet beauty, like the world after a storm.

7

By six-thirty, on cue with the sunset, the first guests start arriving. There's a birthday being celebrated tonight, and the reasons why I have been alone all afternoon become apparent; deep vessels of food are brought out, freshly cooked—crispy prawns, basmati rice, a rich mutton curry, cottage cheese in pureed spinach for the vegetarians. Bottle after bottle of liquor arrives, mostly wine, for it's the favorite of the lady of the house, whose birthday it is. Everybody air kisses, because this is a European town, but takes their footwear off, because the earth herself, even here, is Indian.

A joint is lit and passed around. The drummer and I take it only briefly, by tacit concurrence; we have hashish and Kodaikanal mushrooms in the rooms upstairs, so we let the social partakers have their fill. The night grows both cooler and mellower, the laughter increasingly louder, the conversations more disorderly. The lady of the house retires to her bed after a last round of kisses and presents. "The night is young though I no longer am," she calls to the party, and, as we are meant to, we take this as permission and raise another toast.

And sure enough, there it is, someone drops your name, and I know it is solely because I am within earshot. I smile politely and change the subject. The only reason anyone else remembers you around here is because of me. Because even when I am far away, I am always here. You do not know how many other ghosts I carry. Neither do they.

8

Already the night has gone on too long. Someone stands to receive a glass, someone else reaches out to pour more wine for her. There is a moment of disconnection, the glass falls and shatters. The group is at first startled. Then, there is laughter.

I take the confusion of the moment as an opportunity to leave, quietly withdrawing to the house. I refill my own glass in the kitchen and take it up to the rooftop.

I can see them down below—a man and a woman have started to dance. I wonder how many of these people will sleep here tonight. There are beds enough, and warm bodies, and the ride back through the forest road will be too dark at this time for all but the bravest.

I lie down on my back and look up at the sky, one arm under my head, the other across my belly. This is one of my favorite things to do here. I was doing it when I met you, or at least, the first time I noticed you—how strange that I cannot remember being introduced to you. It is as though the memory of you only began from that night we were up here talking for hours—me stretched out like this under the stars, you with your back against the roof's inner border. Your words in the darkness slipping under my skin at the beginning of an embroidery I did not even observe until it had become a tapestry. Until all your needles were in me, and I was stitched through with that sweet, sweet sting. You were jetlagged and I could not sleep. I liked you. I didn't know then that I could love you.

Look at all that loves me back, I whisper to myself. I fall asleep like this. Down below, someone has driven their car into the compound and is blasting the Gypsy Kings from the speakers. It does not bother me.

9

The bricks under my back grow warm. The drummer comes up and finds me. "You left me here all night?" I am a little hurt.

"*Savasana*," he says. "The corpse posture. Nothing hurts you when it thinks you are dead."

"Except vultures."

"None here, baby." He cackles a little, and gives me his arm. We go downstairs.

For breakfast, we eat leftover prawns with idli. Then we take the bike and go.

Secrets within secrets. This place itself, this house, this town, the sensation of having fallen into a surreal portal—is almost a secret.

And even here, there are still more secret sanctuaries. We ride farther into the rural interior.

It happens so perfectly that it's almost as though we had planned it. The first time I had been here, the drummer had taken me for a long ride so I could clear my heart of the weight of you. We were heading to the lake where he went when he needed peace, but we had gotten lost, having taken a detour along one stunning dirt avenue lined on both sides by coconut trees.

Somewhere on this unfamiliar trail, I saw her.

She faced away from the road but she was unmistakable from any angle.

We stopped and made our way into the undergrowth. "This is Tantric stuff," said the drummer with a low whistle. "Serious shit."

Kali, painted blue, her many arms full, loomed above us in stone. Goddess of weddings and beheadings. I put my hands on her feet and my head on my hands and wept in a way I cannot put into words.

And this much later, here we are, the drummer and I, heading back to the goddess in that grove with offerings to leave at her feet. We seek her as though we know we will find her, with or without maps, within or without memory. Here along this dirt road, in the heart of a village in a forest on the coast, I see them, my friends—the giant red and black butterfly, the wasps, the whispering trees, the wind, the dancing light. Over and over I return, even when all else has become irretrievable, and over and over, what remains, remains. I hold on tight and think, *this is all there is. Look at all there is to love.*

SUSAN McCARTY

ANATOMIES

Corner of A and Fourth/Eye

In New York, there is an important distinction to make between where you live and where you sleep. You sleep in your apartment. You live in the city.

It is a dripping August, which you know by the smell of it: dried urine, rotting garbage, and the unleaded smell of cabs burning off fuel as they idle in the shimmering heat, each a mirage, a promise of something better on the other side. You can't get into a cab today because the ten dollars in cash and change sitting on your desk in your apartment is all you have until payday, which is Friday. Today is Sunday. You don't have a bank account because the check-cashing place is convenient to your apartment. Also, you don't trust yourself with a bank account, the margin of error is always, always so small. Instead, you like to watch the stack of cash dwindle in front of you. It causes you anxiety, but it also makes you feel as though you are in control of something here, in New York. You are in control of nothing, of course, but the illusion helps.

Because you sleep in the East Village, in a studio apartment in an old tenement that you share with a roommate, you walk the streets for entertainment. On paydays, you allow yourself a Cuban sandwich from the takeout counter on Avenue A. Today, however, you simply stand in front of the door for a few minutes, because smelling something is almost as good as eating it, and smelling something other than urine and garbage makes you happy. The smells are engrossing, in fact, which is why you don't notice what has been going on behind you until there is the sound of something whining through the air, not very far from your head, and then the noise of the bystanders, who must have been there all along, suddenly rushes

272

in and you turn in time to see two men grappling with each other, in the street, just feet away. One of them has a hammer. In the moment it has taken you to notice the scene and become confused by it, the man with the hammer bounces it off the side of the other man's head and there is a sound that would, under other circumstances, be satisfying—the sound of a job being completed, of something being forced into it's proper place. You actually see the eye of the struck man wobble in its socket, as if it has just been dropped there to settle. And they are both screaming—one in anger and the other in pain, but the sidewalkers are screaming too and so the scene takes on a kind of miserable white noise wherein no one person's distress can be sorted from another's.

The police sirens are what finally cut through and break the cord that had knotted around you, anchoring you to this place to watch a man maybe get killed. This is true for everyone, and when the cop car screeches up, the men have already run off together, wild elopers, one with his hand over his eye and a trail of blood down his shirt, the other just behind him, brandishing the hammer like a cartoon wife with a rolling pin after a mouse.

St. Vincent's/Lower Left Quadrant

David Beckham has broken the second metatarsal in his left foot. You do not care very much except that the picture of him in the sporting publication open on your lap—he sits on the ground, one hand over an eye, one hand on the foot, worried and in pain—is the only thing distracting you from your own pain (back, lower left quadrant) which is unlike any pain you've had before. It is also distracting you from the St. Vincent's ER which is the least comforting place you've ever been. Everything is a shade of grayish green. There are no plants or tissue boxes. There are spots of dried blood on the floor in front of you. You sit facing the windows and feel like you're in prison. You are trying not to pay attention to the couple seated to your left. You try to focus instead on the lesser pain of Becks, but your neighbors are difficult not to overhear.

It's the meth, the boyfriend says, he's been doing it all weekend. The ER attendant asks the man who is not the boyfriend how much meth he has done this weekend. The man is weeping quietly. He sits straight up in the green vinyl chair, one hand gripping the chair arm, the other twisting his boyfriend's hand, which has gone white and slightly blue from the pressure. His eyes don't look anywhere. I don't know, all of it? says the boyfriend, grimacing at his twisted hand, but content to bruise, to share. The expressionless attendant makes a note on a clipboard. And when did he do the, uh, procedure? she asks. I don't know, says the boyfriend. I just woke up and went to the bathroom and he was sitting on the toilet like that. Like what? asks the attendant just because she wants to hear it again. With his...the boyfriend whispers but can't talk too quietly because his man has started to make a low whining sound in his throat. With his testicles stapled to his thigh, he finishes and puts a hand on the head of the whining man who is wearing loose, dry-weave exercise shorts.

You have glanced up from Becks to catch this glimpse and you'd almost forgotten yourself but here is the breathless punch again. You jerk in your seat and pant. Your vision tunnels, momentarily, the periphery dark and fogged out. You seem to pulse in empathy with your neighbor. Later, you will learn that a UTI has crawled up your urinary tract to your kidneys, which are infected, which can be life threatening but is also easily treatable.

The man with the staples in his balls lets out a thin howl, which is unlike a dog howl. It is not rounded and full and conclusive. It's the sound of pure pain. The bemused ER attendant has come back out of the triage station and even she looks concerned now. You look back down at the photo because you feel very strongly that you would also like to howl, that you would like to hold this man's hand and go a little hysterical with him.

There is a bustling—the attendant and the boyfriend are trying to coax the patient into a wheelchair. You can't imagine how he got here, how he walked at all, down the stairs of his apartment building, to the curb to hail a cab. It must have taken tremendous reserves of strength. He must be exhausted. There is a yelp and a moan followed by some rustling, and the squeak of rubber tires on sanitized linoleum.

David Beckham looks very tired and perhaps as if he is about to cry or has just finished crying. Probably just about to cry—there is something like disbelief in his face. It is 2002 and his foot is worth several million pounds. Something knocks at you from the wrong side, from the inside. You close your eyes, and Beckham's gleaming shin guards stay with you, ghost your retinas for a moment, then dissolve.

World Trade Center/Head

You meet a friend for dinner at Molly's, which is full of the usual regulars—undocumented Irish construction workers and investment bank lackeys: the administrative assistants and data enterers and mailroomies. You are eating a medium-rare burger with one hand and decadently smoking with the other. It is almost as if you intuit that this won't be possible for very much longer. You haven't been following it, but the bill will be passed in December; the bars and restaurants, smoke-free by spring.

You are on your second Guinness, which makes you want to put on music. You like Molly's juke because it has the most Pogues albums in the city, plus it's been one of those days—frequent lately, it seems. You feel funny but you don't know why. You don't even know what you mean by funny. Which is what you say when your friend, who is having the shepherd's pie and also smoking, asks. Tomorrow's the anniversary, he reminds you. How have you worked in an office all day, printing letters and time-stamping materials to be copyedited and proofed, penciling dates in your boss's calendar even, without seeing?

I walked, he says without prompting, seven miles home to Brooklyn. I drank an entire bottle of whiskey that night. When I woke up the next morning I thought it had all been a nightmare. Really? you ask. No, he says, not really. I spent the night throwing up in my bathroom, completely sober.

So you didn't drink an entire bottle of whiskey?

No, I did that. But I didn't forget. That part's wishful thinking.

You weren't living here then so it's not your memory to share, but you listen to him talk a little more about the dust and the fear and the posters, some of which still hang in gray swelled strips on the lamp posts and scaffolds around town. They are unreadable now, but no one will take them down. As you listen something uneasy swells inside you. The room darkens a bit and the sound of the other patrons is suddenly deafening. You stand up, unsure of where you are going, until he puts a dollar in your hand and requests "Fairytale of New York."

The jukebox swims in front of you—you can't make out the numbers next to the track listings and you seem to be having trouble drawing a full breath. The door is two feet away and you leave the jukebox queued with money to get some fresh air, to get out of this cave for just a minute.

The street is empty and in the deepening dark of the night, you see that the blue lights are on. There is no cloud cover tonight, so they rise up from Ground Zero as far into the sky as you can see. You wonder if there are astronauts out there right now and if they can see these other twin towers, these ghosts. You have never looked at them for very long because, even though you have no religion, and the thought is frankly stupid, you are afraid that if you look at the lights long enough, you will see the spirits of the dead being sucked up in them, like some tractor beam to heaven, a pneumatic salvation. Like jumping off a building in reverse. You try to take a deep breath but your breath won't come. The lights go out.

When you come to, you see the upside down faces of strangers and between two of their heads, the blue lights. You are extremely confused. If someone asked you your name, you would not be able to say. There is no sound but a soft ringing. Then your friend's head juts into view and his voice cuts through the white noise: What happened? Where'd you go? Jesus Christ you're bleeding.

You decide not to say anything until someone tells you what's going on. Your friend sets you up and cradles you and puts a napkin

—where did he get the napkin?—to your chin and if you are glad for something its that the tower lights have left your field of vision. You sit on the sidewalk while concerned people bird-walk around you and make noise on their cell phones and then there is an ambulance and then you are inside it and your friend holds your hand and your hair when you throw up into a white bag, but until you turn to go crosstown to Bellevue, to stitches and the diagnosis of a concussion, and some half-baked hypotheses about undercooked meat and low blood sugar, you make yourself look at those two lights through the portholes in the back of the ambulance doors, as if your looking could mean anything at all.

Empire State Building/Phallus

You have been inside twice now and up to the top once, but you can't remember much of the trip except that the lobby ceilings seemed too low, too gray, and the elevator went so fast your ears popped. When you think of the Empire State Building it is always an exterior view, jutting beyond the tops of the Village brownstones, a guiding beacon at night, when the streets creep together and the city rearranges itself. When the grid seems to disappear, there is always that great glowing pyramid tip. They change the lights on it according to the seasons or holidays, but in your mind, it always glows red, white and blue—a sign of American optimism, a great anchor of capitalism, that directional daddy, standing guard.

You look at it now, reassured you're headed north. This part of the city feels friendly. The old tenements crouch close. The shop windows are lit and full of the kinds of business you never have need for—a stationery shop, a designer pet clothing boutique, a restaurant that serves $30 macaroni and cheese. It is not even late, only freshly dark, which is why you are not scared, but merely surprised, when the passenger door of a semi-cab parked on the street opens as you come parallel to it and a man in a gray hoodie, eyes wide but expressionless, yells to you from the depths of the truck. He looks you straight in the eye and asks a simple question.

How does it look? he says. And you, stopped now, the Empire State eclipsed by the massive brow of the cab, can only ask, What? Your voice hangs in the air for a frozen moment and in that moment you see that the man has his cock in his hand, is yanking on it violently. You can't help but be transfixed by the head of it, squeezing past his white-knuckled hand. You realize that he is about to pull his own dick off in front of you.

Then the man is talking again, and automatically your eyes move back to his face. His own eyes are still wide, but now they are worried too. I'm going to see my girl, he says. But I been driving on mini-thins all night. Is it hard enough?

Your legs have realized, before your brain, that it is best to leave quickly, that the ladies selling French paper twenty feet away will not be able to help you should this man decide to drag you into his cab and make material his question. But really, no, that is not what you think. That is what you should have thought. On some level your brain has responded mechanically to the danger, but consciously, the only situation you know that resembles this one is a joke. And so you laugh. You turn around and trip away nearly screaming with it. Later, you spend your last five dollars on a cab ride home.

Ridge and Rivington/Mouth

Your first mistake is that you are wearing headphones. You try to remember to take them off on the subway platforms and at night, on the street, but there are so many rules to remember. This one sometimes escapes you, especially when you are listening to very good music, which occasionally makes you feel as if you are starring in a movie and the movie is your life, which is one of the more pleasant feelings New York inspires in you. Occasionally, New York makes your life feel much bigger and more interesting and possible than it is. This makes it easy to forget.

You are also wearing heels—the tall and tottering kind. You can't run in them—you can barely even walk. But you are walking, alone, from a bar in SoHo to your boyfriend's apartment on the Lower East

Side because it is faster to walk across this part of town, even in tippy shoes, than to take a cab.

You see him first as you turn onto Delancey. He is walking alone. He wears a white t-shirt and a green stocking cap and looks like everyone else on the sidewalk tonight, which is why you forget him almost as soon as you see him. He drops back and you stutter-step on to your mix CD. It is only when you turn again onto Clinton that you sense someone behind you and stop to pretend to look at a menu in a restaurant window. Your Discman is in your coat pocket and you turn it off. Out of the corner of your eye, you see the man, the white t-shirt. He has turned the corner too, and he is walking slowly. You don't know if he slowed his walk when you stopped to read the menu or if he has been walking that way this whole time and you are just being paranoid. But your paranoia is not unfounded—lately, more than usual, dead girls have been in the news.

In fact, you realize, as you read the description of a rosemary-lemon lamb risotto for the third time, that the bar you have just left is very near The Falls, where just a couple weeks ago that grad student was abducted and later found raped and strangled, bound with packing tape and dropped off near the Belt Parkway like a gift. And the actress, last year, not two blocks from your boyfriend's apartment, one block from where you stand right now. You were out that night too, doing what you can't recall. You remember her last words from the newspaper though. What are you going to do, shoot me? she asked them. They did. This is how you remember to be good.

You should go into the restaurant. You should go into the restaurant and order a drink and call your boyfriend and tell him to meet you here. But when you look around again, the man is gone. You begin to get mad. This fucking city, you think. You tell yourself a joke. A girl walks into a bar…there is a punch line. Something to do with putting out, with being put out. The punch line is she didn't keep her mouth shut, of mouths taped shut, a bullet in the lung. You'll be goddamned if you'll slink into that restaurant. You turn and begin to walk determinedly up the street. You find your keys in your pocket and poke them like claws through your clenched fist. You clench your jaw to match your fist. Soon there are footsteps behind you again. You barely turn your head and get a glimpse of white cotton. The city thickens its breath.

Here's something funny you know: The Falls is owned by the Dorrian family. They also own Dorrian's Red Hand, which is where Robert Chambers met Jennifer Levin the night he walked her to Central Park, raped and bit her then strangled her to death. Once, a man you were seeing took you to Dorrian's and you walked back to his place through the park, past where she was killed. He wanted to spook you. Just a bit of fun.

You are running unsteadily now, really more of a lope than a run, certainly this lead-assed shamble will not save your life. You can't hear him behind you over your own breath and the shod clop of your heels. Somehow, you manage to dial your boyfriend with your free hand. Open the door right now, you say as you round Rivington, his door half a block away. There is something in your voice because he doesn't say a word over the phone, but in a few more seconds you see him emerge onto the lit stoop. He is waving, but not smiling. You rush up the steps and pull him into the hallway and push the locked door shut behind you. There is no one on the sidewalk or the street, just your own reflection in the glass door, your pale, translucent face laid over the night, eyes like drill holes, lips parted and mute.

Manhattan/Hands

An Australian tourist has brought you here, has attached himself to you in the cold gray moments before dawn. You shiver in your down parka after so many hours in the club, and that after-hours dive, and when he grips you closer, the feathers in your coat puff from the sudden pressure. You smell of sweat and whiskey and his cologne, something cheap and strong and chemical, but somehow not unpleasant. His hand twists softly in yours in a way that means he is about to say something.

Here's a spot, he says and stops walking and you both look around. Here? you ask. You are standing at Twenty-third and Eighth, a monotonous Chelsea corner without charm or color. Your tongue is sore from the hours you've spent twisting it into improbable shapes in his mouth. You'd gone to Centro-Fly with some friends late last night, dressed to get the cover waived—something artfully shredded, glittering webs of fabric.

It happens every so often that you crave the kind of release you can find in a place like Centro-Fly, with all those beautiful strangers, each one a possibility, it doesn't even matter of what. What matters is by the end of the night you are abandoned to it all: the low lights and the bass pulse of the music, a sweaty flirtation in every corner, the anonymous press of curious limbs.

You don't know his name because he told you, but you couldn't hear, and so you asked him to repeat it and you still couldn't hear, but you nodded as if you had. This is probably why he calls you "Love" instead of your own name and you don't mind. He'd started a conversation by asking if you were French—the best pick-up line you'd ever heard, worthy of reward. You'd tried on a Parisienne pout in response, allowed him to buy you a drink and become quickly entangled in a misty corner of the club, all legs and mouths and fingers. Tomorrow, he will leave with his friends and return to Sydney and you will never see him again and this is the way it should be—his presence now perfect because of the totality of his absence later.

He has brought you here to witness. There's this thing he'd read about in the paper yesterday, this thing that happens twice a year, once at dawn, once at sunset, where the sun aligns perfectly with the cross-streets of the city, the grid, and...here he frowns.

And what? you ask, but he doesn't know. It's a thing you're supposed to see at least once in your life, he says, the sun barreling down the streets of Manhattan like a huge, spectral taxi.

Of course, you say. And there is nothing more important to you right now than to stand on this corner, next to this dark Baskin Robbins, and look down the barrel of the cross-street for the dawn. Sometimes things are that simple. You smile as he puts his nose in your neck and sighs.

The streets are nearly empty this early on a Sunday morning and this makes the city seem like a wilderness. As you watch, the sun begins its crawl over top of the edge of that wilderness, the East River. It angles through the tall muddy buildings thrown up around it like canyons, as if they had always been there and always would be. The buildings on either side of the street seem to cup the sun, but cannot hold it, begin to disappear behind its needle-thin spikes which creep toward you until they engulf you too and you feel yourself begin to disappear. But when you look behind you, your shadows belong to giants. Your Australian smiles at you and for a moment you're in love, entranced, held by him, by the city, kept safe in these palms and looking back down 23rd street, you think how the city proffers so many kinds of darkness, but here, on this corner, just now, a new kind of light.

DAWN PAUL

KOMODO DRAGON

Lawrence's phone went off when we got the dessert menu. He picked up, so I knew it was no ordinary call. "I'll be right over," he said. "Don't let some idiot poke it with a stick."

Lawrence is an expert at dangerous animal removal, the guy the police call when someone's got a tarantula in their cookie jar. We'd been dating for a month and this was the first time he'd gotten an animal call. He specializes in exotics, mostly escaped pets. He won't do rabies cases or anything that flies. On our first date he was quick to tell me that he is a non-credentialed expert, totally self-educated, as though he didn't want that to surface as a deal-breaker later on. He barely finished high school in Florida, he said, was more interested in working at his family's roadside reptile world. He'd moved north when the place went bankrupt.

It wasn't the police calling. It was Lawrence's friend Chip Reed at the local animal rescue no-kill shelter. "He says someone called about a Komodo dragon," Lawrence laughed. "Probably a big iguana. Do you mind if I just pay the check now? You can come along." It was fine with me. I'm a real estate agent so I know you have to be ready when the client is. Also, it was nice that he offered to pick up the check. I'm not in high-end real estate. I mostly do desperation sales, can't seem to sell anything unless it's dirt cheap. We had my car so we drove to Lawrence's place to get his van and gear.

How do you picture Lawrence? Burly, tanned, pith helmet and khaki shorts? Think again. I met Lawrence at a chamber music concert. He's a Baroque cello fan. He's wiry, wears big, black-framed glasses, has reddish-blond hair that's going thin on top and he's not self-conscious about it. For some reason, I've never asked why, he wears a huge stainless steel watch that slips around his skinny wrist.

I think he's gorgeous, green eyes, lightly muscled, graceful.

Animal removal is his hobby, a way to still work with animals since moving north. He has a job with the electric company, keeps track of their underground wires, transmission lines and whatnot. That's how he explains it, the whatnot is a direct quote. I thought of him as Clark Kent, a mild-mannered man occasionally called upon to do feats of daring. I'd always had a theory about guys like Clark Kent, that they can afford to be quiet and humble because they're sure of themselves. Gentle giants. I've been dating on and off since my divorce five years ago, and gentle giants are rare.

He came out of his house with a beat-up duffle bag, still wearing his dinner-out clothes, slacks, sport shirt and Italian loafers. "You going to duck into a phone booth on the way and change your outfit?" I said.

"Phonebooth? What are you talking about?" He whipped the van into reverse, checked his GPS. My joke was wasted, but that was okay. I was eager to see Lawrence at his best with the Komodo dragon.

Lawrence pulled up in front of a triple-decker in a part of town that I know well, full of rat-trap apartment buildings with immigrant tenants afraid to complain. I'm not proud of the fact that I've sold quite a few to absentee landlords who slap on vinyl siding and jack up the rents. No one was around so we walked into the back yard. The land sloped down so the porch on the first floor was nearly a full story off the ground. Chip Reed was standing with a middle-aged woman looking through the lattice screening under the porch. Chip is short and stocky. When he and Lawrence are together they remind me of the two Star Wars robots. Chip is about twenty-five and looks up to Lawrence as a mentor. He used to be in vet school but dropped out when he realized he could never put an animal down. Now he works the night shift at the no-kill shelter.

The woman had tightly permed hair and a sleeveless cotton dress that might have looked stylish on someone else. She was not my idea of a person who would own a Komodo dragon, but Lawrence is always telling me that exotic pet owner stereotypes do not hold true. Chip waved us over.

"Mrs. Kozlov, this is Lawrence, he's going to take care of this lizard for you! And this is Gretchen, his fiancée and assistant." Neither of which is true. Chip is sweet but a bit of a dreamer. We all peered through the lattice.

"It's a Komodo dragon all right!" Lawrence was pleased.

"Yes," Mrs. Kozlov said, and with that one word conveyed very clearly that she was neither foolish nor prone to exaggeration. Komodo dragons, Lawrence had explained to me on the ride over, are very rare as pets. They grow longer than three meters—that's nine feet, for those of us who have to do the conversion—and are carnivorous. They have been known to attack humans and win. Also, it is illegal to capture or trade in them. It was dusk and even duskier under the porch. I couldn't see the lizard until Lawrence flashed a light on it. It was in a corner against the foundation and was only about the length of a baseball bat. It looked pathetic rather than vicious, curled up in a pile of dead leaves and trash. A wrapper from a drinking straw was twined around its tail. It looked bloated through the middle, like it didn't get much exercise.

"You be careful with him," Mrs. Kozlov pronounced. I placed the accent—Russian.

"Don't worry, I'll get him out alive and take him off your hands."

"What do you mean, take him?"

"I'm sure I can find a zoo that will be happy to have him."

"No. He stays with me."

Lawrence looked at Chip. "What's going on here?"

Chip shuffled his feet. "I tried to explain. Mrs. Kozlov, I told you, you need to have a license to keep an animal like this. You have to know what you're doing."

Mrs. Kozlov whirled on Chip. "You said this man would help me!"

"I am trying to help you," Lawrence told her. "Obviously he's gotten too strong for you to handle. That's what always happens with a species like this. You can't keep him. It's illegal and dangerous."

"You," she said, with a finger in Chip's moonish face, "said nothing about taking away. This is a free country. This is not like some places I know, where they come in, they take what they want."

She turned to Lawrence. "Get him. Put him in his tank. I will not make the mistake and let him out on the sun porch again. I thought he would enjoy that. This is how he repays me."

The sun was gone and we could see only by the lights from the neighbors' windows. It was getting chilly and I hadn't brought a sweater. I agreed with Mrs. Kozlov. Just put the lizard in his tank so Lawrence and I could go back to the café and I could have a chocolate martini, maybe even invite Chip. I looked at the Komodo dragon, which was blinking dreamily in the beam of the flashlight. I wondered what it was thinking. Did it slip away from the tank, then the sun porch, imagining that the tropical jungle it longed for was just outside the door? Was it depressed to find itself under a porch with old Dunkin Donuts cups and a deflated soccer ball?

Lawrence said, not looking at Mrs. Kozlov, that he was going to go get his stuff. From the stories Lawrence told, I knew this was not the way it was supposed to go. He was usually a hero. People applauded when Lawrence took an offending creature away. He still had a handmade card taped to his refrigerator, signed by sixteen daycare kids, that said in rainbow colors, Thank You For Taking the Cobra Out of Our Coat Room.

Lawrence came back from the van with his duffel bag. He pulled out a crowbar and said he'd have to pry off a section of the lattice. Mrs. Kozlov flung herself against the lattice and spread her arms. "No! You will not do this. This is my son's lizard. I promised him I would take good care."

"Where is your son?" I asked.

"In the hospital."

"That's excellent, why didn't you tell us that before," Chip piped up. "Let's give him a call, I'm sure he'll understand the situation."

"What hospital is he in?" Lawrence pulled out his phone.

"Is he well enough to take a phone call?" I asked, while Lawrence hovered his fingers over his phone.

"He is in a hospital for people who take drugs. No phone calls allowed. Only visits." Mrs. Kozlov stopped guarding the porch and folded muscular arms over her chest. Lawrence swore softly and tapped his fingers on the lattice.

"I'm sorry to hear that," I said.

"Never should I have brought him here. I wanted him to study computers. But he was older than the other kids. They make fun, his clothes, his accent. I tell him, you wait. A few years, they will be begging you for a job." She looked like she had more to say but Lawrence cut her off.

"Do you know when he's getting out? He has a problem here."

"He's in, he's out. He has lots of problems," Mrs. Kozlov said.

"Where did he get this big fella?" Chip asked. "It's a protected animal. It must have cost thousands."

Mrs. Kozlov shot him a look. "He has money sometimes. For lizards, tattoos all over his back, even his neck. But no money for school, not even the cheap little business college in the mall."

Lawrence nudged Chip and said, "Sometimes guys will take something like this in trade for, you know..." He pinched a nostril and made a snorting gesture, as though Mrs. Kozlov was a child who shouldn't hear the word.

"When I visit my son I will tell him to get a license."

Lawrence looked offended. "They don't distribute licenses to anybody who wants an unusual pet." He made an impatient gesture with the crowbar. "How about if I just do my job here."

"I won't let you sell my son's lizard."

"Who said anything about selling—"

Mrs. Kozlov cut him off with a wave of her arm. "Quiet down!" She pointed at the surrounding apartment buildings. "They will all come out, looking for excitement. You think they'd know how lucky they are, to be in a place with no excitement in the night."

"Mrs. Kozlov," Lawrence started again, each word clipped and quiet. "Do you know your son could go to jail for keeping this animal when he isn't licensed?"

"What do you know about jail." Mrs. Kozlov gave a short, ugly bark. "You will go to jail for stealing my son's lizard and selling him. How do I know you have one of these licenses?"

287

"I do and I'm one of the few people who has an individual license, not through an affiliation with an organization. I am a self-educated—"

I stepped forward. "Mrs. Kozlov, please. Lawrence isn't going to sell him. Honest. This is his hobby, rescuing exotic animals. I'm sorry your son has had problems. And I know you must feel bad after promising him you'd take care of his pet. But you can't keep this lizard. It will just bring more trouble."

Mrs. Kozlov nodded slowly and trudged up the rickety porch stairs to her apartment. I let out a big breath. In my work I deal with a lot of situations—displaced tenants, foreclosures. If you stay calm, things usually end well. I hoped Lawrence had learned something from me for a change. He turned away and started prying off the lattice. When it was off, he crouched down into the space under the porch and motioned for Chip to shine the flashlight. The lizard lifted its head and licked the air with its tongue. Lawrence moved quickly, reached down, grabbed the lizard around its mouth and with his other hand, lifted the animal and held it out, keeping its scaly back away from his clean shirt. He stepped out from under the porch, smiled and said, "Camera!" The lizard waved his legs in the air. I fumbled with my phone, made sure the flash went off.

"Chip, hold the bag open. He's going to be heavy."

Mrs. Kozlov had come out during the excitement of the capture and was standing next to Chip, who held the bag out like a Halloween trick or treater.

"Do you want a photo?" I asked her. "Maybe for your son?" I realized we had never asked her the lizard's name, or her son's for that matter. Lawrence held the lizard out for another photo, his dirty underside exposed from neck to tail. Mrs. Kozlov whipped out a small kitchen cleaver and chopped the lizard's neck. Chip and I screamed. Lawrence yelled and dropped the lizard, which was bleeding but still alive. Mrs. Kozlov bent down and finished the job. The headless body twitched.

"There! Nobody gets him now. Not you," she said, waving the bloody cleaver at Lawrence, "not my son. Maybe I take this to him," she gave the head a little kick, "and tell him this is what happens when you hide away in your drugs and leave me to take care of everything." Chip Reed leaned into the darkness and wretched.

"Lady, you shouldn't have done that," Lawrence was furious, the tip of his nose white as though the cartilage might poke through. "Killing a Komodo dragon is an international offense." I put my hand on his arm and he flicked it off. "Do you know how much trouble you're in now?"

She laughed again. "It is you who has trouble now. You have come a long way for nothing. You have come with nothing and you will leave with nothing." She spit on the dirt at Lawrence's feet. Then she bent down, wiped the cleaver on a tuft of weeds and climbed the stairs to the porch.

"I can have the feds here in ten minutes!" Lawrence screamed.

Shadowy heads appeared over the second floor porch.

"Just let her go!" I hissed at him.

"She killed a rare and endangered animal. She just spit at me!"

"Hey, buddy," said a voice from above, "what's going on?"

"Lawrence, let's go, I mean it."

"We can't just leave the body," Chip whispered.

"Miss K, are you all right down there?"

"She can put it out with the trash, for godsake, let's go."

In the end, Lawrence kicked the carcass back under the porch. Chip offered to nail the lattice up but Lawrence said to leave it. He drove the van to his place in a silent fury and I got into my car and drove home. I called Chip to make sure he made it back to the shelter. He sounded like he'd been crying.

I haven't seen Lawrence since that night. I didn't call him. I waited for a few weeks to see if he would call me. When he didn't, I was sad but relieved. It would have been hard to explain to him that he wasn't a gentle giant, after all.

Yesterday I was driving through that neighborhood with a client. A typical November day, spitting rain, trash blowing along the streets. I heard myself chattering about high-yield investments as I drove past storefronts with hand-lettered signs in swirly Cambodian and blocky Russian, paper Thanksgiving turkeys and Pilgrim hats.

"My only question is," my client said, "are these people going to squawk if I raise the rents?"

I assured him they would not. "They don't want trouble." I thought about Mrs. Kozlov, and hoped she did bring the lizard's head to her son in rehab. I thought of the poor Komodo dragon, killed in a cold backyard so far from where he belonged.

"Gretel?" my client said, and I knew I had missed a question, probably about cheap financing or how to get around zoning laws.

"It's Gretchen. This is the house." I pulled up in front of a faceless triple-decker. "If you don't want it, I'll take you back to the office and have you meet one of the other agents. Because this is my last day." Which became true as soon as I said it.

DEBORAH POE

FRAGILE MAGNETS

It becomes her.

What I mean is the costume she wears, what she calls high modernism.

Hilda Doolittle.

Her hair slicked back with coconut oil I can smell when she leans in to laugh, to hand Brandon and I her strange open Chinese fabric box with poetry inside. Each one of us is allowed one poem. It is folded haphazardly, and stapled. The staples are bright, hot pink.

I have not met her before though I have seen her name.

There is something about her. A matchbox. An orange slice. A lemon under the tongue.

I am this way for her too. She looks at me, at moments like the north pole looks to south.

She is trying to guess why the circles under my eyes are so dark. She sees someone healthy when I smile.

*

That night the red wine chez moi, the daydreams of Ezra pinning back my hair, the rapidly etched words on the Japanese calendar paper left from our trip. Only there was no Ezra, so it was only my words, not his circus-tent noises adding to my night. Only red wine.

And my sea violets. My sea garden. My anemones. Fragile agates.

When I met this young poet, I was suddenly older. Not old, mind you, older. Fourteen years to be exact. A young poet's tugging.

We exchanged ages. I'm sure I brought it up. And ages pounded through me.

I recognized the slate grey expanse in the eyes. Like my sea garden, they were green.

*

Earlier tonight I was in the emergency room. It was my second time in the last three weeks. I was flicking my matches out the car window on the way. When I got there, stoned, no one knew. When the medicine is there, it's there.

A woman had cut her arm, she was there alone, and she read *Reader's Digest* like the Torah.

A guy, younger than me, was cracked out. Nervous, his foot articulating the ache. His knee up and down. I wanted to grab and stop him.

I start writing again. I'm working on this poem. I have to do this, to write, or else I lose it, my mind and the words. The nurse asks me for my insurance information at which point I tell her she's interrupted my process. She apologizes, and I laugh.

*

Freud knew that what we call madness and what we call inspiration come from the same source.

I should like this feeling. More than any silver spoon. Or teacup. The orange slices of sun sipping me for breakfast that morning. Or the shower of black umbrellas I imagined under then slate-grey electric skies, pulling hazard to the ground.

I wanted to reach out to the swift sky, to say "come beautiful rain, beautiful rain, welcome."

I want no barrier between myself and the earth. If I could break him, I could break a tree.

*

When she gives me her number, she says "We shall talk poetry." Brandon isn't sure about her and wonders about her motives.

It is almost midnight, and in the back room, we are smoking pot,

292

and she comes in to say goodbye. Nikki persuades her to rest for a moment. You can see she doesn't smoke often. It affects her almost immediately.

When she smokes, she sucks with her mouth I imagine younger.

Murmuring "this is why I shouldn't smoke pot," she comes to the edge of the bed where Brandon and I are sitting next to each other. And she leans in closer, closer to my mouth.

She leaves, and Brandon laughs. I tell him he has it wrong.

*

My head is trampled coral. Last night blows through me like sea grass. Freud was wrong, wrong, wrong. Why conflate insanity with language. Does it have to be a slippery negative?

The image of the young man with the circles under his eyes slips through like Annie's long hair.

Shall I apologize, dear Freud, for my gestures of kindness? Would you call it penis envy?

Mysteries remain, after all, to swirl in these unknowns. This is what kisses mean.

*

I open my eyes, and the clock beside my pillow says 4am.

A stomach is on its backward cycle, and mother is too far away. With my mother it is complicated. When she brings the medicine, she comes with her dog-heeling boyfriend who acts like someone's got his balls in their fist and is squeezing so tight he can't speak. I doubt very seriously he knows what to do with someone sick. Tonight Brandon stayed with his girlfriend.

I roll over and see Hilda's number. I pick up the phone. It's 4am.

*

I am dreaming of Ezra. In the dream phone call, he admonishes me, tells me I'm moving within the same boundaries. I need to swim out of them. He is talking about the snake in his toilet that has crawled out to parrot his mutterings. As he's speaking the phone keeps ringing.

I wake and look at the clock. After 4am.

It's Brandon's friend. It's Ariel.

Ariel, I was dreaming of Ezra.

*

I saw your number on the floor—need a ride.

*

Rubbing my eyes I put on my goulashes, my dark green pants, and my un-ironed white shirt and lock my apartment behind me.

I can hear Ezra warning me one of these days I will learn. I am too sensitive, too something. Too open. Unable to say no. The way Ezra's mixed messages stick like moisture.

A gaze. A focus. Pan and zoom. How I long for that Spanish water to dive into. The memory of San Sebastian locks my apartment behind me.

*

My stomach is an African ant uprising. I imagine the earth is my stomach, and the ants are making their way through me, eating everything in sight.

Is it too much to ask, just to rest?

*

Annie would do the same.

I knock on the door, and he comes.

*

294

My eyes are open in the third ward of the west wing of a hospital. Rat in a cage.

My eyes search for language, but I can not squeeze the light from between the swelling words. I squeeze my eyes tighter and then open them wide.

I smell and taste sulphur. There is a train, the sound of it passing, it is barreling towards Albany. I believe everyone is sleeping except for the engineer who is barreling across the snow which is light and an endless sea of sleeping swans.

Wind, rend, cut, rend, tatters. Hilda mutters like a spell.

*

Ezra, what would you do? What would you have me do?

I am unsure when his mother will arrive. He wakes, and we talk of poetry. His music and mine. I tell him when he wakes that his eyes are like Annie's. I tell him of Annie, and he nods and smiles.

There are dark circles under my eyes.

I ask him if he's gotten what he's looked for in writing and art. Yes, he says, it has unwrapped itself like foil and wrapped itself around his windpipe.

He is a child in a gown.

I imagine his mother driving with a cigarette hanging out the window. Her boyfriend is sleeping. It smells like upstate New York, moist, and it does not smell like the sea.

Night has tricked itself into the room, outside it is snowing, the snow is thick on the branches, and the golden light of the street lights holds the large flakes aching for the ground.

I push the hair back from his head, and I kiss his forehead.

In my mind I have wandered east and west, wandered through the anemones, somehow still breathing.

What do I tell him? What wisdom? At least Freud showed me something. How do I prepare the boy?

I am a gatepost, wrought iron and long. I am the hell-hazed street lamp. Or only a fixture, another structure in the room. The consistent smell of a hospital has always made me faint. When I lean into him, his hair smells a sweet smoke. His eyes are green like my sea garden. Fragile as an agate.

The nurse has come in, and with her lime-green-silence, she is gone. His mother is not here.

I step out of my shoes. I climb in next to him.

Hold.

He is the edge of a mist where salmon wait their day.

The whitewashed room is keen and sharp.

Heather Sappenfield

Coloring Beyond the Lines

Elinor slid into a silk blouse. She brushed on her mascara and out her long hair. She moved mechanically but paused at her reflection in the mirror. Her nostrils and eyes flared in an untamed way that had started a month ago.

"Go away!" she said.

After providing a hot, nutritious breakfast, she sent off her husband Dirk with a kiss and his lunchbox. She drove her two daughters to elementary school and delivered her son to preschool. Next, she was supposed to organize a Halloween Party for the second grade, then a cut-and-paste-the-mustard-tree activity for Sunday School. After that, it was the grocery, starting a brisket in the Crock-pot, and scouring the bathrooms before she picked up the kids. Then the cheerful, numb-eared chit-chat with Dirk when he returned home. But as Elinor eased her minivan back into the garage, the story-book assembly-line of her life unfurled as a bleak vision before her, and some breakable thing within her snapped.

She bounded up the stairs to the master bedroom and stuffed clothes in a plastic grocery sack. She rushed to her son's room and toppled a tower of blocks as she yanked his backpack from under his bed.

In the kitchen, she scribbled a note: *Mommy's gone on an adventure. I'm not sure when she'll be home. There are leftovers in the freezer.* She drew a smiley face on the bottom, adding big-arch eyebrows with a flourish. She couldn't resist setting the table.

She untangled the car seats from their belts, lined them along the garage's wall, and loaded up the van. As she reached for reverse, she paused and rested her head against the steering wheel. She found her face in the rearview mirror.

"I have beautiful children. I have a beautiful husband. A beautiful home. I'm living the dream." Her eyes widened and her head reared back. She threw the van in reverse.

As she backed out, Barb, her neighbor, stood on the sidewalk with her schnauzer, Sweetie-Pie. Barb waved. Barb had a knack for making Elinor divulge words she regretted, words that would boomerang back to Elinor from someone else. Elinor grabbed the sippy cup filled with day-old juice from the console and rolled down the window, ready to pelt Barb with it. But she suppressed the urge and simply waved. She's sure I'm headed to the grocery, Elinor thought. Elinor headed west on I-70.

She opened up the van to eighty, slid in a Prince CD that was too raunchy for the kids, and sang at the top of her lungs, hitting all his falsettos just right. When she glanced in the rearview mirror and saw the yawning back seat, littered with Goldfish and Happy Meal toys, she sang louder. The CD ended, and she played it again. And again. Three hours later, she crossed the border from Colorado into Utah and entered the vast, red plains. Her throat was raw, her tongue ached, so she turned the stereo off and cranked the windows open to let her hair gallop in the air.

At Crescent Junction, Elinor turned south on 191, a ribbon of black with that dashed yellow line charging down the middle, flanked by the two solid white. It cut through the red earth and grew, narrower, narrower, till it met the cerulean horizon. Driving toward that expanse satisfied a craving Elinor had suppressed for too long.

She reached her arm out the window, dolphined her cupped hand on the wind, and whooped. She flew over a rise and passed a parked state patrol car. She braked and frowned. She reined herself in by thinking Dirk would kill her if she got a ticket. She glanced in the rearview at the patrol car then at herself, half-expecting to see her face split right down the middle.

"Where are we going?" she said. She sat back and sighed. Yet after a minute, she heard thudding in dirt. "Hooves!" she said. She listened to the rapid thuds, leaning close to the steering wheel and squinting, until the road descended between cliffs into Moab.

Elinor parked at an Alco. She bought a sleeping bag, three bags of apples, beef jerky, donuts, crackers, and cheese. She remembered she had a case of bottled water behind the van's seats from Back to School Night a month ago. She noticed Teddy Grahams were on sale and couldn't resist buying two boxes of the honey flavor.

"Do you know anything about the wild horses south of here?" she said to the checker, an acned, slump-shouldered teen, wearing a blue smock with Alco written in white across the front. Elinor straightened her own shoulders.

"I've never seen 'em." The girl turned to a stout woman behind a glass counter of cameras and watches. "Georgie, you ever seen the wild horses?"

Georgie looked up from a box of envelopes of developed film. She eyed Elinor. "You wanna find 'em?"

Elinor nodded.

"How come?"

The checker held out her hand to take Elinor's hundred-dollar bill.

Elinor handed it to her and shrugged. "I need to see them. Not sure why. I just do."

"You alone?" George said.

"Yes."

"Not real outdoorsy, are you?" Georgie's eyes met the checkers. She returned to sorting envelopes. "People that see 'em, they get way back there. And just see 'em. That's all."

"Someone saw 'em in a meadow once," the checker said.

"So they're there," Elinor said.

"Oh, they're there," Georgie said.

*

Elinor opened the Teddy Grahams as she continued south on 191 toward Monticello. The asphalt wound through spectacular red canyons, down juniper-forested hills, and beside a giant rock arch. Elinor barely noticed. She leaned forward, listening for hooves. All she could hear were her teeth crunching cracker bears and the van's

299

engine.

The wild horse article came to her. It had been in *The Denver Post* and told of their tenuous hold in crannies of openness. Two photos had accompanied it. One of a herd running in Utah grass, another of a mustang being broken by an inmate. The inmate held a saddle poised over the mustang's golden back. Its head was imprisoned by disembodied hands on each side of its halter. Its mouth gaped open as if screaming, tongue outstretched, and a rind of white lined its eye.

As she'd read the article, Elinor's son had been in her lap, coloring a picture of Snow White encircled by happy birds and rabbits and deer. Elinor had finished the article, and noticed the way his coloring strayed beyond the lines. She studied her own fingers, vaguely aware of the conflict when his sister, who was wild for Snow White, discovered this page in her book. Elinor remembered how she, too, had loved Snow White as a girl. How after a debutante's adolescence and college, she had dreamed only of motherhood. How she had married Dirk, who she found a little dense, not for love, but because he was handsome and would make a charming father. She saw her regal mother at their 300-guest wedding. Elinor thought of true love's spark and of freedom. They seemed at the edge of her world. Then her son had knocked his juice onto the newspaper and his picture and into both their laps and had begun to wail. Elinor had lifted her eyes to the horizon and felt her legs trample through the red, yellow, and blue plastic toys in the backyard, felt herself bound over the wooden fence, let loose a whinny, and stampede toward that intersection of earth and sky.

Elinor turned the van onto a dirt road that led to distant mountains, seven peaks that fit in her windshield's expanse. The afternoon sun stung her forehead. The van skittered across a section of washboard, and she turned the wheel to pull over. She corrected and drove on. She turned. She corrected. "What do you want?" she yelled. She stomped on the brake and skidded to a stop in the road's center. She clambered out of the van like it was on fire, a Nerf Ball bouncing behind her. She stumbled to the shoulder, hunched with hands on her knees, and scanned the rolling countryside. A raven cawed from a lone tree. She squinted at the peaks. She thought of Dirk, the kids, the heaps of laundry, the empty fridge, the kitchen floor with bits of food stuck to it, the uncooked meals, and Barb. Elinor rolled her head, and her neck went *crack, crack, crack*. She sighed with a fatigue she hadn't let herself feel for ten years.

"I've been under a spell." She gulped her words' reality.

The road ascended, switched back and forth, and grew less passable. Elinor steered over holes and rocks, up short, steep climbs, and down descents. Goldfish bounced off the seats. On one descent, a Snow White pop-up book gone missing for weeks, whizzed from the van's back, banged the console, and Elinor swerved. On another, a toy robot slapped her heel as she pressed the brake, and she yanked back her foot. The van screeched over a rock. A rhythmic *clank* started from under the hood, so she squeezed it into a slot between trees and turned it off. She climbed out and smelled pine, grass, and hot engine. The forest was silent but for the engine's clicks as it cooled. She faced the van, hands on her hips as if regarding her kids' messy bedrooms.

"Well, noble steed, I guess this is the end of the line."

Elinor arranged all her clothes and food on the middle seat, planning for one, maybe two nights. She realized she might not have enough food, so she munched on Goldfish from the floor, thinking she'd been meaning to clean the van anyway. She opened the van's back and took out three bottles of water. She put two on the seat and drank from the third. She slid out of her silk shirt and tugged on a khaki T-shirt that read *GAP*. Into her son's backpack, which was the shape of a purple dinosaur head, she packed a pair of socks, one bag of apples, all the food, and the water. She added gloves, her hairbrush, a hand mirror, and a hat. She rolled a second bag of apples up in the sleeping bag, but had to leave the third. She tightened and retied her sneakers' laces. She climbed into the passenger's seat and looked in the rearview mirror. She wiped a smudge of mascara with her pinkie.

"Damsel in distress." Her laugh was high-pitched.

She cinched her pink parka round her waist, loosened the straps on the pack, and eased it on. She left the van, toting her sleeping bag in her arms. She imagined the purple dinosaur on her back grinned and nodded.

Elinor followed the road for an hour then left it for a trail. The sun dipped below the mountain, and the shadows yawned. The forest was mute. Her steps crackled. Birds silenced at her approach. Squirrels and chipmunks scurried out of her way.

"This didn't happen to Snow White," she announced.

At dusk, the trail ended in a meadow. She remembered the checker's words, so found a spot on the edge and stomped flat an oval in the grass. As she rolled out her sleeping bag, she paused on all fours and dropped her head. She imagined her children crying. She knelt, crossed her arms on the sleeping bag, and rested her head there. She rocked back and forth till they stopped. She opened the backpack and pulled out her dinner of cheese and crackers.

The stars emerged. They seemed so close, Elinor reached out her tongue and imagined catching one, savored its sugary-minty light. But the star shot back into the sky, dragging her by the mouth, a shower of silver glitter across the sky. She saw herself as a speck in this vast world. Her ears realized every snap and rustle. An owl glided low overhead, perched nearby, and hooted. She pursed her lips and thought of bears and howling things. She hunched into her sleeping bag and pulled the drawstring tight around her face.

*

The first morning, Elinor brushed her hair and checked it in the mirror. Her reflection's eyes and nostrils flared.
"I don't trust you with my children." she said.

She wore the jeans and T-shirt she'd slept in. The pale grass was thick, and with her blonde hair, she felt camouflaged. The birds sang, and the sun was warm. Two deer strolled into the meadow's far side. Elinor imagined herself wearing a crown and bursting into song. She laughed, and the deer bounded away.

She tried resting her hands like a Buddhist and meditating.

Grasshoppers leapt around her. At first she startled at each, slapped at some, but she grew used to them. A butterfly winged above. Bees droned on asters and lulled her until she collapsed to the side, snoring.

Late afternoon, she woke just as a fox trotted into the meadow. It caught Elinor's scent, halted, studied her, and moved on. She thought how it was hunting for its family, how mice had scurried around her all day. She remembered that last book she'd read to her children. It was about a mouse and his friends the jay, the rabbit, the porcupine, and the fox. Elinor thought of how many mice this fox must carry home to her hungry kits. She wondered if this furry mother ever bent truth.

Elinor explored the meadow. Near where the deer had crossed, she found hoof prints. They were round and curved to a flared opening in the back. She traced their edges with her fingers.

*

The second morning, Elinor looked in the mirror before brushing her hair.

"My mother won't like you. You're nothing like me."

She attempted meditation again, resolved not to conk out. She crossed her legs and placed her hands on her knees, palms up. She closed her eyes and breathed deeply. She listened to the sounds nearby, then into the trees beyond, and imagined her exhalations reaching them. She discerned the rush of a stream. Crashing burst from of the forest, and she hunched low.

A gray horse with a silver mane and tail galloped into the meadow. A herd followed. They slowed to a trot and circled, a storm of sound and motion. Elinor counted eleven mares and two foals.

They stopped. One of the foals had a white stocking. One was plain with a white star on his forehead. Each stayed close to his mother. The gray horse walked to the side and turned, scanning the meadow, and she saw he was a stallion. She covered her mouth, afraid she might call out.

The stallion marched to the meadow's opposite edge. The other horses started grazing. He sniffed the ground, skirting the perimeter in reverse of Elinor's route. He paused at the spot where she'd touched the tracks. He pawed the dirt, lifted his head, and nickered. The mares' heads snapped up. They hustled together, and the foals squeezed into their center.

The stallion raised his nose with his ears pressed back, making a line from his neck to his nostrils. His head arched toward Elinor, and their eyes locked. She straightened.

"You're awake you're awake you're awake," she whispered.

The stallion strode forward till he towered over her. He flared his nostrils and breathed fast. Elinor sat still. He let out a deafening scream and reared. His legs circled, threatening blows. She had time only to recoil onto her palms, legs crossed in front, as his hooves thudded inches from her knees and his head dipped toward her. His breath was hot, his scent a slap, and he reared again, screaming.

Elinor wept but did not speak, did not even move.

He paced away, circled back, and stomped. Elinor's arms ached. Her face itched. The stallion strode to the herd and sent them before him, but he paused for a last look at her.

She pushed off her palms, arms numb, and dropped her hands to her thighs. They met wet where she'd peed her pants. Elinor had imagined, while under the stallion's glare, that she'd bawl when he left. She collapsed back, legs unfurling, and grinned.

*

The third morning was chilly. She brushed her hair and yearned for her children as if she were the north half of a magnet, and they were the south. If they were here, she would have been awake already, cooking breakfast, wiping noses, tying shoes, changing diapers, applying sunscreen, answering question after question after question. She sat up and peered in the mirror. She saw flared eyes.

"Oh good. You know, having it all is a myth." She flopped back down and felt like sleeping forever.

When the herd walked cautiously into the meadow, Elinor had constructed a tower of apples. She waved, and the stallion started. The herd echoed his movements like a dance. He lifted his head higher.

"Hey there." She covered her mouth.

He tossed his mane.

"Grumpy," Elinor said through her fingers.

The stallion yanked bites of grass, careful to pull his head right back up. His ears swiveled. He snorted and took five cautious steps toward her.

Elinor dropped her hand. "Bashful."

He continued toward her. Elinor resumed her cross-legged position. For strength, she imagined she was indeed Snow White, in that dress with the blue bodice, yellow skirt, and bouffant sleeves, even the headband with the bow, and if she needed to, she could sing this animal tame. "Whistle While You Work" came to her but evaporated in his approaching smell. He stretched his neck until his nose was at her knee. He snorted a blast of hot air and stepped closer. He ran his nose up her arm, never touching it, breathing loudly in, out, and stopped when he reached her ear. His breath rushed into it, and she winced. The stallion jerked back. Elinor inched her hand to her ear and rubbed. He stepped forward and sniffed it. His nose was velvet against her knuckles, her cheek. He snuffled her hair, tangling it. She giggled, and the stallion flinched.

She reached out, and he stepped to the side, watching. Elinor considered his white-edged eye and was sure this horse saw her truer than Barb, Dirk, her children, her mother, or anyone back home would see her, if they took the time to look.

He pawed out and struck her thigh. Elinor sucked in her breath at the bloom of pain. He discovered the tower of apples, lipped one off the top, and chewed loudly. Apple bits flew at her. The foals stepped forward, but he stomped, and they stopped. The stallion took another apple, toppling the structure, and trotted to the foals. He bit it in half and let it drop.

"Shining armor." A tear pearl traced Elinor's cheek.

The mares pressed forward and searched the ground. The stallion brought more apples. Elinor inhaled their sharp scent and bit her lip. She imagined herself building a little cabin before the snow fell. Something easy to keep clean.

*

On the fourth day, Elinor did not look in the mirror.

The horses arrived as she limped across the meadow's center. Only apples were left, and she was dizzy with hunger. She'd been fetching water at the stream down the draw. When she'd stopped to pee, she'd discovered a bruise on her thigh that matched the grape-juice stain on her new carpet back home. She'd shouted and cried over that stain, turning her children's eyes to moons. She pressed her shamed lips. In each hand, she held a refilled bottle with orbiting green and brown bits inside. A twig snared her hair. Her clothes were stiff and rank.

The horses galloped in a circle around her. They swished their tails and tossed their heads. She dropped the bottles and spun with them, arms up, laughing. On their haunches, their muscles were curved and lean. At their shoulders, they were bunched. Their legs reached out and back, out and back. The horses struck Elinor as lovelier than any art. They seemed to spin her, to lift her on the air. Her life's monotony fell away, and she felt possibility all around. She reached into the sky, spinning with her herd. This was the beginning. She would mend here and return to her life, redeemed by the trials and integrity of wild things. Be a brave, authentic mother. A foal squealed, a child's cry, and Elinor collapsed.

Everything stopped.

The mares looked at one another. The foals stayed still. A tail swished. The stallion took one step. Two. The mares stepped closer. When the stallion stood over Elinor, he nickered. She didn't respond. He nickered again and nudged her hard with his nose, pawed out and struck her other leg.

A metallic *thwoop-thwoop-thwoop* sliced the air.

The stallion yanked back. He scanned all around, but not up. He yelled, and the herd fled to the forest's edge, but he paused halfway and looked back.

Elinor's legs would not support her as she tried to rise, and she fell to all fours. She saw the machine in her mind's eye, and her love for her children clamped around her. She thought of the women in the Alco and grew appalled at feeling thankfulness.

"Mommy's adventure is over." Her words were swallowed by the din.

The helicopter grew deafening and skimmed the pines. The meadow's grass swirled. The trees swayed in a berserk dance. The stallion lunged to the side and galloped into them. His silver tail was the last of him she saw. Elinor closed her eyes to seal its glimmer and arc in her memory, would not look at her reflection in the machine's chrome belly.

JESSICA SMITH

A STAR MEANS QUIET

She felt a sick settling in her bones. It was July—the hottest month—and she imagined her bones were on strike.

"It's the heat," she told her boyfriend. "It could kill a girl."

Neither said what they were really thinking: it was back. The lymphoma, it had hibernated, turned restless circles in her marrow for years, snuffled out of deep sleep for one more go.

A month later her doctor confirmed it. He paced in front of the X-rays on the wall, chewed at the tip of his glasses. Nodded once.

"Yes," he said, and she collapsed against her boyfriend's shoulder.

She didn't cry, just rested there and tried to pull strength from inside her—deep parts, places and reserves she never used. She started to make lists in her head.

Her bathrobe, she'd need that. The good slippers, too. The pink ones. A new laptop. The throw her grandmother knitted before she died. That lucky statue of the CN Tower.

The doctor said he'd give them some time and left the room.

"I need a pen and paper," she told her boyfriend. She turned herself away from his shoulder and leaned back to look him in the eye. She knew he would understand the lists, the way she needed to tuck words into neat columns. Control. It was the only thing she had now—control over the small things. A clean piece of paper, white with possibility and purpose. Short words written in black ink. Incomplete sentences. Fragments of thought.

The first time she had cancer she papered her room with lists. She and her boyfriend had spent long hours making them, tacking them up with staples or clips or tape.

Places We Want to Go When I'm Better
Best Rib Joints in Arizona
Sassy Words

People Who Made Fun of Us in Middle School
Best Slow Songs
Famous People (Dead) We Want to Meet

Each list had rows and rows of information—things about her, things about him—that she was afraid would be lost if she died. Things that would go with her, swallowed down with her last breath.

"Pen," she said again, "and paper."

He wasn't listening. Instead, he was staring off toward the door—his eyes focused on the small window near the top. He stared into the corridor—all those yellow neon lights—and didn't even notice when she moved off his lap and to the corner where she picked up her coat, her purse, his briefcase.

*

She got a room in the Green Wing and her name spelled out in glitter on a plaque on the door. The nurses in the Green Wing all wore pins shaped liked unicorns and rainbows. Even the men wore them.

"Oh, you must hate that," she told her favorite nurse, Nurse Gary.

"So hate it," he said.

The Green Wing was famous. The nurses used Shakespearian verse when they delivered the evening meals. There were whole days when members of the staff spoke only in quotes from their favorite movies. These nurses came to the unit specially trained. There was a waiting list to be employed in the Green Wing. It took Gary three and a half years to get a call back.

"It was worse than an audition," he said. "I had to know the stages of AIDS and Iago's soliloquy from *Othello*."

And because of those things—those eclectic touches—this time it wasn't so bad. Not like the first time, when she was in that hospital in Phoenix. Her wing there had been ruled by older nurses, the type who wore the thickest orthopedic shoes. Those women smelled like death—like a natural gas leak and oil from a deep fryer—which didn't inspire much confidence. They talked about Jesus and frowned when she watched HBO.

In Phoenix, the food was gray. The walls were puce. Her boyfriend had to sleep on the bathroom floor because her room was small—too small for a cot or a recliner or even a sleeping bag.

But here, in the Green Wing, things were different. Even the bathroom procedure with the toilets that measured her bowel movements then held them there floating in wait—which she hated more than anything—seemed somehow less horrifying. In the Green Wing, there were thousands of names for bowel movements—the big BMs.

"Come to take note of your Big Muddies," the nurses would say. Or Blond Marsupials or Blazing Muffins or Bowling Marxists.

The first time this happened, it had been confusing. It was Gary who came in, with a clipboard and a backward hat.

"Time to talk Blustery Milwaukees," he said. When she looked confused, he wheeled a chair around to the side of her bed, sat, and patted her hand. "In this wing," he said, "the term *bowel movement* is for sissies."

The ever-changing terminology gave her something to look forward to. She catalogued her favorites, listed them in a special notebook. She put stars next to the ones Gary came up with.

Still, even though things were better in the Green Wing, it was hard adjusting again to hospital life, and she tried to rebel as much as she could. The first week she insisted on eating only green food. It was her one bargaining chip, and she wouldn't have it for long. Already she could feel her stomach rolling over on itself, making new rules for what was digestible and what was not.

"Stop being a pain," her boyfriend told her when she made neat piles of peas and beans and asparagus and zucchini. "They're just trying to help, and you fight them all the way."

"I better fight something," she said and scooped forkfuls of green into her mouth. She thumped her forearm. "Because I sure didn't do a good job fighting this."

*

Week four, her boyfriend showed up unshaven and with a fashion magazine under his arm. "Here," he said, and slumped in the corner chair, the one that doubled as his sometimes-bed.

She paged through and examined the new totes and clutches of the season.

"You know what word I hate?" she asked. "*Blouse*. I hate the word blouse. People tell you it's fun to say, but it's not."

"What people say that?" he asked.

She waved her hand at the magazine. "Just people."

His face was grim under the new crop of stubble. He looked like a judge or a coroner. He'd never been more handsome.

He shifted in his seat. "I can't do this anymore," he said.

She thought he meant the commute. "It's bad," she agreed. "You don't need to come every day. Rush hour is awful."

"No," he said. "Not the commute. This. Everything. I just don't want to do it anymore. Not again."

She thought of the first time. The hospital in Phoenix. There, when she fell asleep and a meal came, he would spell things in her vegetables. Messages. LUV ALWAYS in her wax beans. Back then, he always came clean-shaven and wearing a suit. He came with gifts: videos, books, smuggled cupcakes. His posture had been excellent. Now, though, he was half a body, a man cut in two, always walking as though he were as segmented as a worm.

They didn't argue or yell. There was no crying, no hysterics.

"I found an apartment," he said. "I don't have time for this. I've got a pretty full winter."

Pretty full. He didn't even have the courtesy to say "full." Straight full. Like his calendar was completely blocked off and solid. But no. She got a qualifier. Pretty full—like full, except for those relaxing weekend jags to Hilton Head he had planned.

She narrowed her eyes and picked up the magazine again. She knew he expected her to say something. He needed her to finalize it, to bring everything to a close. He was fond of neatly-wrapped packages. She refused to indulge him. With her index finger, she traced the hip—glowing, peachy, healthy—of the girl in a liquor ad.

Gary was in fifteen minutes later. "Bright Mojo time," he said.

He bent over her IV and assessed her tubing. "You'll need a new one soon." He tapped the place where it entered her arm, the place that was irritated and red and covered with tape.

She shrugged and didn't lift her eyes. She was thinking of the Christmas before, the $1,000 she spent buying her boyfriend new ski equipment for the trip to Vail they wanted to take but never did.

"Was that brother or boyfriend?" Gary asked.

She frowned at the model who floated in a pool and wore a leopard print bikini. "Boyfriend," she said.

"Can I be rude?"

She looked up for the first time.

"It's just that he seems like he's kind of a dullard," Gary said and then shrugged.

"He broke up with me," she said. "I was talking about blouses."

"Awful word," Gary said and crossed his eyes, pretended to choke himself.

"He already has a new apartment," she said. "You can't find one overnight in this town. He must've started looking as soon as I came here."

Gary crossed the room and took her hand in his, pressed the backside to his lips for a long time. He finally broke away and headed toward her bathroom. "I'm just going to measure your urine levels," he said, "and then I'll let you be."

When he left, he turned the lights out and she sat in the dark and told herself enough lies to make it through the night. She was going to be fine. Her boyfriend was coming back.

*

She got a star on her door. A star meant *Quiet*. A star meant *Terminal*. A star meant, *Ssssh, I'm dying*.

She hadn't had a visitor in six weeks. Her boyfriend—her *ex-boyfriend*—had been serious about the breakup. At the beginning she'd thought maybe it was a phase, some sort of grieving process he needed to attend to on his own, and that maybe he was coming to grips with love and mortality.

But he'd proven himself determined. Not a word. No letters, no phone calls. He severed her as easily as if she were an extra appendage, a third limb that had never really had a purpose, just an aesthetic interest.

She didn't really miss him. The staff made sure to fill the suddenly large space he used to occupy with extra balloons and giant cards featuring talking squirrels. They lingered longer, tested out new stand-up, read from the Arts & Leisure section of the newspaper.

Gary and the other nurses memorized lines from her favorite movies and performed long scenes when she was too tired to watch TV. Instead of infomercials at three a.m., she fell asleep to a live version of *Last of the Mohicans* or *Footloose*.

When Gary woke her up from her afternoon nap on the anniversary of her fourth month in the Green Wing, someone else was in the room.

"Who's that?" she asked Gary, who was stretched out on the bed next to her, rubbing the crown of her head with tented fingers.

"A visitor," he said. "Are you feeling up to it?"

She tried to focus. Her eyes had gotten worse over the last few days. They had almost completely stopped obeying when she tried to get them to concentrate on a spot or person for longer than two seconds. It felt like they were loose and spinning farther and farther away from their axes, spinning off into the black hole that was stretching through her head.

"Sure," she said, even though she was less than so.

"Alright then." Gary lifted himself off the edge of her bed. "This is Caroline, and she's from our Wishing Well department."

"Okay," she said.

"It's a division of the Green Wing," he explained. "It specializes in last wishes and requests." When he said the phrase *last wishes* his voice dipped through the octaves and skimmed the lowest so it was almost a whisper, almost like he'd never said it at all.

"You understand?" he asked.

313

She nodded.

"Hold the call button in your hand for me, will you?" he asked and placed the buzzer in her palm. "You use it if you need me, okay? For anything at all."

She nodded again. Already she could feel her eyelids drooping. She felt warm and dark like mold. She wanted to sink back into her bed sheets and go to sleep, a place where she didn't have to fight to keep things in focus.

But instead this lady—this Caroline—came and sat in the divot where Gary had been only a minute before. She talked. She said the hospital had special funds, funds for patients who were terminally ill and had less than a year to live.

"We do things," Caroline said. "Lots of things. If you wanted to eat fried bologna while straddling the foot of the Sphinx, we could do it. If you wanted the world's biggest goldfish pond built in your honor, we would find a home for it."

She understood what she was being told. There needed to be a plan. Something that the hospital could do. A going away party, of sorts. Something they could point to and say, *See? See? She didn't die alone, didn't die without having had a chance to touch her dreams.* It must have lightened the weight on their collective conscience.

"You should think of some things," Caroline said, rising and straightening the hem of her skirt. "Take a few days and think it over."

A few days. They were giving her a few days to figure out how to leave this life without regret or want. Somehow the hospital administration thought a trip to Egypt and a good sandwich could erase the last years where her body tried to disown itself. They thought one last wish could heal the hurt of an empty room and no visitors, the fact that her whole family was gone, her boyfriend too, and that she might as well have died the first time around rather than delay the inevitable.

"New England," she said quickly, before Caroline left the room and it sealed back in—just green walls and a buzzing television set. "Vermont, probably."

314

"You already know?" Caroline asked.

"I saw it on TV once," she said. "Some ballet company did a performance, kicking through the leaves in their ballet slippers. I've always wondered what it felt like to dance like that. I always wanted to take ballet, but my mom got sick before I was old enough."

Caroline flipped open a small notebook and made some notations. "And what about some company?" she asked. "Is there anyone we can contact? Anyone you want to take with you?"

She thought about her ex-boyfriend, who was probably living in some downtown apartment and going to work and to movies and the theatre like he didn't even remember her, the girl he'd left limp and white under hospital linens.

She could ask for him. She could ask for her cousin who lived in Utah. Besides them, there was no one except a ninety year-old grandmother in a nursing home in New York.

"Gary," she said and pressed the buzzer. "I want Gary."

*

When she told him her dying wish was to go to Vermont with him and dance in the leaves, Gary looked confused and a little nervous.

"Sweetheart," he said and stroked the lobe of her ear, "we aren't supposed to fraternize with patients. I love you, and you know it, but not *that* way. I lean more toward the male persuasion."

"Who better to take dancing?" she asked. "Besides, this isn't fraternizing. This is just a long *au revoir.*"

He leaned in to adjust the tangle of her IV. "Alright then. I'll take off."

And so there was a helicopter flight. They removed her IVs and wrapped her in extra blankets—it seemed she was always cold now—and strapped her down to a stiff gurney in the back of the helicopter.

Gary showed up in a leather jacket and a beret. "I'm ready to jet-set," he said and bent to say hello. He traced the line of her chin all the way up and around, past her ears, up to the top of her head. "You

315

look beautiful."

She knew she didn't. The Green Wing was suspiciously absent of mirrors, but while they were readying her for flight, having her stand on legs that shook like tiny picks of wood, delicate matchsticks, she caught sight of herself in a mirror behind the nurse's station. Her blue eyes were sunk deep in her face and her skin shone gray and oily under halogen light. Her hair had fallen out and grown back already, and the crown of her head looked like a threshed field. Her once-red hair had come back in blond-brown clumps.

"Oh," she'd said when she saw herself in the mirror. It was the only word, only sound she felt capable of.

The nurses moved quick and sure, blocking her view of the mirror and smoothing their hands down her shoulders and back.

"It's always worse in your head than it really is," one nurse said. "Mirrors can be tricky things."

But now in the helicopter things didn't seem so bad. The fall air felt thick and beautiful against the tufts of new hair. And Gary was holding her hand, looking utterly ridiculous in his beret and bomber coat. Already this was better than any string of moments she'd had with the ex-boyfriend.

When the helicopter coughed to life, rose, and hovered above the hospital, she got her first look at how massive the compound really was. Different wings stretched out like never-ending limbs from the center round, making it look like an octopus or a spider that had been crushed under someone's heel.

When the helicopter tipped and swung left for a turn, she looked down, considered all the limbs and wings and rooms, and could almost feel millions of eyes turning toward windows as they heard the thrush of propellers. They must have been wondering if someone was lucky enough to be getting their escape, finally scaling the walls and lifting like a star or some other bright thing into the sky and flying far, far away from there.

*

316

They landed in a field somewhere in northern Vermont, on the edge of a tree farmer's land.

"I always thought tree farms were myths," Gary said. He shook his head and folded his hands into the pockets of his jacket. "You know, like leprechauns or something."

The other on-duty nurses rolled her to the edge of the helicopter, then lifted her into a wheelchair. Gary reached up and held the wheels and brought her down safely.

After she was on the ground the pilot and the other nurses backed away, settled down into the helicopter, opened lunchboxes. "Take your time," they said. "Just come back whenever you're done."

She looked up at Gary. He was looking down at her and adjusting his beret.

"Now what?" he asked.

*

They toured the property for an hour. Gary often had to stop pushing to go up ahead and drag stones or fallen branches out of the way. She slept on and off, and it was easy. Easier than usual. She imagined it was something in the way sunlight hit her face in patches, always moving.

When she woke the last time, in the middle of a clearing dotted with sugar maples and poplars, Gary was standing a ways off, partly obscured by a birch that was peeling and shedding twists of bark as if they were great curls of soap. Gary held the trunk with one hand, struggled to force his feet into tights, thick and white.

Underneath her covers she could feel something new. A foreign attachment. Something not quite hospital regulation. She pulled back her blankets and sheets and found her green scrubs and dressing gown gone. Green had been replaced with pink and white. A tulle skirt was tucked around her waist, and her feet came to graceful points in a pair of ballet slippers.

"You did all this?" she asked.

With one last powerful stretch, Gary pulled the tops of the

leggings up around his hips before turning toward her. He pretended to slump, exhausted, against the tree. "I haven't had to wear tights since my high school did *Macbeth*."

"I didn't wake up when you were dressing me?" she asked.

He shook his head. "Your body's getting used to going under."

That should've scared her, those words, but she just sank back into the chair and rearranged the tulle. She couldn't stop touching the fabric. She pushed against the armrests of the chair but couldn't lift herself. Her bones were dissolving. They were pocking with pores and sucking at the rest of her, hungry as quicksand.

"How do we do this?" she asked. "Is there protocol? Do we have to take photographs as proof I got my wish?"

"Only if you want to," he said and knelt in front of her wheelchair. He pushed the rest of her coverings aside. "I'm going to lift you up now, okay?"

She nodded then felt the whole world tip as Gary raised her from the chair.

"If you feel sick in any way, you let me know," he said and balanced her on his hip. "Anything. Runny nose or headache. I don't have anything out here. It's all back at the helicopter."

She nodded and pushed her head into the leather of his jacket. It was warm from sun and smelled like man, like Gary: campfires and dry red wine.

"You smell good," she said. She felt her feet touch ground. The pointed shoes scraped against soil and rock. For the first time in months she was standing on something other than cold tile whose chill leaked through slipper bottoms and thick socks. It felt divine.

Gary bent and pushed the heels of her feet together, turned her toes outward. Then her arms and hands. "Shoulders up," he said and brought her hands together near her waist. "This is First Position. This is where we start."

"You took ballet?" she asked. "You really studied?"

Slowly, he drew his arms away from her sides and tested to see if her balance was true. "I was the Arabesque King in high school," he said. "I wasn't very popular."

Without his arms to brace her, her body trembled under the weight of its new responsibility to keep her straight and tall. But it did.

He crossed to stand behind her and fitted their bodies together. "Follow me now," he said. He picked her arms up and threaded their fingers together. "Just move with me."

And they started to move. Her limbs seemed new and somehow longer as they followed his. And then the legs. She couldn't believe what her body was letting itself do. Her knees were working and bending. Her ankles felt airy, like springs. She was suddenly well-oiled and renewed. Leaves were flying everywhere, kicked up by their toes, toes that scuffed through the heavy piles that smelled of wood and moss.

She thought for a second of her ex-boyfriend and what he was doing now. She wondered if he called the hospital—maybe every other week or so—just to check, just to see if she were still alive. She wondered how the nurses' answer felt. Yes. Yes, she's still alive. Still in the small room with the yellow star out front, the one that means *Sssh* and *Quiet* and *I'm dying*. He must feel sad and sorry for her, but not enough to come back.

She did not miss him—not really. She missed small things like Sunday mornings and thick newspapers, doing crosswords together. She always figured out the tough clues, the answers like *loquacious* or *adenoids* or *Gary Marshall*. Her boyfriend made her a medal once—a gold star he cut from construction paper after outlining its points with a cookie cutter. He hung it on their bedroom door. *World's Brightest Crossword Star* it said. It stayed there for at least a year and a half before she took it down. She was hosting a baby shower for a girl from work, and she was afraid of being tacky. Things went away. Throw pillows and decorative lamps. The picture of a rhinoceros that hung in the bathroom. And the star. She'd tucked it underneath the pile of extra towels in their linen closet and forgotten it.

He might have found it when packing his things, sifting through closet after closet and trying to define his versus hers. Maybe he found the star, traced its points, thought how smart and good she used to be before her body turned on itself. Maybe he packed it and took it to his new place. Maybe he used it as a bookmark. Maybe he would find it again after he called the hospital for the last time and heard the answer *no*.

"Doing good," Gary said. He put his hands on her hips and lifted so that her waist rested high above his shoulders. His lips pressed against her stomach. "Arms out," he said, and she put her arms out. He spun her then. Spun her in a sweeping arc so that the trees and sky and grass blurred.

"What am I supposed to do?" she asked. Her arms were cumbersome. They didn't look right. They didn't feel right. The wind blew thick across her body, all the newly exposed flesh.

Gary eased her down slowly. He kissed her chin, her lips, her nose, her temple on the way down. "You've never been more beautiful than you are right now," he said.

"I'm not right," she said, even though he was moving her again, repositioning her.

"Second Position," he was saying. "This time we'll start here."

"I'm not right," she repeated. "Everything feels syrupy. The air is syrup."

The hands on her arms and legs stopped moving. They tightened where they lay.

"It's making me hungry," she said. "I want breakfast. I want pancakes."

The world was moving slowly now. Slower than ever before. Even her voice sounded old fashioned in her ears. Like maybe she was hearing a tape of herself—filled with static and other interference— that was being played underwater. She didn't understand why her ears couldn't filter everything out. Her eyes, too. Nothing seemed right.

"I'm hungry," she said. She reached her hand out and it seemed to stretch forever. She touched the flounce of her skirt and the pink ribbon that hung around her waist. "I'm tired."

And then she was falling. Her body lurched forward, but Gary was there and holding her and rocking her and telling her to stay awake.

"Breakfast," she said.

Gary nodded and pulled her closer to his chest as she sagged, became fluid and unstable in his arms.

"Pancakes with maple syrup?" he asked.

She could feel his pace quicken, sensed it somewhere in the middle of her head where her equilibrium was still hard at work while things around it failed, burned out, burned up. She was sure of only two things: she wanted pancakes, and she was upright.

"Hang on," he said. His voice was close, so close it could've been in her head. "Hang on, and we'll get some."

And he was running then, carrying them both so fast toward the helicopter that was miles away. His leather jacket was cool on her cheek, and when she tried to open her eyes so she could look at him and say *no* and *don't hurry* all she could see was the sun through the leaves. The sky was red and gold, the trees were red and gold. And when she closed her eyes again it was the leaves she saw against the black of her eyelids. A great crush of leaves and leaves and leaves, burning yellow stars into the dark of her head, into all that was left.

SUZANNAH WINDSOR

IN KOOLIKARI

The airport is one room only, and filled with a dozen or so locals returning from more exciting places. Adelaide or Melbourne, places next to the sea. Places I haven't seen, except to pass through them on the way to Koolikari.

My mother, in the midst of this desert, is like a Canadian bird who's taken the wrong migratory path. Her skin is pale with winter, my arms brown against hers. At first we embrace tentatively with nervous laughs, then firmly. Her breath is stale like the inside of an old car. Between her tongue and cheek, peppermint gum shriveled hard as a raisin.

"There was nothing at all to see in the last flight," she says. "Nothing but dead-looking trees."

"You've made it then. You must be so tired."

"Kevin's not with you?" She cranes her neck for emphasis, like she could possibly have missed him in a half-empty room.

On Saturdays, Kevin speaks at three different churches in surrounding towns. Ghost towns, barely dots on the map, remarkable only for their wheat silos jutting out of the barren landscape. A few crumbling homesteads where cattle farmers still manage to survive without air conditioning. Places they can't get a preacher to live. "He's doing the rounds. He'll be back tonight."

Two days of travelling have made my mother an invalid. She slips the strap of her handbag off her shoulder so I can carry it for her, and we step out the doors into the parking lot—a field of sunburnt grass, much like the runway. Hot wind blasts us as we wait for the man with the little luggage cart to drive across the dirt. My mother wipes the back of her neck and looks at the sweat on her fingers like she's drawn blood. I've gotten used to the sweat of the heat, and now regard only the burn, deep in my skin.

Her suitcase is easy to spot, wrapped with orange tape which says, "oversized." I haul it off the cart with both arms. "What, you got a body in here?"

"Essentials," she says.

"Like?"

"Stuff I need." She looks me up and down. "Stuff *you* need."

My shorts and t-shirt are secondhand from the church charity box. My hair is too long and uneven at the back. It hasn't been cut in the year-and-a-half since Kevin and I left Toronto, not because there isn't a hairdresser, but because I can't afford to pay one. I volunteer to teach music at the Koolikari area school—show kids how to tap spoons and pat rhythms on the bottom of tin cans—but there's no funding for nonessential subjects, for nonessential teachers.

I appreciate plain soap and water now.

*

My mother doesn't understand why there are no savages. We drive through the centre of town toward the manse, and she is confused—I daresay, disappointed—that the people walking up and down the main street don't wear loin cloths or carry spears.

"I've told you what it's like in my letters."

"But there's no internet."

"There's dial-up."

"That's primitive, darling. And you have to go to the library to use it."

I don't mention that Kevin declined the church's offer to buy us a laptop. *I want to experience life free of distractions,* he says. He writes all of his sermons using dusty books in the church office. He prays in the backyard at high sun with no hat, as if to build endurance. I don't play or write my music while he's in the house, anymore.

"I don't understand why you're here at all. This doesn't seem like the kind of place that needs missionaries. Everyone here speaks English. Can't they just read a Bible for themselves? I thought you were *supposed* to be missionaries."

"We are, sort of."

"But not like Greta."

Greta is the only missionary my mother has ever known. She lives in the Congo and speaks Swahili. Sends Christmas postcard pictures of herself hugging smiling African children. "Not exactly like Greta. But the churches needed a Pastor, and Kevin needed to get his feet wet."

She turns her head to the side window, to the twisted gum trees with bare trunks. "Aside from your wedding, I don't think I've stepped foot in a church since your father's funeral."

I remember only pieces: the pew hard beneath me, hard as a coffin; a pink dress fanned over my knees; the pastor standing behind the lectern; my mother's hand entwined in the back of my hair, holding tightly like I'm a handful of dust—like if she loosens her grip, she might accidentally blow me away.

*

There is no meat in the freezer, and no money left in my wallet.

"We'll have lamb tomorrow," I promise. Someone is sure to give Kevin a leg tonight. He never comes home empty-handed on Saturdays, especially now that people are suspicious of our circumstances.

"Shouldn't we wait for Kevin?" she asks, as I fill our mismatched plates. She might as well have said, "What kind of missionary doesn't wait for her husband at dinner time?"

But Kevin will be too late for us to wait. He'll have to drive slowly through the scrublands at dusk when the roos come out. He won't be home until I'm in bed, eyes sore from reading, feet sticking out the from under the sheets to keep cool. He'll kiss me on the forehead, ask me if I'm feeling okay, and say he's tuckered.

We eat fried rice, vegetables, and canned pineapple for dinner. Just the two of us, like it was for so many years. The kitchen fan is on and the room is dim because we keep the blinds mostly shut until the sun falls out of the sky.

I apologize again for the simpleness of the meal, knowing I should have planned better. My mother looks into her carrots and rice and says, "I should be watching my weight, anyway." She's sparing me the embarrassment of explaining why there's no meat, which makes me even more uncomfortable because I know she's worried.

I wash the dishes, she dries. Her silence, her judgement, builds inside my stomach. I spill out words of fortitude—Kevin's, mine, the locals—in the face of adversity, as if we are warriors. How we brave rainwater tanks and water shortages; spiders the size of my hand; places so hot, people live in underground houses; a lake so dry, it only fills up a few times a century. But my mother knows me too well. She shivers as she stuffs the end of a tea towel inside a drinking glass.

After dinner, she pulls a dress out of her suitcase and pins it to my shoulders. Blue, knee-length, deep neckline, belted waist. "I thought you could dress it up with a shawl or dress it down with a jean jacket," she says, and shrugs. She tosses the dress onto my shoulder, and hands me a clear plastic bag filled with mascara, lipstick, eye shadow, creams, sprays, conditioners. "Super-Mart had a sale. They were practically free."

I think of the plain clothes I usually wear to church. Of the ceiling fans whirring over my head at the piano, the back of my thighs wet against the bench. Of flies burrowing into my nose. Of trying to play hymns on keys that stick when they're swollen with heat. "Thank you," I say, and wonder where I will store makeup in our bathroom, which has no cabinet, and how I will keep it all from melting.

*

This is the height of Saturday night entertainment in Koolikari: in the centre of town, shop fronts blocking out the dipping sun, we sit on the concrete bench near the fountain. Ice cream cones from *Shirley's* streaming down our hands faster than we can lick them. When Kevin is away, I sometimes come here by myself to watch the recycled fountain water. Out and down and in and back it goes, round and round.

"One day, before you leave, we'll drive to the coast," I say. Kevin will take a day off work, and we'll travel the two hours it takes to get there. Maybe we'll even stay overnight at one of the camping grounds so we can wake to the fresh sea air.

"So, I've been meaning to tell you," my mother says. Her feigned nonchalance makes it painfully clear that she hasn't been *meaning* to tell me—she's been waiting for the right *time* to tell me. "There was a teaching job in the newspaper last week. One of those fancy private schools you were looking at when you first graduated."

"Music?"

"Full-time, permanent."

She suddenly looks uncomfortable. Like a fire ant has made its way into her shorts and she's too polite to scratch. "What's wrong?"

"When are you coming home?" she asks. It's a hopeful question, but her words sound as weak as a child asking when her dead father will live again.

"I don't know. It depends on a lot of things."

She passes me her ice cream to hold, digs in her purse. Hands me the itinerary for her return to Toronto two weeks from now. "My travel agent said you could still get on the same flights, at least as far as Vancouver. You could be home for summer and start working this September." There is no mention of Kevin.

"Mom."

"I never wanted this for you. This isn't the way your life was supposed to be."

She doesn't understand that I never expected my life to turn out this way, either. Now, those expectations are little better than parched dreams, bound by a waiting place, a place of suffering, of self-denial. A place where ghosts are made, a place no one can ever quite belong. I don't belong in Koolikari, but I can't belong in my former life, either. I know too much, now. This sunburn runs too deep.

"You're so young. You should be picking out curtains for your new home and having dinner parties and decorating a nursery. That's what people do when they get married. Not this." She motions from my head to my feet. "Not this"—as if I have grown up to be a stripper instead of a pastor's wife.

I wonder if it's the right time to tell her that, soon, there will be a nursery. That there's a little dust-baby, ten weeks old, growing inside my belly. That, like her, I'm going to be a mother. That I often sit alone at noon in my darkened kitchen and decide what the baby might be: a pianist, a composer, a teacher, a dreamer. And any expectations I have will be crushed one day, too, when that baby becomes somebody different. Someone I would, or could, never have become myself.

Dallas Woodburn

Three Sundays at the Grove

When Deepti was born in San Francisco in the summer of 1989, her parents were living in a tiny apartment above an Indian restaurant called "The Golden Sari" and they were in their Hindi phase. Deepti often wondered whether the Indian restaurant and the samosas her mother craved during pregnancy influenced their sudden conversion to Hinduism. It would make sense, knowing her mother. She judged a culture based on one thing: its food. Once she found a type of cuisine she liked, she immediately embraced all aspects of that culture. Over the years she had acquired a wide mishmash of cultural affectations to match her ever-growing palate, trying on religions and customs, discarding some aspects while keeping others, as if the world were an immense shopping mall waiting to expand her cultural wardrobe. Deepti wondered, if her parents had lived above an Italian restaurant instead of "The Golden Sari," would they have had a Catholic phase? Would Deepti instead be named Mary or Teresa or Anne?

Regardless, that was twenty-one years ago and the Hindi phase was long gone—as was her father. Still, Deepti was left with two ever-constant reminders: her vegetarianism and her name, Charusheela Deepti, which roughly translates to "beautiful jewel full of light" in Hindi. These two things, combined with her honey-freckled skin, almond eyes, and unruly wiry curls, made her into what a classmate in high school once called a "character." It was meant as a compliment, Deepti thought; this was America, after all, where individuality is praised and prized. Still, Deepti often felt she was a part of many groups—part Asian, part black, part Hindi—and yet not *really* a part of any group. She was a one-woman species. Unclassifiable.

*

"So what is it that makes someone an American?" the T.A. said. She stood close to the whiteboard, marker in hand, ready to write down whatever morsels of insight her students offered. No hands raised.

Deepti slouched in her chair, pulling down the hood of her sweatshirt.

"I don't think there are specific traits that make someone an American," said a boy in the front row. "I mean, we don't even all speak the same language anymore. Did you know the government is printing ballots in Spanish now?"

"Why's that a bad thing?" another boy put in. Deepti lifted her head at the passion in his tone. "That's what makes America great—there are so many different cultures and people living side-by-side, neighborhood-by-neighborhood, in the same country. People still remember where they came from. They keep alive the traditions and cultures and languages of their homelands, but they also forge a new life in America. It's like when you move away from home—you don't need Mom and Dad anymore, but that doesn't mean you forget about their existence, does it?"

The room was silent save for the rapid squeaking of the TA.'s marker on the whiteboard. After a moment she turned around, straightening her glasses. "Thank you for that, Greg," she said, addressing the second boy, who was now doodling on the cover of his notebook. Greg—that was his name, Deepti remembered now, he had sat next to her the first day of class and had leant her a pen. "So, Greg," the T.A. continued, "If I may ask, where is your family from?" Greg hesitated, his cheeks slightly flushed. He had short-cropped blonde hair and sunglasses perched atop his head. He took them off, then slid them back on again. "Actually, I'm not exactly sure," he said.

"My ancestors came here before the Revolutionary War. We don't know where they lived before then. Maybe England, Scotland—someplace like that."

It took Deepti a moment to digest his words. Since *before the*

Revolutionary War? Imagine possessing such a sure foothold on American identity, having a sense of belonging so strong nobody could take it away. Not pieces of different cultures, shadows of ancestors brought to light in your name, your complexion, the shape of your eyes. Rather, wholeness.

"Does that mean you're not American, then?" a corn-rowed guy put in. "You just said that being American is having a sense of where you came from."

"Yeah," Deepti said. "He's American." It wasn't until twenty-six pairs of eyes turned to look at her that she realized she had spoken it out loud. Very loudly.

She cleared her throat. "Of course he's American. Just because you can't pinpoint your past doesn't mean it doesn't exist."

Greg smiled at her, and there was a warmth in his eyes that caught Deepti off guard—as if when he looked at her he didn't just see her honey-freckled skin, or kinky hair, or dark almond eyes, but rather all of her, together. A person. Whole.

*

For their first date, they went to The Grove, an outdoor shopping mall in West Hollywood. Deepti thought of it as "Disneyland for Grown-Ups"—rich with fountains, palm trees, and towering storefronts strung with white lights like gigantic gleaming pearl necklaces. There was even a trolley cavorting back and forth down the middle of the street. Deepti's ex-boyfriend, Thun, the son of a wealthy Vietnamese rice merchant, used to take her here after they had an argument. He would ask her to try on clothes and, as an apology, would go back later and buy them for her. At first it made Deepti feel cared for, but gradually the shopping excursions became more frequent, and before long wearing the clothes Thun bought made Deepti feel sick inside. That was seven months ago. Now, Thun was likely buying clothes for some other girl. Probably an Asian girl. He'd told Deepti once, "You're the only non-Asian girl I've ever dated."

"But I *am* Asian," she'd said. "You met my grandparents, Thun. I'm half-Chinese."

"Well, sure, you're *technically* Asian." He'd actually rolled his eyes. "But look at you. You're not *really* Asian. Not Asian-Asian. You know what I mean."

Deepti said no, she didn't know what he meant, and Thun said never mind, and she said what exactly were you implying, and he said just let it go dammit, and she said don't yell at me, you don't have to yell, and he'd shown up at her apartment the next day with bulging shopping bags. But his comment stuck with her, buzzing at the collar of her shirt. Stinging her.

The more she thought about it, the more Deepti hated The Grove. But Greg had suggested it. "They have a great farmer's market here," he said.

"Let's go," Deepti said. Greg took her hand and led the way, only a half-beat away from skipping. He was like a child—excited about the smallest, most everyday things. They wove their way through the tented stalls, zig-zagged past the booths of bulging pumpkins and squashes, sizzling meat with peppers and onions, tubs of live lobsters, cloves of garlic hanging from the rafters alongside ribbon-tied bunches of dried flowers. People pushed children in strollers, their shopping bags swaying, jostling against each other in a pleasant Sunday-afternoon way. Greg bought Bing cherries, a loaf of cinnamon-cranberry bread, and two thick bars of dark chocolate.

Then, "I'm starving!" he declared.

They found a stall selling cheap Chinese food—the American version, of course, with greasy noodles and deep-fried orange chicken that Deepti could not eat. She ordered the mixed vegetables instead, which were mundanely delicious. Deepti only ate "authentic" Chinese food when she visited her maternal grandparents in Oregon, so this was the type of Chinese food she was used to, the watered-down Americanized version she simultaneously recognized for its illegitimacy and loved for the same reason. And, while her own mother had preferred ordering from Panda Express to cooking recipes passed down through the family for generations, at least she had taught Deepti the correct way to use chopsticks. Greg was impressed.

"I'm terrible at using those," he said, gesturing with his plastic fork at the chow mein dangling off Deepti's chopsticks.

"It's not that hard," Deepti said. "Plus, I've been using them all my life. My mom's Chinese. Her parents came to America when she was just a baby."

"Really? That's cool."

Greg didn't ask for further details about her ancestry, but she told him anyway: "Yeah, and my dad's black. They met at Berkeley, in the '60s. You know—civil rights, free love and all that."

"Wow." Greg nodded, his eyebrows slightly furrowed as if he wasn't sure what to say. And what should he say? What did Deepti expect him, expect anyone, to say? The silence stretched, unbearable. Deepti felt a pit open up in her stomach, the greasy noodles sliding down her throat to gnawing emptiness.

"So you, do you speak any Chinese?" Greg asked.

"No, not really. Just little bits and phrases."

"That's still cool. Say something for me."

"Umm ... let me think." In truth, Deepti could not remember a single phrase she had learned eight summers ago, when her mom went back to Berkeley in search of her "roots," or maybe Deepti's father, and Deepti spent a month living with her grandparents in Oregon. Either way, Deepti was looking out their living room window for flashes of lightning when her mom's '89 Mazda pulled into the driveway on a rainy Tuesday afternoon. She could tell from the way her mother heaved herself out of the driver's seat and shut the car door with the full weight of her body, as if crouching between its hinges were cockroaches that needed crushing, that nothing—and yet everything—had changed.

To Deepti, that summer was a fierce line drawn in the gravelly sand of her life, separating the way things were from the way things used to be. Her mother left as a loud voice and a flapping coat, jangling bracelets and jasmine incense—a hippie woman-child who gazed skyward with hopeful eyes, clutching a well-worn copy of *The*

Woman Warrior to her breast and giving crinkled dollar bills to every homeless person she passed on the street. When she returned, she seemed audibly softer, smaller—a question mark slouched inside herself. Whatever she had gone to Berkeley looking for, she had not found it. When she came back, she stopped looking altogether.

Two months later, she began showing. Deepti's brother, Alson Jones, Jr., was born during the first whispered notes of spring. He was dark, too—darker than Deepti. Their mother said they had the same father, though she was no magician and another child didn't make Alson Jones, Sr. reappear.

Now, gazing into Greg's expectant eyes, the only Chinese word Deepti could summon was *kuei*. Ghost. Before that summer, her mother flipped through the pages of Maxine Hong Kingston's memoir every day, as if she could glean magic from the touch of her fingertips to the dusty ink on its pages. She memorized passages, quoted them aloud while they were eating breakfast or driving to school or shuffling through the aisles in the downtown Ralphs, their basket filled with hard green apples and skim milk: "'The difference between mad people and sane people is that sane people have variety when they talk-story. Mad people have only one story that they talk over and over.' That's what Brave Orchid says. She was Maxine's mother."

Deepti's mother referred to Maxine Hong Kingston by her first name, as if they were dear friends. Maxine, the writer of her mother's Bible, eventually became her invisible friend as well. The year before, when Deepti went home for Christmas break, she sometimes caught her mother muttering to an imaginary Maxine. Sensing Deepti there, her mother would abruptly turn around and smile, and pretend she was singing to herself.

"*Kuei*," Deepti told Greg now.

"*Kuei*. What does it mean?" he asked.

"Ghost," Deepti said. It was also the word they used for white people, but she did not tell him that part.

*

Deepti only had a handful of memories of her father. Being carried piggyback along a crowded city street, lulled by the sway of her father's gait and the strength of his sinewed shoulders. The teddy bear her father won at some amusement park and gave to her, though Deepti wasn't sure she actually remembered the broad smile on her father's face as he presented the bear from behind his back. It was possible she was just imagining the memory.

Most of all, Deepti remembered lying in her bed at night, plugging her ears with her index fingers and screwing her eyes shut as her parents' arguments resounded through their tiny apartment above The Golden Sari.

"Who is she?" her mother would scream.

"Who is *who*?" her father would shout. "There's nobody else! You're crazy, Min!"

"Then explain where you disappear to all night. Huh? Huh? Just explain it to me, Alson!"

"Maybe I *should* go find someone else—my own wife don't even trust me!"

"Just tell me where you were, or leave!"

"Fine, fine—I was at Bernie's. Okay? Okay, Minjun?"

"What were you doing at Bernie's? Liar! You were not at Bernie's, don't even expect me to swallow that load of shit—"

"You know what? I really don't have to take this."

"Fine!" her mother screamed, the last time. "Then go! Just go, Alson! Go!"

"Okay. I'll go!"

"GO!"

"I'm going!" her father shouted, the last time. "Don't worry, Minjun—I'm gone!"

Deepti heard every word, despite her fingers plugging up her ears. That was the last time she heard her father's voice. To Deepti, the sharp slam of the front door was the world shattering.

*

"My parents are coming to visit this weekend," Greg said.

"Yeah?"

"They want to meet you."

"Really?"

"Of course! You're my girlfriend."

"I know," Deepti said. "But, I mean, it hasn't been that long."

"It's been four months."

Deepti swallowed. "It's just—that's kind of a serious step, isn't it? Meeting the parents?"

Greg smoothed his palms over his blue-jeaned thighs. "I didn't realize our relationship was a casual thing to you."

"It's not—Greg, listen—"

"Deep, you're an important part of my life and my parents want to meet you. I don't get what's so weird about that."

"It's just ..." Deepti sighed, fiddling with the zipper on her hooded sweatshirt. "Are you sure they want to meet *me*? I mean, look at me, Greg. Do they know I'm not some—some rich white sorority girl?"

"Is that really what you think of me?" Greg asked quietly. Deepti could hear the hurt in his voice. "Nothing but a rich white boy?"

Deepti fumbled for words. "No, Greg—I'm sorry. I didn't mean that." She reached for his hand. "I would be honored to meet your parents. Really."

"You don't have to."

"I want to."

"I was thinking," Greg said, "maybe we could take them to The Grove?"

*

This time they did not eat at a stall at the farmer's market, but instead at a restaurant with tablecloths and linen napkins and menus written in French. *La Tomate Brulante.* They sat at a table on the patio. The sun shone brightly in Deepti's eyes, making her squint, but she thought it would be rude to put on her sunglasses. Beads of sweat coalesced on the back of her neck.

"So, Deepti, what is your major?" Greg's mother asked. She wore her hair in a loosely coiled knot at the nape of her neck, with sideswept bangs that accentuated her high forehead. Her eyes were blue and heavily mascara-ed. Only twice could Deepti remember seeing her own mother wearing make-up: when she left that summer day for Berkeley, and in the wedding photo that Deepti had uncovered, framed and dusty, in a box in her grandparents' garage.

"I'm studying philosophy," she said.

"Philosophy, eh?" said Greg's father, his tone like an elbow in the ribs. "What do you plan to do with that?"

"Well, you actually have a lot of options with a philosophy degree. Students become doctors, lawyers—"

"Law, huh?" Greg's father was a tall man, even when seated, with broad shoulders and impeccable posture and a closely cropped salt-and-pepper beard. *Is he a lawyer?* Deepti tried to remember if Greg had mentioned his father's profession. She didn't think so. They didn't talk much about their families.

"Yes, but I don't know if I want to go into law," Deepti said. "I'm thinking of applying for the Peace Corps."

"Really?" Greg's father raised his eyebrows. "I didn't know kids still did that."

"It's a very competitive program, Pop," Greg said, his hand finding Deepti's beneath the table.

Later, after a round of appetizers, salad and soup, rack of lamb marinated in lemon and garlic that Deepti had to politely refuse, and after the coffee cups and sugar spoons had been cleared away, and after Greg's father made a big show of calculating the tip for the waitress, and Deepti said, "Thank you for lunch," feeling strangely unsettled at the whole ordeal of it—later, after the meal was done, they left *La Tomate Brulante* and strolled along the fake cobblestone streets, past the stores with the big windows and the strings of pearl-lights gleaming nearly translucent in the bright sunshine. There was a bridge over a man-made pond, a gaudy fountain, a grassy park swathed with trees and a small stage set up with a band playing live music. Keyboard, drums, bass, guitar.

"Oh, I love this song!" Greg's mother said. "Remember, George?" She smiled at Greg's father. The four of them settled down amongst the cluster of families on the grass as the notes swelled and the pianist sang, "Hey Jude, don't be afraid, you were made to go out and get her ..."

Deepti closed her eyes, letting the music seep into her chest, golden and warm. Greg sat beside her, his hand on her knee, singing along: "Hey Jude, don't let her down, you have found her, now go and get her ..." Maybe she worried too much. Maybe it would all be okay.

*

"Hey Pop, everything okay?" Greg said into his cell phone. Deepti paused the DVD they'd rented, *Mr. and Mrs. Smith.* Greg shrugged apologetically and mouthed to her, "Sorry." Into the phone he said, "I'm glad you and Mom made it back safe."

Deepti got up to refill their glasses of Diet Coke. When she returned, Greg's brow was furrowed and his voice was taut. "Pop, you're out of line—"

Deepti sat down beside him, but Greg slid his arm out from behind her and stood up. "I don't understand—" he said into the phone, slipping into his bedroom. He closed the door, but the walls were thin and Deepti could still hear his end of the conversation.

"That's ridiculous—of course she has a future. What do you mean, what is her family background? What does that have to do with anything? Her mom's Chinese and her dad's black. No, Pop, I'm not—you sound crazy, do you even hear yourself? She's not pregnant —"

Deepti stared at the frozen image on the television screen, of Angelina Jolie crouched with her back to the wall, gun poised and ready to shoot. She wanted to plug her ears with her fingers, but she had learned long ago that the words you least wanted to hear were often the most impossible to keep from hearing.

*

"They found her," Alson said. His voice was too calm to belong to a fifth-grader.

"Hey, bud, it's two in the morning." Deepti was still half-asleep. "Why are you up? What's going on?"

"It's mom. They found her."

"What?" Deepti sat up. She could feel the blood rush to her temples.

"Grandma's gonna call you tomorrow. I heard them talking about it. A policeman came to our house. I'm not supposed to know. Grandma was crying."

"It's okay. I'm glad you called me. It's good you called."

"She's never coming back, is she?"

"I don't think so, Al. No."

"Deepti? When are you coming home?"

*

Deepti stuffed a couple T-shirts into a duffel bag. Bras, panties, jeans. Deodorant. Greg came up and wrapped his hands around her waist. "I'm gonna miss you," he said.

"It's only three days."

"You're sure you don't want me to come with?"

"Midterms are almost here. I don't want to burden you with this."

"I've told you, it's not a burden."

"I know, but really, Greg. This is something I need to do myself." As the words left her mouth, Deepti felt a surge of guilt—Greg was trying, wasn't he?—but he just didn't understand. He had the perfect All-American family. His mother with her blush and pearls, his father with his beard and law firm. Their pre-Revolutionary-War lineage. Greg wouldn't understand a mother who one day didn't pick up Alson from school, who wasn't there when he got home, who, they later found out, didn't go into work that day, either. She just disappeared. No note, no goodbye—nothing. On the kitchen table,

338

she left her faded, dog-eared copy of *The Woman Warrior*. That was how Deepti knew she wasn't coming back.

Deepti took *The Woman Warrior* from her bookshelf and placed it gently in her bag. "I'll see you on Thursday," she said to Greg. She kissed him, hard, closing her eyes so as not to see her mother lurking in the corner of the room, gazing at her with a ghostly vacant stare.

*

When Deepti left her apartment the next morning, her *kuei* mother followed, sliding across the backseat of the taxi that took them to the airport. She followed Deepti onto the plane, plopping herself down on the carpeted aisle floor beside her daughter's seat, 43C. She was oblivious to the other passengers stepping on her, grunting as they heaved bulging travel bags into the overhead compartments, and the stewardesses pushing carts right through her as she lay sprawled on her side, sleeping, her thin arms folded underneath her head. Deepti had forgotten how sharply angular her mother's elbows were, how hollow her cheekbones. Even when she was alive, she had been thin and ghostly. The last time Deepti hugged her, saying goodbye after Christmas break, she had been too scared to squeeze at all, as if the slightest pressure would cause her mother's frail bones to break.

"Miss? Chicken or pork?" The stewardess's high-heel was planted squarely through Deepti's mother's chest. She was awake now, blinking up at Deepti expectantly.

"Actually, can I have your vegetarian option?" Deepti asked. In truth, the ghostly form beside her was not new. Her mother had always been pervasively half-there. Even now, even dead, she still affected Deepti's life. Her whimsical choices, trying on religions and cultures as if she were a little girl playing dress-up, determined who she, Charusheela Deepti, was and who she would always be. Deepti shifted in her narrow seat, waiting for her mixed vegetables and rice. She would always have to ask for the vegetarian option, because of her mother.

*

Deepti held Alson's hand as they leaned against the boat railing, watching their mother's ashes swirl away into the dark ocean waves. Their grandparents stood a few feet away, gazing down into the water with unreadable wrinkled faces. Nobody spoke.

Deepti's ghost-mother was there, too. She had followed Deepti from the airport to her grandparents' home, standing silently in the corner as Deepti ate her grandmother's dumplings and played endless games of checkers with Alson. Her ghost-mother sat on the edge of Deepti's bed all night, and Deepti couldn't sleep. She just wanted it to be over—she wanted to say goodbye and be done with it. Now, Deepti hoped her mother's *kuei* would dive in and float away with her ashes.

She didn't. But as her ashes disappeared, ocean water seeped into her clothes and weighed down her hair, spilling out of her eyes and causing her feet to squish in her shoes as she walked. Her mother, the drowned ghost. Deepti had stuffed *The Woman Warrior* into the pocket of her coat before they left her grandparents' house, in case she needed it at the funeral. She wanted to throw it into the ocean's choppy waves. Feeling the cover's flimsiness between her fingers, she almost pulled it out. But she couldn't. She couldn't just throw it away, not like that, not with her ghostly mother standing beside her and reproaching her with vacant eyes. Eyes that knew nothing and yet also seemed to know everything—everything, at least, that mattered. Everything Deepti feared. She looked into her mother's ransacked stare and saw a future chosen and waiting for her that she never wanted to claim. Deepti did not want to be her mother's substitute. She gripped the railing tighter.

"Ow!" Alson said. "You're hurting my hand!"

"Sorry," Deepti said. They turned away from the railing as the boat headed back to shore. Deepti's other hand hung limp and empty at her side. She wished Greg were there.

340

*

On her way back to school from the airport, Deepti stopped at The Grove. It was a Sunday, and families milled about. The band was back, though the bassist was out sick, the singer informed them between songs. Deepti leaned against a tree and listened to "Piano Man" and "Your Song." She left before they played "Hey, Jude."

The trolley was parked at a stop, so Deepti got on. She let her arm dangle off the side and savored the breeze against her face. Her ghost-mother sat beside her, dripping wet, muttering to herself or maybe to Maxine. Her voice was the unintelligible whisper of dried leaves.

Deepti stayed on until the last stop, by the farmer's market. Her mother followed. Deepti strolled past rows and rows of stalls, the striped tents selling gyros and rogan josh, pot stickers and palenta. Finally, she came upon what she wanted. "Big Billy's Burgers!" a sign proclaimed, strung across the front of the stall. "America's Best!" Deepti could smell meat sizzling from the grills behind the register.

"One cheeseburger, please," she told the cashier. And, six minutes later, she had an All-American burger in her hand. Nobody stopped her. Nobody could tell she had never before done this in all her life. Deepti sat down at a grease-streaked table with hard plastic chairs. There was a sticky pool of soda left from someone's spilled drink; she wiped it up with a napkin. Her ghost-mother sat down across from her. Deepti met her mother's eyes as she brought the burger up to her lips and took a bite. It tasted strange, a taste Deepti would associate forever afterwards with forgiveness. She took bite after bite, knowing that within an hour she would be kneeling in front of a toilet in a public bathroom stall, her body repelling this foreign substance, poison to her innocent herbivorous stomach. Yet she kept eating, not really tasting anymore, just chewing and swallowing, swallowing and chewing. Thinking. About the way her mother used to sing her to sleep when she was little, a lullaby, *Just let the west wind carry your cares away, Wei shenme? Mei guanxi.* About how her mother had been found curled up underneath the fire escape beside The Golden Sari restaurant, not breathing but with a peaceful expression on her face. Deepti chewed and swallowed, swallowed and chewed, thinking finally about Greg, his hand on her knee, the way he smiled at her and she felt her own wholeness expanding inside her ribcage like a hopeful balloon.

When she had licked every morsel of meat and fat from her fingers, Deepti scrunched up the wrapper in her fist and tossed it at the nearest trash can. She unzipped her duffel bag and took out *The Woman Warrior*. Always she was surprised at how small it was, how little it weighed. You could carry it around with you all day, in your purse, your pocket. So light a ghost could carry it. Deepti set the book carefully down on the table, smoothing the cover flat. When she got up to leave, her mother did not follow.

NOTES

HEIDI KOELZ: Sources consulted include Philip McFarland's *Hawthorne in Concord* (New York: Grove Press, 2004) and Patricia Dunlavy Valenti's *Sophia Peabody Hawthorne: A Life, Volume 1, 1900–1847* (Columbia: University of Missouri Press, 2004).

ANGELIQUE STEVENS: Works cited include "Decisive Moments." *American Photo.* September v.8, issue 5, 1997: 47. and "HCB on Photography." *American Photo.* September v.8, issue 5, 1997: 76.

DEBORAH POE: Acknowledgement is made to H.D.'s poetic impulses which can be heard throughout the piece.

BIOGRAPHIES

JUDITH ARCANA writes poems, stories and essays. Her most recent books are poetry collections—*The Parachute Jump Effect, 4th Period English,* and *What if your mother*—these all followed her third prose book, *Grace Paley's Life Stories, A Literary Biography.* One of her new stories about tattooing and abortion was published as a zine in 2013 (Keesha and Joanie and JANE—visit the zine's Facebook page); two more stories from the proposed collection are online at *Serving House Journal* (late fall 2012). She's working on the Maude poems, a project supported by grants from Oregon's Regional Arts and Culture Council and The Celebration Foundation. A native of the Great Lakes region, Judith lives now in the Pacific Northwest. Listen to her read on SoundCloud and visit juditharcana.com for more information about her work.

JENNIFER ARIN is the author of a book of poetry, *Ways We Hold* (Dos Madres Press), and a poetry chapbook, The Roots of Desire (Thicket Press). Her poems and essays have been published in both the U.S. and Europe, in *The AWP Writer's Chronicle, The San Francisco Chronicle Sunday Book Review, Gastronomica, Puerto del Sol, Poet Lore, ZYZZYVA, Paris/Atlantic, Lucero,* and *The Chronicle of Higher Education,* among many others. Her awards include, most notably, a grant from the National Endowment for the Humanities, a PEN Writer's Fund grant, a Poets & Writers Writer-On-Site Residency, and funding from the Spanish Ministry of Culture for collaborative editing of, and research for, a book about the Spanish Civil War. She teaches in the English Department at San Francisco State University.

YVONNE BATTLE-FELTON currently resides in Lancaster, UK where she studies, writes, reads and researches in pursuit of her Creative Writing PhD at Lancaster University. Yvonne's interest in the psychology of character and character influence over plot in both fiction and nonfiction complement her research interests in reuniting the African

American/Black American family after the Emancipation. A writer of short stories, personal essays, radio dramas and screenplays, Yvonne's research and writing explore degrees of truth, legacies of the past and letting go.

JANEE J. BAUGHER is the author of two collections of poetry, *The Body's Physics* (Tebot Bach, 2013) and *Coördinates of Yes* (Ahadada Books, 2010). Her nonfiction, fiction, and poetry have been published in *Boulevard, Nano Fiction, Verse Daily, and Portland Review,* among other places. As an essayist, she was awarded a 2012 fellowship at the Island Institute of Sitka. Baugher's performance venues include Seattle's Bumbershoot Arts Festival and the Library of Congress. Currently she is an associate editor for *StringTown* literary magazine, and she teaches literature at University of Phoenix.

ZEINA HASHEM BECK is a Pushcart Prize nominee and a Lebanese poet with a BA and an MA in English Literature from the American University of Beirut. Her poems have been published or are forthcoming in *Nimrod, Poetry Northwest, Columbia Granger's World of Poetry, The Common, Cream City Review, Quiddity, Crosstimbers, Copper Nickel, Mizna,* and *Mslexia,* among others. Her first poetry collection, *To Live in Autumn,* won the 2013 Backwaters Prize and will be published in August 2014 by the Backwaters Press. It was selected as winning manuscript by distinguished poet Lola Haskins. Zeina lives with her husband and two daughters in Dubai, where she regularly performs her poetry.

Born to a Mexican mother and Jewish father, ROSEBUD BEN-ONI is a 2013 CantoMundo Fellow and the author of *SOLECISM* (Virtual Artists Collective, 2013). A Leopold Schepp Scholar at New York University, she won the Seth Barkas Prize for Best Short Story and The Thomas Wolfe/Phi Beta Kappa Prize for Best Poetry Collection. She was a Rackham Merit Fellow at the University of Michigan where she earned her MFA in Poetry, and was a Horace Goldsmith Scholar at the Hebrew University of Jerusalem. Recently, her story "A Way out of the Colonia" won the Editor's Prize for Best Short Story in *Camera Obscura: A Journal of*

Contemporary Literature and Photography. A graduate of the 2010 Women's Work Lab at New Perspectives Theater, her plays have been produced in New York City, Washington DC and Toronto. Her work appears in *American Poetry Review, Arts & Letters, Bayou, Puerto del Sol,* among others. Rosebud is a co-editor for HER KIND at VIDA: Women in Literary Arts.

TANTRA BENSKO teaches Experimental Fiction and Fiction Writing through UCLA Extension, and her own academy online. She offers many sites for the promotion of avant-garde literature, including *Exclusive Magazine.* She is the author of a few books including *Lucid Membrane,* and has 200 poetry and fiction publications in journals, such as *JEF.* She grew up in Indiana, got her MFA from Iowa, has lived many places, often living outside in the elements as a yogini, but now is settled in Berkeley.

JANE BLUE has been published recently in *Pirene's Fountain, FutureCycle, The Innisfree Poetry Journal, Stirring,* and *Avatar.* In the past she has appeared in *The Chattahoochee Review, The Antigonish Review, The Louisville Review, Quarter After Eight*and quite a few other places, both print and online, including anthologies, books and chapbooks. A new book of poems, *Blood Moon,* is now available from FutureCycle Press in early 2014. She was born and raised in Berkeley, California but now lives near the Sacramento River with her husband, Peter Rodman.

M. L. BROWN's poems have appeared in numerous journals and anthologies, most recently, *Qarrtsiluni, Calyx, Fourth River* and *Shadow and Light: a Literary Anthology on Memory.* When not working on poetry, she devotes her time to raising funds for Planned Parenthood. She lives in Santa Barbara with her husband and their dozen fruit trees.

TARA ISABELLA BURTON's work has appeared or is forthcoming in *PANK, Structo, Arc,* and more. She is a contributor to *The Atlantic, Los Angeles Review of Books,* and *Salon.com.* In 2012 she received *The Spectator's* Shiva Naipaul Memorial Prize for travel writing. Her first novel is on submission.

WENDY CALL has served as Writer in Residence at twenty institutions, including five national parks, four universities, two high schools, two visual art centers, a historical archive and a public hospital. She co-edited *Telling True Stories: A Nonfiction Writers' Guide* (Penguin, 2007). Her book *No Word for Welcome: The Mexican Village Faces the Global Economy* (Nebraska, 2011) won Grub Street's National Book Prize for Nonfiction. Her essay in this anthology was made possible by a grant from the K2 Foundation. Her essays and poetry translations have appeared recently in *Guernica, Kenyon Review* online, *Michigan Quarterly Review*, and *Orion*. She teaches in Goddard College's BFA program and lives in Seattle.

LORRAINE CAPUTO is a documentary poet, translator and travel writer. Her poetry and narratives have been published in over 70 journals in Canada, the US and Latin America, such as *Drumvoices Revue, Canadian Dimension* and *In Other Words* (Mexico). Her works have also appeared in eight chapbooks of poetry, five audio recordings and six anthologies. She has also authored several travel guidebooks. In March 2011, the Parliamentary Poet Laureate of Canada chose her as poet of the month. She has done over 200 literary readings, from Alaska to the Patagonia. For the past decade, she has been traveling through Latin America, listening to the voices of the *pueblos* and the Earth.

EMILY CAPETTINI is a doctoral candidate in English with an emphasis in creative writing fiction and science fiction at the University of Louisiana at Lafayette. Her work has previously appeared in places such as *The Louisiana Review* and *Stone Highway Review*. She is originally from Batavia, IL, once the windmill capital of the world, and sometimes dreams of quitting her job to become a wind farmer.

CAROL CARPENTER's poems and stories have appeared in numerous online and print publications, including: *Barnwood International Poetry Magazine, The Pedestal, Orbis* and *Quiddity*. Her work had been exhibited by art galleries and produced as podcasts (Connecticut Review and Bound Off). Her chapbook, *The Empress of Patton Avenue*, appears online at Heartsounds Press. She received the Hart Crane Memorial Award, the

Jean Siegel Pearson Poetry Award, Artists Among Us Award and others. She lives in Michigan.

KRISTI CARTER has poems published or forthcoming in journals such as *Spillway Magazine, So to Speak, CALYX Journal,* and *Hawai'i Review.* She is originally from the foothills of North Carolina. She currently lives in Nebraska.

ANN CEFOLA is the author of *St. Agnes, Pink-Slipped* (Kattywompus Press, 2011), *Sugaring* (Dancing Girl Press, 2007), and the translation *Hence this cradle* (2007). A Witter Bynner Poetry Translation Residency recipient, she also received the Robert Penn Warren Award judged by John Ashbery. In 2013, she participated in the Pulitzer Remix, which tasked 85 poets from seven countries with creating poems from Pulitzer novels for National Poetry Month. Her work has appeared in anthologies such as *Rabbit Ears: Poems About TV* (2013) and *Journey to Crone* (2013); in journals such as *Feminist Studies* and *Natural Bridge*; and translations in *Absinthe, ActionYes,* and *Rhino,* among others. Ann, who holds an MFA in Poetry from Sarah Lawrence College, works and lives in the New York suburbs.

BETHANY E. CHANEY lives, works and writes in a small house in Carrboro, North Carolina. Her writing has been published on-line or in print by *In the Grove; Al Jadid: A Review and Record of Arab Culture and Arts*; the NC Writers' Network; and Folkmoot USA. She is a 2007 NC Arts Council Fellow, the recipient of the 2008 William Saroyan Society Centennial Prize for Non-Fiction, and an award-winning pine needle basketmaker. She holds a BA from the University of North Carolina and a MBA from Northeastern University, and works as a consultant to non-profit organizations.

SARAH A. CHAVEZ is a mestíza born and raised in the California Central Valley. She is currently a fifth year PhD student with a focus in poetry and Ethnic Studies at the University of Nebraska—Lincoln. Her work can be found or is forthcoming in *The Fourth River, North American*

Review, and *WomenArts Quarterly*, among others. A selection from her manuscript, *This, Like So Much*, won the Vreeland Prize in 2011 and was chosen as a finalist for the 2012 Arts & Letters/Rumi Prize for Poetry. A selection from her chapbook manuscript *All Day, Talking* won the Susan Atefat Peckham Fellowship in 2013.

JOANNE M. CLARKSON is the author of three collections of poems including *Pacing the Moon* (Chantry Press). Her work appears regularly in small press publications including *Nimrod, Visions International* and *Borderlands* this year. Clarkson has a Master's Degree in English and has taught, but currently works as a Registered Nurse specializing in Hospice and Community Nursing. One of her hobbies is reading palms and cards, skills she learned from her grandmother, Esther, who was a professional psychic. Esther often told fortunes in the back of her sister's millinery shop on Green Lake in Seattle, Washington.

CHRISTINA COOK is the author of *Lake Effect* (Finishing Line Press, 2012). Her most recent work has appeared in *New Ohio Review, Crab Orchard Review, Hayden's Ferry Review,* and *Cimarron Review*. Christina is a contributing editor for *Cerise Press* and an assistant editor of *Inertia Magazine*, and works as the senior writer for the president of Dartmouth College.

NINA CORWIN is the author of two books of poetry, *The Uncertainty of Maps* and *Conversations With Friendly Demons and Tainted Saints*. Her poetry has been nominated for the Pushcart Prize and has appeared in *From the Fishhouse, ACM, Forklift OH, Hotel Amerika, New Ohio Review/nor, Poetry East, Southern Poetry Review* and *Verse*. Corwin is an Advisory Editor for *Fifth Wednesday Journal* and curator for the reading series at Chicago's Woman Made Gallery where she co-edited *Inhabiting the Body: A Collection of Poetry and Art By Women*. Corwin has read and performed her work across the country, at times set with musical or choreographic compositions. She lives in Chicago, where she is a practicing psychotherapist known for her work on behalf of victims of violence.

BARBARA CROOKER lives and writes in rural northeastern Pennsylvania, and her poems have appeared in journals such as *The Hollins Critic*, T*he Beloit Poetry Journal, America, The Green Mountains Review, and The Denver Quarterly*, and anthologies including *The Bedford Introduction to Literature, The Bedford Introduction to Poetry, and Good Poems American Places* (Garrison Keillor, editor) (Viking). Her books are *Radiance*, which won the 2005 Word Press First Book competition and was a finalist for the 2006 Paterson Poetry Prize; *Line Dance* (Word Press 2008), which won the 2009 Paterson Award for Literary Excellence; *More* (C&R Press 2010); and Gold (The Poeima Poetry Series, Cascade Books, 2013). Her poetry has been read on the BBC, the ABC (Australian Broadcasting Company), and by Garrison Keillor on The Writer's Almanac. She's won a number of awards, including three Pennsylvania Council on the Arts Creative Writing Fellowships.

CAROL V. DAVIS is the author of *Between Storms* (Truman State University Press, 2012). She won the American 2007 T.S. Eliot Prize for *Into the Arms of Pushkin: Poems of St. Petersburg*, 2007. Twice a Fulbright scholar in Russia, she was the 2008 poet-in-residence at Olivet College, MI and teaches at Santa Monica College, CA. Her poetry has been read on NPR, Radio Russia and at the Library of Congress. Her poems hae been published in *Ploughshares, Prairie Schooner, North American Review, Mid-American Review, Bellingham Review, Verse Daily* and Ted Kooser's *American Life in Poetry*.

EMARI DiGIORGIO makes a mean arugula quesadilla and has split boarded the Tasman Glacier. She is Associate Professor of Writing at The Richard Stockton College of New Jersey and a NJ State Poet-in-the-School. She was named a Distinguished Teaching Artist by the NJ State Council on the Arts for 2012 and received the Governor's Award in Arts Education. Her poetry manuscript *Bullets in Honey* is a four-time finalist for the Crab Orchard Series in Poetry First Book Award,and recent poems have appeared in *Anderbo.com, DIAGRAM,* and *Poetry International.* She also was featured on the Dodge Poetry Foundation's Poetry Friday Blog.

SUSAN ELBE is the author of *The Map of What Happened*, which won the 2012 Backwaters Press Prize and *Eden in the Rearview Mirror* (Word Press), which won Honorable Mention for the Council for Wisconsin Writers Posner Poetry Book Award, as well as two chapbooks, *Light Made from Nothing* (Parallel Press) and *Where Good Swimmers Drown*, winner of the 2011 Concrete Wolf Press Chapbook Prize. Her poems appear or are forthcoming in many journals and anthologies, including *Blackbird, Diode, North American Review, Prairie Schooner, A Fierce Brightness: Twenty-five Years of Women's Poetry* (Calyx Books), and *A Face to Meet the Faces: An Anthology of Contemporary Persona Poems* (University of Akron Press). You can learn more about her at www.susanelbe.com.

SUSAN J. ERICKSON's poems appear in *2River View, Crab Creek Review, Museum of Americana, Raven Chronicles, Switched-on-Gutenberg,* and *The Lyric*. She is working on a manuscript of poems in women's voices. She lives in Bellingham, Washington where she helped establish the Sue C. Boynton Poetry Walk.

REBECCA FISH EWAN, once a SCUBA instructor in Berkeley, where she grew up and spent most of her time wet, now writes poetry, nonfiction and young adult fiction in the desert Southwest...and uses gobs of moisturizer. She has an MFA from ASU where she teaches landscape architecture in The Design School. Her nonfiction book, *A Land Between,* won a national ASLA award. The first kiss scene from her yet-unpublished YA novel, *Hold My Hand,* is excerpted in the Fall 2013 issue of the fashion publication, *I.T. Post*. The novel is one of a work-in-progress series that explores how time travel can improve everyone's love life...eventually. In nonfiction, she is working on a tragicomic memoir in verse and cartoons about karma, loss and being a middle school dropout living in a kid's commune. She posts on her blog, underourbootsoles, when something in her garden and beyond gives her Whitmanesque thoughts. Other work online includes "The Quiet of Trees," for *The New Nature,* and a guest blog post for *Brevity,* "Is Writing Better than Sex?"

NANCY FLYNN hails from the anthracite country of northeastern

Pennsylvania where at an early age, she fell in love with words instead of into a sinkhole or the then-polluted Susquehanna River. She attended Oberlin College, Cornell University, and has an M.A. in English/Creative Writing from SUNY/Binghamton. Her writing has received the James Jones First Novel Fellowship and an Oregon Literary Fellowship. Recent poems have appeared in *Blood Orange Review*, *PANK*, and *qarrtsiluni*; Burning River published her second chapbook, *Eternity a Coal's Throw* in 2012. In 1998, after many years living on a downtown creek in Ithaca, New York, she married the scientist whose house once hosted parties where Vladimir Nabokov chain-smoked cigarettes. They packed up their Conestoga Volvo 850 and headed for the foothills of the Oregon Coast Range, finally settling near the mighty Columbia in Portland, Oregon in 2007.

JUDITH GILLE divides her time between Seattle and San Miguel de Allende, Mexico where she writes about Mexican art and culture and current immigration issues. Her work has appeared in the *Los Angeles Times*, *The Dallas Morning News*, *The Florida Sun-Sentinel*, in magazines, online literary journals and in a number of anthologies. Her memoir *The View from Casa Chepitos: A Journey Beyond the Border* is due for release in October 2013.

COREY GINSBERG's prose and poetry have most recently appeared in such publications as *PANK*, *Gargoyle*, *the cream city review*, *Subtropics*, *The MacGuffin*, and *Puerto del Sol*, among others. She currently lives in Miami and works as a freelance writer.

PATRICE GOPO, the child of Jamaican immigrants, was born and raised in Anchorage, Alaska. Her essays have appeared in *Relief* and *Literary Mama*. She has also been a commentator for Charlotte, North Carolina's National Public Radio station WFAE 90.7. Patrice's essays often focus on issues of cultural identity, immigration and race with occasional diversions into her Alaskan childhood. She lives in North Carolina with her husband and her two daughters.

JANE HAMMONS teaches writing at UC Berkeley. Her writing appears in several anthologies including *Hint Fiction: An Anthology of Stories in 25 Words or Fewer* (W. W. Norton); *The Maternal is Political: Women Writers at the Intersection of Motherhood and Social Change* (Seal Press); and *California Prose Directory: New Writing from the Golden State* (Outpost 19). Her most recent collection of short stories was short-listed for The Scott Prize by Salt Publishing. She has published fiction and nonfiction in a variety of magazines and journals, such as *Alaska Quarterly Review*, *Columbia Journalism Review*, *San Francisco Chronicle Magazine*, *Southwestern American Literature*, and *Word Riot*.

LOIS MARIE HARROD's 13th poetry collection, *Fragments from the Biography of Nemesis*, was published by Word Tech (Cherry Grove 2013). *The Only Is* won the 2012 Tennessee Chapbook Contest (*Poems & Plays*), and *Brief Term*, a collection of poems about teachers and teaching was published by Black Buzzard Press, 2011. *Cosmogony* won the 2010 Hazel Lipa Chapbook (Iowa State). She is widely published in literary journals and online ezines from *American Poetry Review* to *Zone 3*. She teaches Creative Writing at The College of New Jersey.

BRANDI HOMAN is a cofounder and former editor-in-chief of the feminist poetry press Switchback Books and is a doctoral student at the University of Denver. Probably, she loves you.

LOUISA HOWEROW's work has appeared in American, Australian and Canadian journals. Her poems are also included in the anthologies, *Letters to the World* (Red Hen Press, USA), *Possessions* (London Museum, Canada), *An Unfinished War* (Black Moss Press, Canada), and *For Rhino in a Shrinking World* (The Poets Printery, South Africa).

SUZANNE KAMATA is the author of the novels, *Gadget Girl: The Art of Being Invisible* (GemmaMedia, 2013) and *Losing Kei* (Leapfrog Press, 2008), which was just published as an e-book, as well as a short story collection, *The Beautiful One Has Come* (Wyatt-Mackenzie Publishing, 2011). She is also the editor of three anthologies including *Love You to*

Pieces: Creative Writers on Raising a Child with Special Needs (Beacon Press, 2008). She is currently working on a series of essays about traveling with her daughter who has special needs, for which she received a grant from the Sustainable Arts Foundation. She lives in Japan with her husband and their fourteen-year-old twins. "The Heart Finds a Home" was previously published in slightly different form in *Real Simple* in June, 2011.

JULIE KANE was the 2011-2013 Louisiana Poet Laureate. A former George Bennett Fellow in Writing at Phillips Exeter Academy, New Orleans Writer in Residence at Tulane University, and Fulbright Scholar to Vilnius Pedagogical University in Lithuania, she currently teaches at Northwestern State University in Natchitoches, Louisiana. Her poetry collections include *Jazz Funeral* (2009), which received the Donald Justice Poetry Prize, and *Rhythm & Booze* (2003), a winner of the National Poetry Series and finalist for the Poets' Prize. Recently she wrote the libretto for Starship Paradise, a one-act opera with music by Dale Trumbore that was produced by Center City Opera Theater of Philadelphia. Her poems appear in over forty anthologies and in journals such as Barrow Street, Prairie Schooner, Rattle, and The Southern Review. They have also been featured on *Poetry Daily, Verse Daily*, and *The Writer's Almanac* with Garrison Keillor.

VASILIKI KATSAROU's first poetry collection, *Memento Tsunami*, was published by Ragged Sky Press in 2011. Her work has appeared in *Poetry Daily, wicked alice, Press 1*, and *US 1 Worksheets,* and she also co-edited the anthology *Eating Her Wedding Dress: A Collection of Clothing Poems*. She directs the Panoply Books Reading Series in Lambertville, NJ. Vasiliki holds an MFA from Boston University and a degree in literature from Harvard College. In a previous life, she wrote and directed an award-winning 35mm short film about utopia called *Fruitlands 1843*.

BETH KEEFAUVER has taught creative writing and literature at Warren Wilson College, Western Carolina University, and University of Tennessee, where she earned her PhD in English and Creative Writing. Her fiction and nonfiction has appeared in *Pisgah Review, Blue Lotus Review, Press 53 Blog, ISLE*, and *Grist,* where she is a former fiction editor. Before entering the academic life, Beth worked as a sea turtle biologist, forklift operator, and a writer/performer for LYLAS, an award-winning female comedy troupe. Aspiring huntress and mini-homesteader, she bikes, hikes, and writes in the mountains of Asheville, North Carolina with her husband, toddler, and cat.

VANDANA KHANNA was born in New Delhi, India and received her MFA from Indiana University. Her first collection, *Train to Agra*, won the *Crab Orchard Review* First Book Prize and her second collection, *Afternoon Masala*, won the Miller Williams Prize and is forthcoming from the University of Arkansas Press in 2014. Ms. Khanna's work has been nominated for a Pushcart Prize and has appeared in journals such as *Crazyhorse*, *Callaloo* and *The Indiana Review*, as well as the anthologies *Homage to Vallejo*, *Asian American Poetry: The Next Generation* and *Indivisible: An Anthology of Contemporary South Asian American Poetry*. She lives in Los Angeles.

MOLLY SUTTON KIEFER's chapbook *The Recent History of Middle Sand Lake* won the 2010 Astounding Beauty Ruffian Press Poetry Award. Her second chapbook, *City of Bears*, will be published in 2013 by dancing girl press. Her work has appeared in *Harpur Palate*, *Women's Studies Quarterly*, *Berkeley Poetry Review*, *you are here*, *Gulf Stream*, *Cold Mountain Review*, *Southampton Review*, *Wicked Alice*, and *Permafrost*, among others. She earned her MFA from the University of Minnesota, is in the mentorship program at the Loft Literary Center, serves as poetry editor to *Midway Journal*, and runs *Balancing the Tide: Motherhood and the Arts | An Interview Project*.

KATHLEEN KIRK is the poetry editor for *Escape Into Life* and the author of five poetry chapbooks, mostly recently *Nocturnes* (Hyacinth Girl Press, 2012) and *Interior Sculpture: Poems in the voice of Camille Claudel* (Dancing Girl Press, 2014). Her work has appeared previously in the Sundress Publications journals *Stirring*, *Intentional Walk*, and *Wicked Alice*, and in a variety of print and online journals, including *Arsenic Lobster*, *Confrontation*, *Eclectica*, *Waccamaw*, and *Poetry East*. Never an actual cheerleader, she reviews books of poetry as The Poetry Cheerleader for *Prick of the Spindle.*

CHRISTINE KLOCEK-LIM received the 2009 Ellen La Forge Memorial Prize in poetry. She has four chapbooks: *Ballroom - a love story* (Flutter Press), *Cloud Studies* (Whale Sound Audio Chapbooks), *How to photograph the heart* (The Lives You Touch Publications), and *The book of small treasures* (Seven Kitchens Press). Her poems have appeared in *Nimrod, OCHO, Diode, Riffing on Strings: Creative Writing Inspired by String Theory* and elsewhere. Her work has been nominated for the Pushcart Prize and Best of the Net anthologies and was a finalist for 3 Quarks Daily's Prize in Arts & Literature. She is editor of *Autumn Sky Poetry.*

HEIDI KOELZ grew up in St. Louis, Missouri, before moving to New England. She manages communications for a nonprofit arts organization in Boston, Massachusetts. Her essays have appeared in the *Antioch Review* and in *Paige Leaves: Essays Inspired by New England*, from the Harvard Book Store.

SANDRA GAIL LAMBERT lives in Gainesville, Florida and writes both fiction and memoir. Her work has appeared in *New Letters, The North American Review, Arts and Letters,* and *Big Fiction.* She also won the 2013 Saints and Sinners Short Fiction Contest. The essay in this anthology was first published in *The Alaska Quarterly Review. The River's Memory*, her debut novel, is due out in the fall of 2014 from Twisted Road Publications.

JJ LYNNE is a recent graduate of Merrimack College, where she received the Bishop Markham Medal for her achievements in the Humanities. Her poems have won first and second prizes in the annual Rev. John R. Aherne Poetry Contest and her writing has appeared in *Treehouse Magazine* and *Meat for Tea.* Lynne currently works as a library assistant who spends her time bandaging paper cuts and scribbling micropoems on the backs of due date slips. She looks forward to seeing her work in the forthcoming first issue of *Mock Orange Magazine.*

MARJORIE MADDOX is Director of Creative Writing and Professor of English at Lock Haven University and has published *Local News from Someplace Else* (Wipf & Stock); a 2013 ebook of *Perpendicular As I* (Authors Guild/Stone Steeple Books); *Transplant, Transport, Transubstantiation* (2004 Yellowglen Prize); *Weeknights at the Cathedral* (WordTech Editions); *Perpendicular As I* (1994 Sandstone Book Award); *When the Wood Clacks Out Your Name: Baseball Poems* (Redgreene Press); five chapbooks, and over 450 poems, stories, and essays in journals and anthologies. She is co-editor of *Common Wealth: Contemporary Poets on Pennsylvania* (PSU Press 2005) and author of two children's books from Boyds Mills Press: *A Crossing of Zebras: Animal Packs in Poetry* (2008) and *Rules of the Game: Baseball Poems* (2009). The recipient of numerous awards, including Cornell University's Sage Graduate Fellowship for her MFA and Pushcart Prize nominations in poetry and fiction, Marjorie lives with her husband and two children in Williamsport, PA.

SHARANYA MANIVANNAN is the author of a book of poems, *Witchcraft*. She has received a Lavanya Sankaran Fellowship, an Elle Fiction Award, and been nominated twice for a Pushcart Prize. Her fiction, poetry, and essays have appeared or are forthcoming in *Drunken Boat, Hobart, Wasafiri, Prairie Schooner, Cerise Press, Killing The Buddha,* and elsewhere.

ANDREA MARCUSA is a fiction and essay writer. Her writings have appeared in *The New York Times, The Christian Science Monitor, The Ontario Review, Copper Nickel, NewSouth,* and other publications. She was a finalist in the *Ontario Review*'s 2007 Fiction competition, and winner of the *Antigonish Review* 2008 Fiction competition. She divides her time between writing fiction and essays and working in the areas of health care and sustainable agriculture. For fun she tweets about flora and fauna in Central Park at @My_Cen_ParkNYC. She lives in New York City with her husband, two sons and pet cockatiels, Turko and Luna.

SUSAN McCARTY's stories and essays have been published in the *Utne Reader, Conjunctions, the Iowa Review, Willow Springs* and elsewhere. She is an assistant professor of English at Salisbury University on Maryland's Eastern Shore.

LISA McCOOL-GRIME loves Sappho, wallflower women and collaborations. Her wallflower women are or will be appearing in *DIAGRAM, Weave, Rabbit Catastrophe Press* and elsewhere. Her poem "My Tongue, a Cutting Board" was recently nominated for a pushcart by *Stone Highway Review*. A few of her collaborative publications include *qarrtsiluni, elimae,* and *PANK.* Tupelo press awarded one of her poems first place in their Fragments of Sappho contest.

KARYNA McGLYNN is the author of *I Have to Go Back to 1994 and Kill a Girl,* winner of the Kathryn A. Morton Prize from Sarabande Books, and a book of flash fiction, *Alabama Steve.* Her poems have appeared in *Fence, Salt Hill, Columbia Poetry Review, Subtropics, Court Green, Ninth Letter* and *Phoebe.* Karyna received her MFA from the University of Michigan, and is currently a PhD candidate in Literature & Creative Writing at the University of Houston. She is the Managing Editor of *Gulf Coast* and coordinator of the Houston Indie Book Fest and Gulf Coast Reading Series.

CLAIRE McGUIRE is a lifelong poetry lover whose work has been published in several literature magazines and reviews in the Hudson Valley. After growing up in Upstate New York and receiving a degree in art history from SUNY New Paltz, she packed a suitcase and moved to Germany. She currently lives in a small city near Berlin, where she studies world heritage. Most of her inspiration is drawn from the day-to-day experience of living, both in familiar and foreign cultures.

JENNIFER MILITELLO is the author of three collections of poetry: *Body Thesaurus* (Tupelo Press, 2013), named by Marilyn Hacker as a finalist for the Alice Fay di Castagnola Award, *Flinch of Song* (Tupelo Press, 2009), winner of the Tupelo Press First Book Award, and the chapbook *Anchor Chain, Open Sail.* Her poems have appeared in *American Poetry Review, The Kenyon Review, The New Republic, The North American Review, The Paris Review, Ploughshares,* and *Best New Poets 2008,* have been awarded the

Barbara Bradley Award from the New England Poetry Club, the 49th Parallel Award from *Bellingham Review*, and the Ruskin Art Club Poetry Prize from Red Hen Press, and have received grants and fellowships from the New Hampshire State Council on the Arts, the Barbara Deming Memorial Fund, Writers at Work, and the Millay Colony for the Arts.

JENNIFER MOFFETT completed her MA in Creative Writing at The University of Mississippi and has been a freelance writer for more than 10 years. Her novel-in-progress was a short-listed finalist in the Faulkner-Wisdom Creative Writing Competition. Her essays and book reviews have appeared in various print publications, including *Jackson Free Press*. She has published short fiction in the *New Orleans Review*, *The Citron Review* and *Marco Polo Arts Mag*. She lives on the Mississippi Gulf Coast where she teaches creative writing and literature at a community college.

DIANE LEE MOOMEY is a sculptor, a painter, a gardener, a dreamer, and a storyteller who lives in El Granada, California. She has had gallery exhibitions in Ontario, Quebec and in California showing claywork and framed paper sculptures accompanying poems. Her current art project is a series of watercolors on the theme "Paths, Portals and Elements." Her poetry and short prose have appeared in *Northwest Literary Forum, Earth Prayers,* (Roberts/Amidon, HarperCollins, 1991,) *Two-Twenty-Four Poetry Quarterly, Blis, Icon, The Love Project* (Anabasis), *The Sand Hill Review, FaultZone* (an anthology) and *Writing For Our Lives*.

JENN MARIE NUNES is the author of 3 chapbooks: *OBJECT REFERENCE NOT SET TO AN INSTANCE OF OBJECT*, dancing girl press (2014), *OPERA TRANS OPERA*, with Mel Coyle, Alice Blue Books (2013); and *STRIP,* online at *PANK Magazine* (July 2011). Her work appears in numerous journals, including *Black Warrior Review, Ninth Letter, Bateau and Horse Less Review*. She lives in New Orleans where she co-edits *TENDE RLOIN*, an online gallery for poetry and co-curates the associated ColdCuts reading series. Some say she has pretty eyes.

DAWN PAUL is the author of two novels, *The Country of Loneliness*

(Marick Press) and *Still River* (Corvid Press). She has worked with painter Ben Johnson for the YouTube literary journal, *Shape of a Box* and choreographer Kelley Donovan on dance/poetry pieces. Her work has appeared in the anthologies *Going Alone—Women's Solo Wilderness Adventures* and *Steady as She Goes—Women's Stories of the Sea*, both from Seal Press. She has just completed a new collection of short fiction, working title *Upper Enchanted Township and Other Stories*. She teaches writing at Montserrat College of Art and kayaks, backpacks, skis and bikes in New England and elsewhere.

RACHAEL PECKHAM is the author of *Muck Fire* (Spring Garden Press) and the recipient of the 2010 Robert Watson Poetry Award. Her essays have been nominated for a Pushcart Prize and received a notable mention in the *2012 Best American Essays*. Most recently, her work appeared in *Hotel Amerika,* and *Under the Sun.* She currently teaches Creative Nonfiction at Marshall University in Huntington, West Virginia.

DEBORAH POE's books include three poetry collections *the last will be stone, too* (Stockport Flats), *Elements* (Stockport Flats), and *Our Parenthetical Ontology* (CustomWords), as well as a novella in verse, *Hélène* (Furniture Press). In addition, Deborah co-edited and authored the introduction for *Between Worlds: An Anthology of Fiction and Criticism* (Peter Lang). Her fiction and cross-genre work have appeared in journals such as *No Contest, Fact-Simile Magazine, Conversations Across Borders, Night Train,* and *Sidebrow.* Deborah is assistant professor of English at Pace University and founder and curator of the annual Handmade/Homemade Exhibit.

JANEEN PERGRIN RASTALL lives in Gordon, MI, population 2. Her poetry has appeared or is forthcoming in several publications including *The Raleigh Review, Prime Number, Heron Tree, The Michigan Poet, Great Lakes Review, Midwestern Gothic* and *The Way North: Collected Upper Peninsula New Works* by Wayne State University Press.

MARTHE REED is the author of four books: *Pleth*, a collaboration with j hastain (Unlikely Books 2013), *(em)bodied bliss* (Moria Books 2013*)*, *Gaze* (Black Radish Books 2010) and *Tender Box, A Wunderkammer* (Lavender Ink 2007). A fifth book of poems will be published by Lavender Ink (2014). She has also published four chapbooks as part of the Dusie Kollektiv; a fifth is published by above / ground press. Her collaborative chapbook *thrown*, text by j hastain with Reed's collages, won the Smoking Glue Gun contest and will appear in 2014. An essay on Claudia Rankine's *The Provenance of Beauty: A South Bronx Travelogue* appears in *American Letters and Commentary*. She is Co-Publisher of Black Radish Books.

CAROLE ROSENTHAL is the author of *It Doesn't Have To Be Me*, a collection of short stories. Her fiction appears in a wide variety of periodicals, ranging from literary magazines like *Transatlantic Review*, *Confrontation, Other Voices*, and *The Cream City Review*, to *Mother Jones*, and *Ellery Queen's Mystery Magazine*. Her frequently anthologized short stories have been dramatized for radio and television, translated into eleven languages, and her articles and reviews published in newspapers and with presses including Dell, Arbor House, Doubleday, Bowker, and the Modern Language Association. She teaches at Pratt Institute, in Brooklyn, where she is a Distinguished Professor. She lives part-time in New York City and part-time in the Catskills.

HEATHER SAPPENFIELD's stories have won the Danahy Fiction Prize and The Arthur Edelstein Prize for Short Fiction. Her work has appeared in *Meridian, Tampa Review, So To Speak, Joyland*, and *Shenandoah*. They have also received a Pushcart nomination. "Coloring Beyond the Lines" is part of a collection which was a 2012 finalist for the Flannery O'Connor Award. In the same year, Sappenfield's novel *The Phases of Water* placed second in the Writer's Digest Writing Competition. She lives in Vail, Colorado, with her husband and daughter.

JENNIFER SAUNDERS is an American living in German- speaking Switzerland with her Swiss husband and their two Swiss-American sons. Her poetry has appeared in *Adanna, Found Poetry Review, Heron Tree, Literary Bohemian*, and elsewhere; and just when she thinks she's mastered

German, something comes along to remind her that she hasn't.

KELLY SCARFF works as an editor and adjunct instructor. She is a graduate of Chatham University's MFA in Creative Writing program, where she was a teaching fellow and won the Best Thesis in Poetry Award. Her poems have appeared in *5AM, Nerve Cowboy, Chiron Review, Pear Noir!* and elsewhere. Kelly's poetry chapbook, *I Fall in Love with Strangers*, was first runner-up in Liquid Paper Press's 2011 competition. A resident of Greensburg, she has been featured at the Carnegie Library of Pittsburgh Sunday Poetry & Reading Series, and at the University of Pittsburgh-Greensburg's alumni authors Written/Spoken Reading Series.

MARISSA SCHWALM is a Ph.D. candidate in English Literature and Creative Writing at Binghamton University in New York, where her fields of study include contemporary poetry and creative nonfiction. Her creative work has been published most recently in *Clockhouse Review, First Inkling, Decompression,* and others.

DANIELLA SELLERS is originally from Key West, FL. She has an MA from The Writing Seminars at Johns Hopkins University and an MFA from the University of Mississippi where she held the Grisham Poetry Fellowship. Her poems have appeared or are forthcoming in *Subtropics, Smartish Pace, Cimarron Review, Poet Lore, Prairie Schooner, 32 Poems,* and elsewhere. Her book, *Bone Key Elegies*, was published in 2009 by Main Street Rag. She lives in Winter Springs, Florida where she edits *The Country Dog Review.*

PAULA SERGI is the author of three poetry chapbooks: *Brother, Family Business* and *Black Forest Love Songs*, as well as co-editor of three anthologies; *Boomer Girls, Meditations on Hope* and *A Call to Nursing*. She received a BS in Nursing from U of Wisconsin, Madison and an MFA from Vermont College. A Wisconsin Arts Board recipient, her poetry is widely published in literary magazines. She lives in Fond du Lac, Wisconsin at the confluence of the Dutch Gap and the Fond du Lac River and fantasizes about owing a dachshund pup some day.

DIANE SEUSS's third book of poems, *Four-Legged Girl*, is forthcoming from Graywolf Press. Her second collection, *Wolf Lake, White Gown Blown Open*, received the Juniper Prize for Poetry and was published by the University of Massachusetts Press in 2010, Her first book, *It Blows You Hollow*, was published by New Issues Press. Her poems and brief lyrical essays have appeared in a range of literary magazines. She received a Pushcart Prize in 2013 for a poem that originally appeared in *Blackbird*. Diane was the MacLean Distinguished Visiting Writer at Colorado College in fall 2012 and she is Writer in Residence at Kalamazoo College, in Michigan.

JEN SIRAGANIAN is a poet, teacher, and co-coordinator of the Lit Crawl, the final night of Litquake, San Francisco's Literary Festival, which features over 80 readings in a single evening in the Mission District. She earned a BA from Brown University and an MFA from the University of Arkansas, and has been nominated for a Ruth Lilly Fellowship and a Pushcart Prize. A past recipient of a scholarship from the Squaw Valley Writers' Conferences, she has published writing in *Barrow Street, Frontiers, Spillway, The Squaw Valley Review*, the anthology *Nothing But the Truth So Help Me God*, and other literary journals.

SARAH J. SLOAT grew up in New Jersey. After finishing graduate school with a degree in language education, she taught in China, for a year cut short by the Tiananmen Square massacre. Afterwards, she rambled around, and has since lived in California, Kansas and Italy. For the past couple decades she's lived in Germany, where she works in Weltschmerz. Sarah's poems have appeared in *Bateau, Harper's Ferry Review* and *Court Green*. She has published two chapbooks with Dancing Girl Press, *Excuse me while I wring this long swim out of my hair* and *Inksuite*. Another chapbook, *Homebodies*, is available from Hyacinth Girl Press.

JESSICA SMITH grew up just outside Buffalo, New York (which explains her love for bleu cheese and the Sabres), and has lived and taught in Minnesota and Maine. She currently teaches writing and literature at

Central Maine Community College and has had work published in *Permafrost, Louisville Review, Portland Review, Berkeley Review, and Arcadia.* She wrote "A Star Means Quiet" while attending Minnesota State University, Mankato for graduate school.

ANGELIQUE STEVENS teaches Creative Writing and Literature of the Holocaust and Genocide at Monroe Community College in Rochester, NY. An activist for human rights, her travels have taken her across the globe. She lived in Chiapas Mexico to be a witness for peace with the Zapatiasta rebels, volunteered in an elephant refuge in Thailand, and drilled a water well in South Sudan. She writes about her travels and her experiences growing up in Upstate New York. She has won the silver in Traveler's Tales Best Women's Travel Writing. She is one of the founders of A Straw Mat, a women's writer's group in Upstate New York.

JENNIFER TAPPENDEN is the founding editor of Architrave Press. She earned an MFA in poetry from the University of Missouri – St. Louis where she also served as the university's first Poet Laureate. Her poems have appeared or are forthcoming in *Flyway, Euphony, Bryant Literary Review* and elsewhere.

JUDITH TERZI holds an M.A. in French Literature. Recent poems have appeared or are forthcoming in publications such as: *The Centrifugal Eye; Myrrh, Mothwing, Smoke: Erotic Poems* (Tupelo Press); *Raintown Review; Times They Were A-Changing: Women Remember the 60s & 70s* (She Writes Press); *Trivia: Voices of Feminism.* She is the author of *Sharing Tabouli* and *The Road to Oxnard. Ghazal for a Chambermaid* was just published by Finishing Line. A former high school French teacher, she also taught English at California State University, Los Angeles, and in Algiers, Algeria.

MEGHAN TUTOLO is the sole writer and editor in marketing for a national Italian foods company [by day] and a poet/painter/ukulele-player/insomniac [by night]. When she isn't romancing olives and spaghetti, she is probably writing about the moon and stars or the mundanity of day-to-day, trying to find meaning in it all. Her work has appeared in *Nerve Cowboy, The Oklahoma Review, Chiron Review, The Pittsburgh Post-Gazette* and on paper placemats and napkins in select diners across the east coast.

SUSAN VOLCHOK is a New York writer who has published widely in journals and anthologies ranging from *The Kenyon Review, The Virginia Quarterly Review, The Massachusetts Review* to *Best American Erotica* and *Tattoos*, in mainstream magazines and newspapers, including *The New York Times*, and online, including *n+1, Mr. Beller's Neighborhood, Hospital Drive*, and *Byliner*.

DONNA VORREYER is the author *A House of Many Windows* (Sundress Publications, 2013) and of five chapbooks, including *We Build Houses of Our Bodies* (dancing girl press, 2013). She loves to travel, but the Chicago area has been home all of her life.

LORENA WILLIAMS is a writer, educator, outdoors enthusiast, and traveler. She received her MFA in Nonfiction from Chatham University in Pittsburgh, PA, where she now teaches writing, literature, and ESL. A native of the American West, she continues to write about rock, sage, and the high desert. Her work has appeared in *Touchstone*, received Honorable Mention in *The Atlantic* Student Writing Contest, was the Third Place Winner of the Torrey House Press Nonfiction Contest, and is soon to appear in *The Fourth River* and *Exclosures* Journals.

SUZANNAH WINDSOR is a Canadian writer whose short fiction and poetry have appeared in *Sou'wester, Grist, Anderbo, Saw Palm, Best of the Sand Hill Review, The Danforth Review*, and others. She is the managing editor of *Compose: A Journal of Simply Good Writing*, an associate editor at *Anderbo*, and the founding editor of Writeitsideways.com. Currently, she lives in Australia with her husband and four young children.

DALLAS WOODBURN is a 2013-14 Steinbeck Fellow in Creative Writing at San Jose State University. Her short story manuscript was a finalist for the 2012 Flannery O'Connor Award for Short Fiction, and her individual stories and essays have appeared in *The Nashville Review, The Los Angeles Times, Prime Number, Arroyo Literary Review, Monkeybicycle, and Louisiana Literature*, among others. Her plays have been produced in Los Angeles by Eclectic Company Theatre and Brand New Theatre, and in New York City as part of the Samuel French Off-Off Broadway Short Play Festival. Recent awards include the Ninth Glass Woman Prize, the Brian Mexicott Playwriting Award, a scholarship to attend the Key West Literary Seminar, and a nomination for the Pushcart Prize. She is the author of two children's books and editor of the anthology *Dancing With The Pen: a collection of today's best youth writing*.

ABIGAIL WYATT has been writing seriously since 2007 when ill health made it impossible for her to continue her career in teaching. As well as having had work published in more than seventy magazines and journals, she is the author of two poetry collections and 'Old Soldiers, Old Bones and Other Stories', which is available online and from *One Million Stories*. One of the editors of *Poetry 24* and co-editor with Duncan Yeates of two 'Murder of Krows' anthologies, Abigail is currently working on two major projects. These are: firstly, a collection of poems arising out of old family photographs and, secondly, *Tales of Little Grey Ted*, a book in verse for children of all ages.

REPRINT CREDITS

Rosebud Ben-Oni: "At Ten I had the Look of Locust," *The Golden Triangle*. Reprinted by permission of the author.

Jane Blue: "Architecture," *Convergence*. Reprinted by permission of the author.

M. L. Brown: "Mother's Home Ritual for Quenching Fires," *Blackbird*. Reprinted by permission of the author.

Tara Isabella Burton: "Fatherlands," *Guernica*. Reprinted by permission of the author.

Lorraine Caputo: "The Fisherwomen of Tilapita," *Mid-American Review*. Reprinted by permission of the author.

Kristi Carter: "Blue Ridge Anatomy," *Poetic Story: An Anthology* (CreateSpace). Reprinted by permission of the author.

Ann Cefola: "Sugaring," *Sugaring* (dancing girl press). Reprinted by permission of the author.

Cristina Cook: "Homing," *The Baltimore Review*. Reprinted by permission of the author.

Nina Corwin: "Born a Midge Doll," *Conversations with Friendly Demons and Tainted Saints* (Puddin' Head Press). Reprinted by permission of the author.

Barbara Crooker: "Question Mark and the Mysterians," *Rattle*. "Willow Ware," *Spillway*. Reprinted by permission of the author.

Carol V. Davis: "This Month in Michigan" and "Roots," *Between Storms* (Truman State University Press). Reprinted by permission of the author.

Emari DiGiorgio: "A Woman Loses Her Country," *Poetry Jumps Off the Shelf* (Woodrow Hall Editions). Reprinted by permission of the author.

Susan Elbe: "Eden in the Rearview Mirror," *Blackbird*. Reprinted by permission of the author.

Corey Ginsburg: *"Her House is Pepto-Bismol Pink*, My Neighbor Says," *PANK*. Reprinted by permission of the author.

Brandi Homan: "What It Means To Be an American," *Denver Quarterly*. Reprinted by permission of the author.

Louisa Howerow: "Elements," *FreeFall*. Reprinted by permission of the author.

Julie Kane: "Purple Martin Suite," *Jazz Funeral* (Story Line Press). Reprinted by permission of the author.

Vasiliki Katsarou: "Swan Boats, Boston Public Garden," *Press 1*. Reprinted by permission of the author.

Vandanna Khanna: "Lemons: A Love Letter," *New Purleiu Review*. "In the Kitchen," *The Atlanta Review*. Reprinted by permission of the author.

Molly Sutton Kiefer: "The Cape," *TRIVIA: Voices of Feminism*. "Chromosomal Geography," *Konundrum Engine*. Reprinted by permission of the author.

Kathleen Kirk: "Little Green Store," *Spoon River Poetry Review*. Reprinted by permission of the author.

Marjorie Maddox: "Cartography," *Perpendicular As I* (Sandstone). "Pennsylvania Round in Four Parts," *Watershed*. Reprinted by permission of the author.

Sharanya Manivanan: "Nine Postcards from the Pondicherry Border" *Flycatcher*. Reprinted by permission of the author.

Claire McGuire: "Pollyanna Smiles," Codhill Press. Reprinted by permission of the author.

Jennifer Militello: "There Remains New Branches," *Verse Magazine* and

Body Thesaurus (Tupelo Press). Reprinted by permission of the author.

Diane Lee Mooney: "Solstice, again," *New Issues Poetry & Prose*. Reprinted by permission of the author.

Jenn Marie Nunes: "The Land Where Plums Abound," *Fell Swoop*. Reprinted by permission of the author.

Rachael Peckham: "Aunt Moreen's Confession," ABZ Press. Reprinted by permission of the author.

Marthe Reed: "Winter Canon: South Louisiana," *Golden Handcuffs Review*. Reprinted by permission of the author.

Danielle Sellers: "Peach Tree, Late Summer," *Prarie Schooner*. Reprinted by permission of the author.

Paula Sergi: "Crumbs," *Primavera Magazine*. Reprinted by permission of the author.

Diane Seuss: "Don't fill the outline," *Black Tongue Review*. Reprinted by permission of the author.

Jen Siraganian: "A House on the Seam," *Spillway*. Reprinted by permission of the author.

Sarah J. Sloat: "Europa," *American Poetry Journal*. "Good Wife of Hunan," *Verdad*. Reprinted by permission of the author.

Jennifer Tappenden: "Invitation to Ms. Brigit Pegeen Kelly," *Bad Shoe*. Reprinted by permission of the author.

Judith Terzi: "Tsunami," *Mad Hatter's Review* and *Sharing Tabouli* (Finishing Line Press). Reprinted by permission of the author.

Meghan Tutulo: "Monday Night in South Greensburg," *Arsenic Lobster Poetry Journal*. Reprinted by permission of the author.

SUNDRESS PUBLICATIONS TITLES

When I Wake It Will Be Forever
Virginia Smith
$14.00   ISBN 978-1-939675-10-1

The Lost Animals
David Cazden
$14.00   ISBN 978-1-939675-07-1

A House of Many Windows
Donna Vorreyer
$14.00   ISBN 978-1-939675-05-7

Gathered: Contemporary Quaker Poets
Ed. by Nick McRae
$16.00   ISBN 978-1-939675-01-9

The Hardship Post
Jehanne Dubrow
$14.00   ISBN 978-1-939675-03-3

Too Animal, Not Enough Machine
Christine Jessica Margaret Reilly
$10.00   ISBN 978-1-939675-02-6

The Old Cities
Marcel Brouwers
$14.00   ISBN 0-9723224-9-3

One Perfect Bird
Letitia Trent
$14.95   ISBN 0-9723224-8-5

Like a Fish
Daniel Crocker
$14.95   ISBN 0-9723224-8-5

The Bone Folders
T.A. Noonan
$14.95   ISBN 0-9723224-6-9

CPSIA information can be obtained
at www.ICGtesting.com
Printed in the USA
FFOW03n1814250218
45230033-45813FF